What People Are Saying About This I

"A scratchbuilder's delight . . . FSM author Charles Adams' Model Design & Bl have for anyone interested in scratchbuilding."

– FineScale Modeler Magazine

"Charles Adams' Model Design & Blueprinting Handbook presents the field of model design from start to finish, covering the basics of analyzing references, sketching multi-view drawings, creating blueprints, and [making] construction patterns for all types of modeling projects . . . [it] is not an 'idiot's guide' to drafting, rather it is a rich, detailed treatment of the drafting and plan making process that could easily serve as the basis of a college course on drafting . . . That having been said, I believe anyone can find tidbits and nuggets that will improve their modeling skills . . . "

– Model Railroad News

"A veritable treasure-trove of techniques from an author well-versed in his subject . . . an unmatched resource for model creation . . . For any budding scratchbuilder, in whatever medium and/or scale, the book is an absolute must and will amply repay careful study of the many and valid techniques its author so graphically espounds. Laid out in logical sections and steps, the whole creative process is outlined from A-Z and beyond in some cases! No mere review can do the content justice . . . even if you are an experienced modeler of many years' standing, I'd be really surprised if you didn't find some fresh, new, workable ideas."

– Windsock Worldwide

"Sometimes you can judge a book by its title . . . This book is precisely what the author intends it to be . . . a valuable reference for the modeler and, with practice, will certainly result in higher quality plans and, hence, better models."

– Nautical Research Journal

"It's a well thought out book that's easy to follow and interesting to look at, with a pleasing layout and well done illustrated examples. I believe that anyone interested in designing models would find a great deal of value in this book . . . All in all, this is one of the best in its category . . ."

– Writer's Digest Book Awards Competition

"The book, while aimed at modelers in the 'scale model' sense of the word, can easily be used by those wishing to build full size. It is not specific to any particular model genre . . . the concepts and methods taught are applicable over a wide range of projects . . . With the copious illustrations accompanying very clear text, you can learn the basics necessary to get started . . . With the information in this book you can build an authentic replica (or 'modification') from the barest of information. This alone is worth the price."

– Steamboating Magazine

"Hands down . . . this new manual and further volumes in the series are going to change the face of future scratch building, all for the better! Overall Rating: 95% – Definitely recommended."

– ModelShipWrights.com

"If you want good solid reference on designing models and creating blueprints for them, this is it."

– ModelGeek.com

"Overall Rating: 10 – a must-have for the serious model builder."

– StarshipModeler.com

"This is cool stuff and all at a VERY reasonable price! Definitely recommended!"

– CyberModeler.com

MODEL Design
& Blueprinting
HANDBOOK
Volume 1
SECOND EDITION

A Note From the Publisher

We'd like to thank you for choosing this title from *ModelersNotebook.com*. Our company was founded to create specialty books and other helpful publications specifically for modelers. As a small specialty press, we need your help to spread the word.

If you find the information in this book to be of value, *please tell your friends*. Each time you let someone know about this book, you can help ensure this and other similar modeling resources will continue to be made available in the future.

Make an announcement at your local modeling group or club. Post a note or message in an online forum or Web community devoted to modeling. Ask your local hobby shop to carry our titles. Let others know what you think! And, of course, please be sure to include a link to our website.

Thank you again for your continued support and encouragement. Enjoy!

www.ModelersNotebook.com

MODEL Design
& Blueprinting
HANDBOOK
Volume 1
SECOND EDITION

An In-Depth Guide for
3D and Traditional Modelers

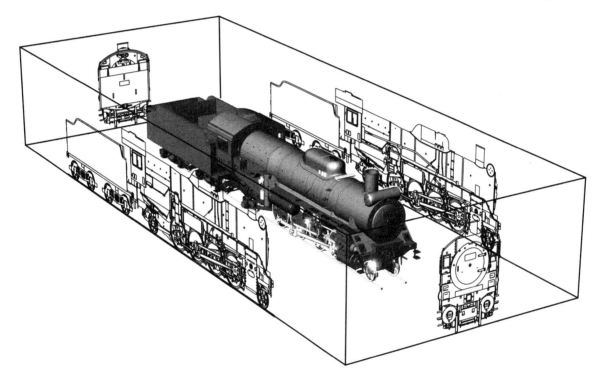

Written & Illustrated By
Charles Adams

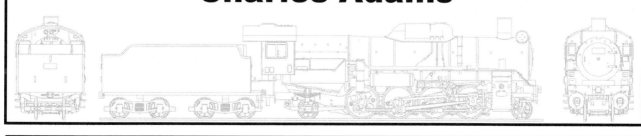

Model Design & Blueprinting Handbook, Volume 1
Copyright © 2007, 2010 Charles Adams
First Edition 2007
Second Edition 2010

Published By
ModelersNotebook.com
Seattle, Washington

Edited by Deborah B. Adams
Cover Design: Charles Adams

ISBN-13: 978-0-9791752-3-7

Printed in the United States of America

First Printing: April, 2010

16 15 14 13 12 11 10   1 2 3 4 5

TRADEMARKS

All terms mentioned in this book that are known to be trademarks or service marks have been appropriately capitalized. ModelersNotebook.com cannot guarantee the accuracy of this information. Use of a specific name or term in this book should be not be regarded as affecting the validity of any trademark or service mark.

AutoCAD and *DWG* are either trademarks or registered trademarks of Autodesk, Inc., in the United States and/or other countries.

Adobe, Adobe Illustrator, Adobe Photoshop, Acrobat, PDF, PostScript, and *Macromedia Freehand* are either registered trademarks or trademarks of Adobe Systems Incorporated in the United States and/or other countries.

CorelDRAW and *Corel PaintShop Pro* are either trademarks or registered trademarks of Corel Corporation and/or its Subsidiaries in Canada, the United States and/or other countries.

Canvas is a trademark of ACD Systems of America, Inc. in the United States and in other countries.

All other trademarks are the property of their respective owners.

WARNING AND DISCLAIMER

Dedication

To all the enthusiasts out there who enjoy this wonderful hobby called modeling –

In memory of my late grandfather, David F. Bullard, who first introduced me to art and drawing at a very early age –

And to my family for their support, for being there, and for always believing in me.

Acknowledgments

Special thanks to my friend **Alan Sinclair**, a.k.a. "Wizard of Flight," for reviewing the reams of material created for this book and for writing the Foreword. Alan is a professional draftsman and instructor who really knows his stuff.

Also, words can't express how much I appreciate my editor for all the many hours she spent working on this book. I couldn't have completed this project without her clear perspective and great eye for details. I am blessed to have her as part of my team.

From the day my father brought home my first plastic model kit, I've been fascinated by scale modeling. So, thanks **Dad** for introducing me to this hobby. From that moment on, I've spent a great deal of time reading articles and books, researching subjects, and drafting plans for a variety of projects. In my teen years, I was greatly inspired by the works of well-known hobby author **Robert Schleicher**. I've also enjoyed seeing the wonderful drawings of **Shane Johnson**, a talented author, artist, and sci-fi enthusiast. Although we've never met or spoken, I've often thought of him as a kindred spirit.

I *have* met some great friends through this hobby. Many of them have inspired me with their creativity, dedication, and talent. They've challenged me to learn new skills and to boldly tackle new modeling frontiers. **Jim Creveling** introduced me to something called "studio-scale." This special and uniquely challenging *niche* of the SF modeling hobby is geared towards recreating some of the great filming miniatures built for movie and television productions. Special thanks also to **Mark Bradley** and **Rick Ingalsbe** for their support, encouragement, and great fellowship over the years. Rick, I know we'll get the chance to work together on a film one of these days.

To **Gene Kozicki**, thanks for being a really good friend and for introducing me to many fascinating and talented people, including some of the greatest names in visual effects. In recent years, I've been fortunate to have had the rare opportunity to design and build a couple of models for film and television. With that in mind, thank you, **Lee Stringer**, for giving me my first chance to work on a Hollywood production. Thank you as well for encouraging me to make the leap to 3D. Once I did, I never looked back. It has changed my career – and my life. This book was made possible in part by what I learned from this process.

Table of Contents

Section 2: Making Construction Patterns

About the Author

Charles Adams is an artist, designer, and writer with 23 years' experience in both drafting and technical illustration. He has long been a traditional fine artist, studying art and winning numerous awards starting at an early age. Even so, while in college he chose to major in engineering where he first learned drafting. Then, his career moved in a different direction when he became a partner in a creative design firm.

Charles has a unique blend of talents in both creative and technical arenas. His wide-ranging experience includes graphic design, technical writing/editing, marketing, and copy writing. He has worked as a fine artist at Walt Disney World, created advertising/marketing materials for a variety of companies, written technical articles/training materials, and even designed computer software while working as an Information Technology Manager.

As a longtime hobbyist and modeling enthusiast, Charles launched the popular science fiction modeling website *StarshipBuilder.com* in 1997, and, more recently, *AirshipModeler.com* in 2006. He has written for *FineScale Modeler Magazine* and has acted as a technical editor on several books.

Charles is currently working as a professional model designer. He has created conceptual designs and built special effects miniatures for both film and television productions. He also enjoys creating technical illustrations and working on a variety of freelance projects. For more information, contact him through one of the websites listed above or visit:

www.CharlesAdams.com

Foreword

Have you ever wanted a model of a subject, but couldn't find a kit? Or, maybe you found a kit, but it didn't meet your expectations? I think it's safe to say we've all been in this predicament at one time or another. The solution is simple: Just build it from scratch.

Well, we all know from experience, it's not quite *that* simple. The key elements of scratch-building are *research, blueprints* and *construction*. In the past, reference material was basically limited to books and articles. With the advent of the Internet, however, all this has changed. The Web has given us the ability to share information with people all over the world. A quick search of the Internet can yield a bounty of excellent reference material. So, this first important element needed to build a project from scratch can now be done quickly.

The next element is often not so easy to come by – the dreaded blueprints. Without a decent set of plans, most scratch-building projects are doomed. Unless you are lucky and happen to find an existing set of plans during your research, you are left to create your own.

This book is dedicated to helping you develop your own blueprints quickly and easily. Just as the Internet helps you with research, the computer is a powerful tool for drawing plans and blueprints. There are a number of programs available that make drawing plans quick and easy. Some are even free. No matter what method or program you choose, the ideas and concepts in this book will show you how it's done.

I've been a modeler for nearly 40 years. I've spent the last 26 years of my life as a professional engineer/draftsman, working on everything from swimming pools to large jet aircraft. Twenty years of that time have been spent using CAD ("Computer Aided Design"). I even taught classical drafting (paper and pencil) for five years.

I have always enjoyed drawing plans and scratch-building everything from kites and R/C planes to fictional spacecraft. But, it wasn't until I began using *AutoCAD* that I started exploring the world of "virtual" model design and building.

The first subject that I used the principles discussed in this book to recreate was the *WarHawk*, a ship from the short-lived 70's TV series *Buck Rogers in the 25th Century*. As the second season of the show opens, Buck is engaged in combat with [a character named] Hawk. This character's ship was designed to look like a bird of prey – from the hooked beak right down to the talons used to capture its "prey." Now, I always liked Buck's *Thunderfighter* ship from the show and I even built the Monogram model kit that was issued. But, Hawk's ship just captivated my imagination.

From the first time I saw it, I knew that I wanted to build a model of this subject. Yet, the reference information needed was practically non-existent. All I could find were a few preproduction concept sketches and a VHS tape of the show – not much at all. For years I held out, thinking someone would build a model or that more pictures would become available. But, neither happened.

In early 2000, I gathered together the numerous sketches and notes I had made over the years from watching the now-worn-out tape. I sat down at my computer with my notes and *AutoCAD*® software and started designing plans for the *WarHawk* from scratch. It took some time, but, using many of the concepts described in this book, I was able to create my first set of blueprints using only photos as reference.

Since then, I have done this for all types of subjects. I feel confident in saying this book will be useful for anyone interested in scratch-building their own models – whether "CG" or real. Any modeler will find this book to be a valuable asset when it comes to exploring the world of scratch-building.

The information here is presented in a way that one does not need to be a professional draftsman to be able to understand and use it. Some of this info cannot be found in any drafting textbook as it represents years of experience and trial and error spent learning what works and what doesn't. I learned most of these same techniques the hard way through many hours studying reference photos and trying to reverse-engineer my favorite starship.

So, the hard work has all been done for you. Now, you get to have the fun.

Alan Sinclair
a.k.a. "Wizard of Flight"

Introduction

From DREAM. . .

Everything starts with an idea or concept in your mind.

To DRAWING. . .

Your thoughts are given form by sketching them out.

To REALITY. . .

The construction process begins.

Bringing Your Model Design Ideas to Life

Do you have an idea in your head you want to get on paper – or into the computer? Then, the next logical step is to make a *drawing* of your design. Being able to sketch out ideas is crucial in the overall process of turning your dream into a finished project. For sure, it's nearly always the *first step* in getting a design out of the idea stage and on the road to becoming a reality.

NOTE: Underlined terms appear in the Glossary.

Just keep in mind, working drawings aren't simply nifty illustrations that are pleasing to the eye. Rather, they provide vital construction information you need in order to get the job done. For this reason, having a good set of *blueprints* can be very important to the success of your project.

In fact, the information contained in this volume lays the *foundation* for a whole new world of modeling opportunities. Once you know how to make accurate plans and construction patterns for your projects, new levels of capability and productivity are just around the corner – thanks to new and exciting technologies. Armed with a good set of plans and some high-tech "digital power tools," just imagine what you can accomplish.

The concepts and techniques presented here apply not only to building models, but also to other design tasks as well. For example, these same methods can be used in many types of do-it-yourself projects. The only limit is your own imagination. . .

What You Need to Know

Written specifically for modelers, craftsmen, and other hobbyists, this book was created to present the model design and blueprinting process in a format that is both easy to understand and to apply. With this volume as your guide, you'll learn powerful techniques and concepts that can help you with just about any project.

You'll quickly get up to speed on the basics, including how to read and interpret blueprints and lay out plan views. Later, you will delve into more advanced topics such as making construction patterns and creating developments and intersections. Before long, you'll be ready to create drawings and patterns for building your own models completely from scratch.

2D Design Basics

Having a set of blueprints is often the starting point for any model design project. Such drawings can help streamline the construction process in many different ways. Being able to create blueprints requires a basic understanding of 2D design fundamentals. For this reason, the material in this book can be considered *foundational* to the model design process.

This foundation involves what is known as <u>drafting</u>. While this may sound technical, don't worry. Rather than assuming any particular level of proficiency, the material covered here will be explained from the point of view of the beginner. With an easy-to-follow format and numerous, detailed illustrations on nearly every page, you'll find plenty of helpful hints and tips along the way.

2D Tools for 3D Artists

Having a good set of plans can be critical if you want to build a physical model from scratch. But, did you know 2D drawings can also be valuable for many 3D modeling tasks as well? For example, you can extract a great deal of information from a set of blueprints that will aid you in building not only the overall form of your 3D model, but also the individual parts. This is particularly true if you are into "hard surface" or "hardware" subjects such as vehicles, buildings, etc.

Before you begin, you may need to determine one or more of the following:

- What is the correct size and shape of my subject?
- Can I determine the cross section I need to build?
- How long and how wide should it be?
- Do I have the correct proportions?

When you're working on a 3D project, these are just a few of the questions a good set of 2D plans can help you answer. Remember, *you always need a starting point*. This is true even when you are creating something entirely in virtual space.

Traditional vs. Digital Tools

In order to provide a useful design course for *all* modelers, the goal here is to cover the general principles of making blueprints. These principles apply whether you want to draw with a pencil and paper or with a computer program.

Until now, the methods for making your own blueprints have been explained only in textbooks and coursework on drafting and engineering graphics. Such material is really intended for engineers, architects, and industrial designers. In contrast, this book was written specifically for modelers, craftsmen, and hobbyists.

Do you build physical models you can hold in your hand or 3D models that exist only inside the computer? Perhaps you are interested in *both* kinds of modeling. No matter what type or genre of modeling you prefer, this book was written for you.

Having a good set of 2D blueprints can jumpstart and then streamline the process of building something in 3D. For example, the complex 3D locomotive model seen on the front cover of this book was made in only a few days. This was possible because 2D plans were used as a starting point.

Whichever approach you choose, this book will equip you with what you need to know to start making blueprints and patterns for your next project.

You may find, however, that computer-based drawing is extremely powerful and efficient. That's why a number of tips and hints in this book are geared towards using digital design tools. If you've never tried drawing with a computer before, you may want to consider the benefits of this approach.

For example, imagine a carpenter going about his work producing something from wood using "basic" hand tools such as a hammer, saw, tape measure, and block plane. As an experienced craftsman, he can do a fine job with these tools and produce beautiful, quality work.

Yet, what if you gave this same craftsman power tools like a table saw, router, and drill? He could not only accomplish his work much faster, but he could do it with more precision and with greater ease. More importantly, even someone who is not an experienced craftsman could produce quality work using this kind of equipment.

In a similar fashion, the advent of computer technology has provided new "digital power tools" for the modeler. Whether you are new to designing model projects or you have a good deal of experience under your belt, just imagine what these digital tools could do for you. Why not open the door to new levels of proficiency, craftsmanship, and productivity?

Computer Design Basics

There are two different approaches for making blueprints using a computer. CAD software is the traditional choice for draftsmen and engineers. In contrast, graphic artists employ illustration programs to make their drawings. Both types of applications are designed for very different purposes. Yet, either can be used to make plans for your projects. Just keep in mind, the process of drawing will be slightly different depending on which path you choose.

Because illustration software is much easier to learn, most of the tips on computer-based drawing in this book will be geared toward using these programs. Refer to **Appendix A** for more detailed information that can help you get up to speed on the basics.

How to Use This Volume

A lot of effort has gone into the design of this book to make it a useful and efficient reference. As an example, the text is fairly large and easy to read. For maximum clarity, illustrations are generous in both size and layout. Most appear on a left-facing page while the accompanying description appears on a right-facing page. Whenever possible, text describing a particular illustration is placed opposite the corresponding figure.

You don't have to use a computer to get a lot out of the material in this book. The basic techniques presented here will work quite well – even if you want to make your drawings on paper the good, old-fashioned way. In that event, all you need to get started is some graph paper, a pencil, a drawing compass, and a good ruler.

Being able to draw in digital format is vital if you want to explore the high-tech world of modeling capabilities made possible by *3D design* and *rapid prototyping*.

Keep in mind, this is not a book on how to draw with a computer. A separate title is available from the publisher that can help get you up to speed on the basics of doing that. Instead, this volume focuses on how to create blueprints and construction patterns for your projects. Many of the tips and hints included here, however, focus on computer-based drawing for both speed and efficiency.

The information covered in this volume has the potential to open up a whole new world of modeling opportunities. Some of the concepts and techniques covered here can prove invaluable for a variety of different model design applications. For more information on some of these exciting possibilities, be sure to read the **Afterword** at the end of this book.

It all starts with what you are learning here in this volume. Once you know how to make drawings for your projects, the sky will indeed be the limit on what you an accomplish.

In addition, substantial margins have been included on the outside edges of every page. Special margin notes appear here. Whenever possible, these are located next to the relevant discussion in each chapter. Keep in mind, these notes *do not* simply repeat key points in the accompanying text. Rather, they provide additional information to enhance some of the points being made. The remaining margin space can then be used for you to write your own notes if desired.

Each chapter begins with an overview that explains what is being discussed and how it can be helpful. Then, it closes with a brief summary of everything that has been covered and how it relates to what will be presented next. The information included is quite extensive.

First, you'll review the basics of how to make blueprints. This is discussed in **Section 1** and includes **Chapters 1-3**. Then, you'll see how to create accurate construction patterns from your finished plans. This is covered in **Section 2**, encompassing **Chapters 4-7**.

The appendices in the back of the book contain lots of useful information as well. Example topics include how art is created in the computer and how to share data between different types of programs. You'll also learn more about how to scan template images and incorporate them into your drawings, as well as how to print your plans on paper.

In addition, you'll find lots of underlined terms throughout this book. These words are defined in the **Glossary**. A detailed **Index** has also been provided.

Be sure to look at the last pages of this volume for more information about related books, as well as future volumes in this series. You'll also find references to some of these titles in the margin notes.

Let's Get Started

You now have a good idea of what this volume is all about and what it can do for you. As you will see, the ability to draw lays the *foundation* for many incredible modeling possibilities. Because blueprints represent the beginning step of just about every model design project, being able to create something completely from scratch – be it in "virtual space" or in the physical realm – may depend on your ability to make drawings and construction patterns.

If you have a dream or concept in mind, this book will show you how to get started bringing your ideas to life. By the time you've read through this material, you will know exactly how to make practical working drawings for your next project. Before you know it, you'll be able to take your ideas from *dream* to *drawing* to *reality*.

Are you ready to dive in and get started? Then, roll up your sleeves and let's get to work!

Section 1
Creating Blueprints

Topics in This Chapter:

Chapter

The Blueprinting Process

1.1: Overview

In this and the remaining chapters of **Section 1**, you will be introduced to some basic blueprinting techniques. This chapter will serve as a quick overview of the blueprinting process. If you first get acquainted with how everything works, understanding the intricate details of making complex drawings will be much easier.

Let's begin with some terminology. When you think of the word blueprints, several different types of drawings may come to mind. You might imagine presentation plans that depict a subject from multiple angles or views. Architects and civil engineers create blueprints in the form of floor plans and elevations that describe buildings and other structures. Designers create design drawings for projects ranging from furniture and cabinetry to crafts and consumer products. And, of course, modelers create plans in order to build their projects. All these things require *blueprints* in one form or another to translate the design from concept into reality.

Drawing blueprints is both an art and a science. It could be argued, however, it is more science than art since many standards have been established for properly laying out a set of plans. Engineers and draftsmen, for example, have long been using these standards to produce "technically correct" working drawings. Modelers have also adopted many of these practices to create construction plans for their own projects. No matter what type of blueprints you wish to create, the techniques illustrated in this book will show you how to make them.

Keep in mind, since this is a book about creating blueprints for model projects, a few techniques may be introduced here that are *not* standard practice for engineers or draftsmen. Everything in this volume, however, is geared to help you create the plans you need to recreate a subject – whether it be in physical form or as a 3D computer model. By providing a "roadmap" to the entire drawing process, this volume can equip you with the tools you need to get started designing your very next project.

NOTE: Underlined terms appear in the Glossary.

Blueprints come in two basic "flavors" – overview or "presentation plans" and detailed "working drawings."

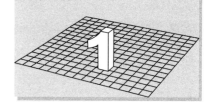

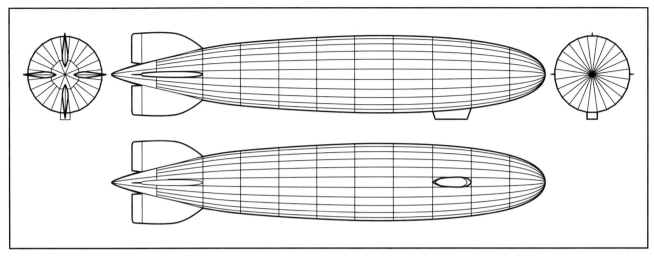

Figure 1.2.1. "Presentation plans" illustrate the form of a subject but not the structure for building a scale model.

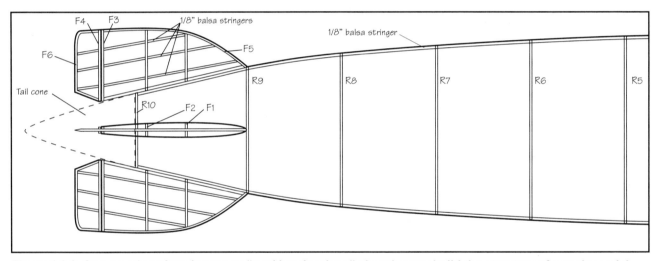

Figure 1.2.2. Construction plans known as "working drawings" show how to build the structure of a scale model.

Section 1 of this volume covers various techniques for making blueprints. **Section 2** demonstrates how to create templates and other useful construction patterns from your finished plans, as well as how to obtain accurate measurements.

1.2: Types of Blueprints

In the context of model design, blueprints come in two basic forms. First, *presentation plans* are overview drawings that show the basic layout of a subject in one or more views. The most common of these are known as 3-view drawings. For example, such plans might show top, side, and front views of a subject similar to that illustrated in **Figure 1.2.1**. Here you can see multiple views of a "rigid dirigible" or airship similar to the type flown in the early 20th Century. While drawings like these might include basic structural details along with the overall layout, they typically do not provide the level of detail needed to build a scale model of the subject. As a result, presentation plans are really only useful as a *starting point* for anyone who wishes to design and build a model from scratch.

In contrast, <u>working drawings</u> are blueprints that are much more useful to modelers. These are often referred to as "construction plans" or, simply, "plans." For example, if you've ever built a model airplane, you may have seen a set of modeler's construction plans. Working drawings such as these contain not only the overall layout, but also key dimensions and construction patterns needed to build a model of the subject completely from scratch.

In **Figure 1.2.2** you can see working drawings created for building a scale model of an airship. Here, the construction details of the tail fin are elaborated. In a similar fashion, plans for a "stick and tissue" model airplane might show not only the framework of the wings, tail, and fuselage, but also the mounting of the engine, propeller, and landing gear. They might also include full-size templates for cutting out the wing ribs and fuselage bulkheads. To be truly useful, such plans should be drawn the same size as the model being built so you can lay parts directly on them as a guide during assembly.

1.3: Multi-View Drawing

The first step in creating a proper set of blueprints is to draw the subject from different angles. These views should be created in such a way as to eliminate any sort of <u>visual perspective</u>. Why is this necessary? The short answer is that perspective introduces *distortion* into any drawing. When objects in a drawing are distorted, you cannot get reliable measurements from them. What is needed is a method whereby a subject can be drawn from any angle without including this naturally occurring visual distortion. The solution is a process known as <u>orthographic projection.</u>

When drawings can be created in such a way that all visual perspective is eliminated, the dimensions shown will then be the actual or *true* dimensions of the subject. This is very important because the primary purpose of blueprints is to provide accurate measurements of your subject. In this way, the drawings themselves become a "measuring stick" of sorts. As a modeler, you can then take this information and use it to build an accurate scale model.

The process of creating blueprints for a subject that include a combination of top, bottom, side, front, and rear views is known as <u>multi-view drawing</u>. The ability to make such drawings is extremely valuable for anyone who wishes to build models from scratch. Not only do you want to know how to orient the various parts you will be building, but you also want to know the correct dimensions of any part or assembly in order to properly fabricate it out of whatever material you have chosen to use. As a result, no matter how simple or complex the subject, you will want a good set of accurate blueprints before you can begin building.

To get started on the road to making your own drawings, take a look at the example blueprints shown in **Figure 1.3.1**. These represent multiple views

Section 1.4 covers the topic of perspective distortion in greater detail. If you plan on using photographs as reference for drawing blueprints, you may want to carefully study this section.

Chapter 3 walks you through a step-by-step example of how to deal with perspective distortion when making blueprints using photographic reference.

Figure 1.3.1. Multi-view drawings of a vintage steam locomotive.

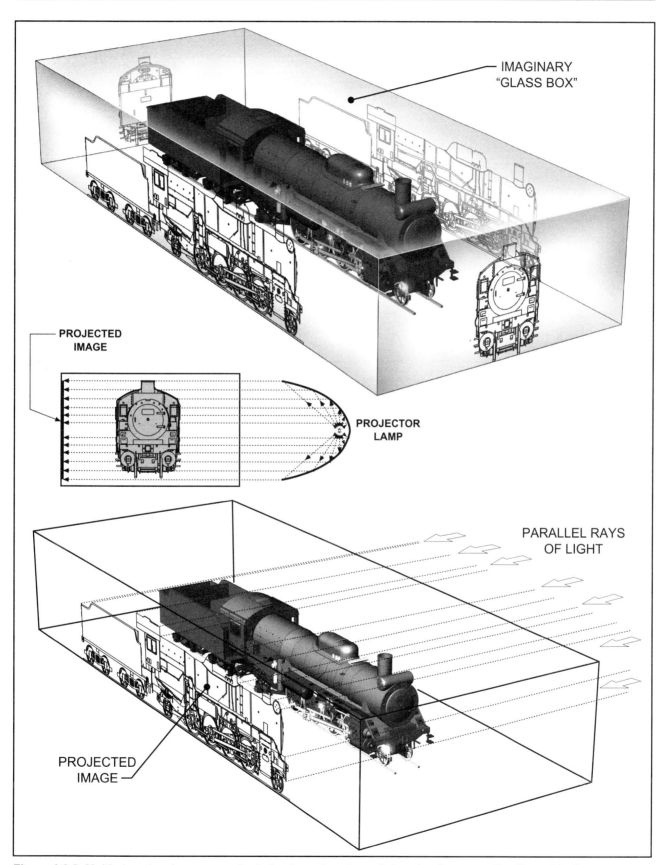

IMAGINARY
"GLASS BOX"

PROJECTED
IMAGE

PROJECTOR
LAMP

PARALLEL RAYS
OF LIGHT

PROJECTED
IMAGE

Figure 1.3.2. Multi-view drawings are *projected* onto an imaginary "glass box" surrounding the subject.

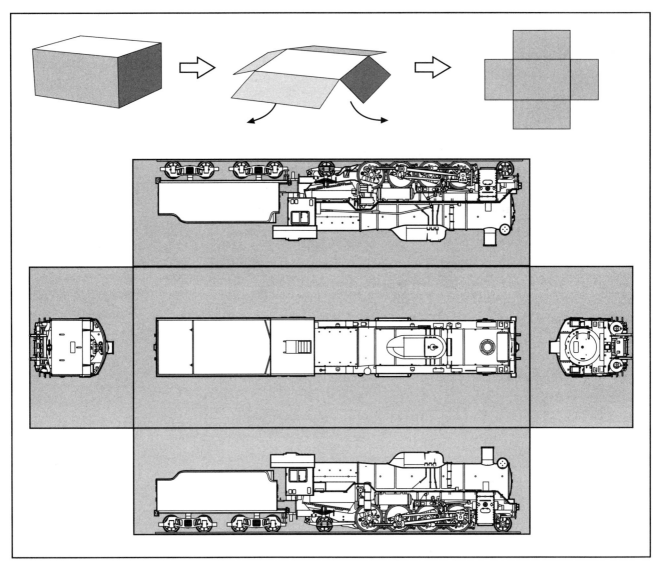

Figure 1.3.3. Create multi-view drawings by "unfolding" the imaginary glass box surrounding the subject.

or "multi-view drawings" of the vintage steam locomotive found on the cover of this volume. All these views were created using orthographic projection. In **Figure 1.3.2**, you can see how the arrangement of the blueprints corresponds with the actual subject. This example provides an important clue to the "secrets" of how the blueprinting process actually works.

As it turns out, orthographic projection – or, simply, "projection" as it is commonly called – is the key to the entire blueprinting process. Projection is used not only to create 2D drawings, but also can be used in 3D modeling as well. Therefore, it is both a concept and a practical technique for the modeler to utilize in a variety of ways.

To understand how it all works, imagine for a moment that your subject is surrounded by an imaginary glass box as illustrated in **Figure 1.3.2**. Such a box must be large enough to completely enclose the subject. Now, imagine a *projector lamp* is aimed at the box in such a way that the rays of light are *perfectly parallel* to each other. Why is this important? When light rays are parallel, any shadows cast by objects in their path are *exactly the same size* as the objects. This effectively eliminates perspective distortion.

If you were to place a projector lamp on the *left* side of the subject, it would cast a shadow on the opposite face of the glass box. If you were to then place a piece of paper over the glass and *trace* the shadow, you would end up with a *right side view* of the subject. Such an outline is known as a projected view. From this point forward, it will be referred to as a plan view.

This process can be taken one step further by imagining your subject itself is semi-transparent. If this were the case, light from the projector would pass not only around the subject but also *through* it. As a result, outlines of all relevant details would appear in the projection. You could then trace everything needed to describe the subject from this particular point of view.

Since the imaginary glass box surrounding the subject has six sides, views can be projected in this manner for each of the six sides in order to generate six different plan views of the subject. These are known as the six principal plan views. If you were to label these views based on the geometry of the subject, you would end up with the following:

- Front plan view
- Rear plan view
- Left side plan view
- Right side plan view
- Top plan view
- Bottom plan view

1.4: A Matter of Perspective

If all this seems like a lot of effort just to make a few sketches, keep in mind the real purpose of creating blueprints is to provide accurate *measurements*. Obviously, you should only measure a drawing if it shows the true dimensions of the subject. When a drawing mimics visual perspective, it will contain some degree of distortion, thereby making it useless as a "measuring stick."

As illustrated in **Figure 1.4.1**, visual perspective is a natural phenomenon that helps you perceive three-dimensional objects. This phenomenon can sometimes create dramatic visual distortion. The degree of distortion often depends both on the size of the object you are viewing and on how far away it is from you when it is viewed. In general, the closer you get to an object, the more noticeable the effect of perspective distortion becomes.

Artists often simulate the appearance of visual perspective in a 2D drawing or painting by using *converging* reference lines. To see just how dramatic

No real-world lamp source can produce perfectly parallel beams of light. The concept of parallel light rays is simply a theoretical idea behind the concept of orthographic projection. It provides a conceptual method whereby visual perspective can be completely eliminated from a drawing.

An easy way to see the effects of perspective distortion is to study photographs taken with different camera lens settings. You may notice a subject photographed with a "wide angle" lens often looks dramatically different than the same subject photographed using a "telephoto" lens.

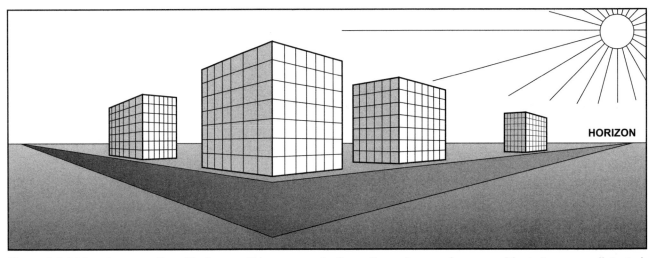

Figure 1.4.1. Visual perspective affects everything you see in three dimensions and causes objects to appear distorted.

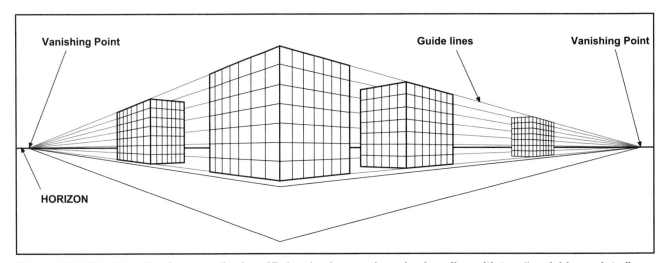

Figure 1.4.2. Simulate visual perspective in a 2D drawing by creating a horizon line with two "vanishing points."

Visual perspective plays havoc when trying to use perspective views as a guide for drawing blueprints. This side view is distorted because the outboard "engine pod" is closer to the camera and thus appears enlarged. The front view is badly distorted because the nose of the ship is so much closer to the camera than everything else.

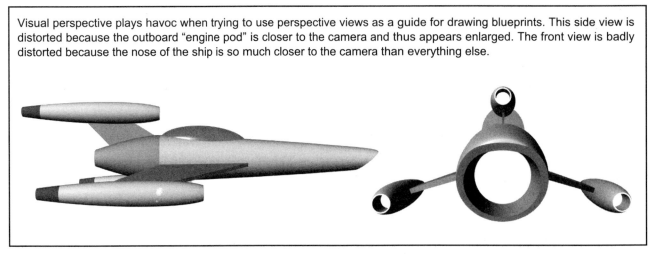

Figure 1.4.3. Visual perspective plays tricks on the eye by causing significant distortion in reference photos.

this effect can be, look at the example shown in **Figure 1.4.2**. Note how the reference lines converge to two different points on the same horizon.

Because blueprints do not include this visual perspective, they are dramatically different from just about all other types of illustrations. Once all perspective has been eliminated, the drawings are said to be "flattened." You can then extract useful measurements from them.

The idea of a "flattened" illustration, however, can sometimes cause confusion. This may be because orthographic views can sometomes look dramatically different from what you might expect. As a result, you may find a projected plan view does not look quite "right" to your eye because you are accustomed to seeing the subject with visual perspective.

This also points the way to another common problem. You may need to rely on photographs for reference in order to make your blueprints. Unfortunately, much like the eye, the camera also "sees" visual perspective. As a result, using photographs as the basis for your blueprints can cause some significant problems. As it turns out, it can be very difficult to take a photograph that successfully approximates or "emulates" a true orthographic plan view.

There can be several reasons for this shortcoming. First and foremost is the inherent distortion caused by the lens of the camera. As you will see in this chapter, the alignment of the subject relative to the lens can also cause a multitude of issues when you are relying on a photograph as a template for your blueprints. Despite your best efforts, most photographs will inevitably be distorted in one way or another. This means subtle differences will nearly always exist between "flattened" orthographic views and the visual perspective seen by your camera.

To illustrate this phenomenon, a series of examples are presented in **Figure 1.4.3** though **Figure 1.4.6**. Although it may not be apparent at first glance, this fictional spacecraft (created specifically for the purposes of this example) has a shape that is somewhat troublesome to draw accurately in plan view form. If you imagine having a model of this craft in front of you, you could rotate the model in order to view it from the side, top, front, and back. You could also photograph the model and use the photographs as reference to begin drawing blueprints of the craft.

Unfortunately, if you simply trace a side view photo of this subject, you will start running into problems right away. Drawing the fuselage of this model in the side view is fairly straightforward. But, what about the engines? Note how the outboard engine is placed on the tip of the "wing" so that it is located far away from the centerline of the ship. As a result, when looking at the model from the side, the engine nearest your eye will appear quite a bit larger than it really is. At the same time, the engine on the opposite side will

Visual perspective is always present whenever you take a photograph. This can cause numerous problems if you are relying on photos for reference when making your blueprints.

Due to the nature of optics, all camera lenses cause at least some degree of distortion. The highest quality lenses (often the most expensive) are designed to minimize distortion as much as possible.

Note the dramatic difference between a front perspective view seen through a 50 mm lens (left) versus the same angle when photographed with a 150 mm lens. A "longer" lens reduces perspective distortion considerably. This makes the resulting image far more useful.

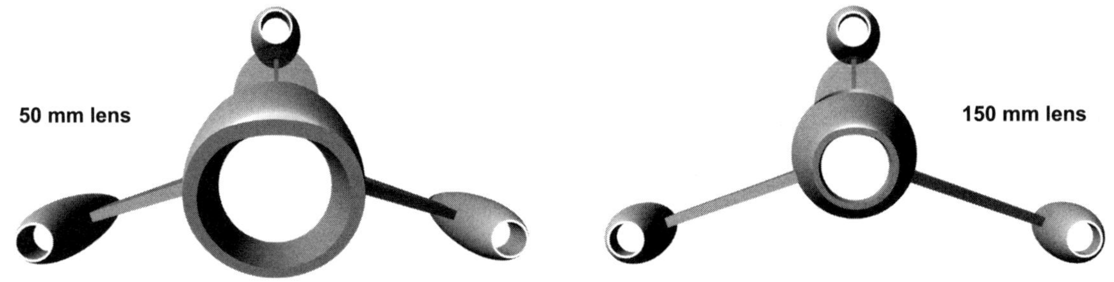

50 mm lens   **150 mm lens**

Figure 1.4.4. The focal length of the lens used can have a dramatic affect on perspective distortion in the image.

ACTUAL SUBJECT   BARREL DISTORTION   PINCUSHION DISTORTION

Figure 1.4.5. Cheap or defective camera lenses can cause either *barrel distortion* or *pincushion distortion*.

Template images will always contain some perspective distortion – even when they have been photographed using a telephoto lens. In this example, orthographic plan view drawings have been superimposed on both side and front template images. Note the dramatic differences between the apparent and the "true" dimensions of certain features.

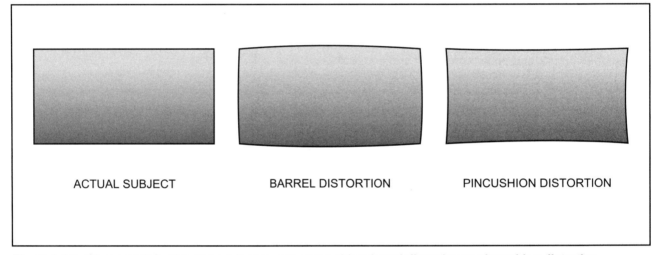

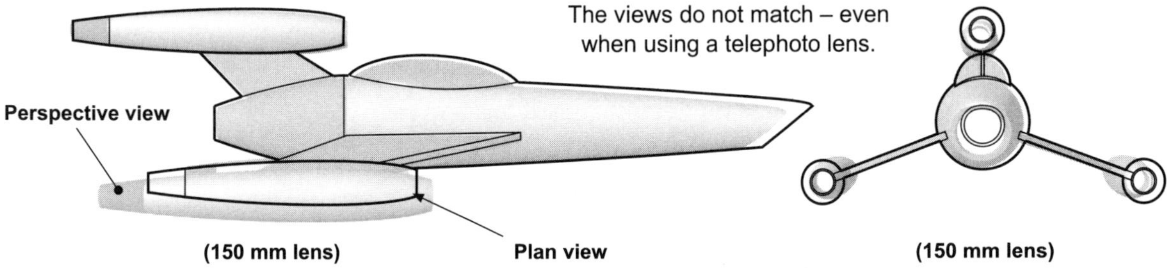

The views do not match – even when using a telephoto lens.

Perspective view

(150 mm lens)   **Plan view**   **(150 mm lens)**

Figure 1.4.6. Template images are always distorted – even those photographed using a "telephoto" lens.

appear much smaller than it really is. Then there is a *third* engine in the middle of the craft. Which one should you trace?

The answer here is to use the *center engine* for reference in the side view while ignoring the other two. Since both the center engine and fuselage share the same centerline, they are located in the same plane. Thus, you can accurately gauge the size of each in relation to the other. On the other hand, the outboard engines should not be used for reference in this view.

Other problems appear as you continue trying to draw the craft. For example, when viewed from the front, the long "nose" will be much closer to the camera than the rest of the ship. This causes *severe* perspective distortion as illustrated in **Figure 1.4.3**. The amount of distortion will depend both on the distance between the model and the camera and on the focal length of the lens used to take the photograph.

According to basic principles of photography, it is generally believed your eye sees objects the same way a 35 mm camera would when fitted with a 50 mm lens. As a result, an object appearing in a photograph taken with such a setup should appear about the same as it would if you were viewing it in person. *Decreasing* the focal length of the lens *increases* the perspective and, therefore, the distortion. This is known as "wide angle" photography. Because the distortion in such photos can be severe, you should avoid using wide angle photos for reference whenever you are drawing blueprints.

Increasing the focal length *reduces* the apparent perspective distortion. This can be very valuable if you need to use photos as an aid when drawing blueprints. For example, in **Figure 1.4.4** you can see an illustration of how drastically different the front view of our example spacecraft will appear when photographed with a 50 mm lens as opposed to a 150 mm lens. The first image is approximately how you would see the model if it were in front of you. It is obvious such a view would not be very useful for reference. On the other hand, using a "telephoto" lens (i.e. one longer than about 100 mm) produces a much better template image.

Perspective distortion is not the only potential problem when using photographs as reference. The lens used to take the photograph can cause other types of visual distortion as well. One common example is called <u>barrel distortion</u>. This is illustrated in **Figure 1.4.5**. Barrel distortion causes the middle of the image to be enlarged relative to the outside edges. This problem is quite common with inexpensive lenses such as those typically found on a consumer-grade, auto-focus type of camera. A related problem is known as <u>pincushion distortion</u>, and this is also demonstrated in **Figure 1.4.5**. This is the opposite of barrel distortion. Here, the interior of the image is *less* magnified than the outside edges.

When studying photographs, beware of perspective distortion based on the shape of the subject, the type of lens used, and the distance from the camera. Whenever possible, choose photographs taken with a *telephoto lens* where the camera was aimed directly at one side of the subject.

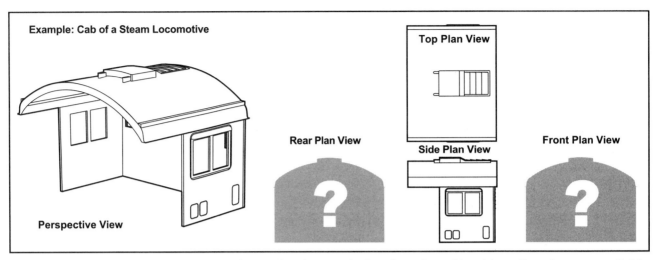

Figure 1.5.1. Orthographic projection can be used to draw a missing view when at least two other views are available.

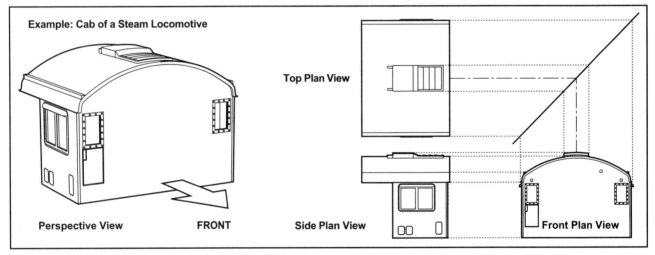

Figure 1.5.2. Use orthographic projection to graphically "calculate" missing information.

Due to potential distortion problems, try to avoid tracing photographs directly when drawing your blueprints. If this becomes absolutely necessary, be certain you understand exactly how the image is distorted so you can compensate. To do this, use actual measurements of the subject to derive the correct dimensions in each plan view whenever possible.

To illustrate how tricky this process can be, look at the example shown in **Figure 1.4.6**. Here you can see an illustration representing both a side plan view and a front plan view of the example spacecraft. These views have been superimposed on perspective images of both angles. The images were created specifically for this purpose and simulate a photo taken with a telephoto lens. Even then, note how dramatically different the craft looks in true orthographic plan view. These types of differences can sometimes fool your eye and trick you into drawing portions of your subject incorrectly.

1.5: The "Power" of Projection

You have now seen how orthographic projection can be used to eliminate all visual perspective and generate up to six principal plan views of any subject. This, however, is only the tip of the iceberg when it comes to the usefulness of this technique. The process of projection has another, even more powerful application. If you have two different plan views of any subject, you can use projection to fill in or *graphically calculate* a missing view.

The best way to illustrate this concept is by example. Look at the cab of our vintage locomotive shown **Figure 1.5.1**. To begin drawing this part of the subject, you might start with published blueprints that show the side plan view. Unfortunately, the side view alone does not provide sufficient information to recreate the cab – another view is also needed to begin mapping out this area. If you can somehow obtain a *top* plan view, for example, you could use the technique of projection to fill in the remaining details.

As you will see in **Chapter 2** and **Chapter 3**, this process begins by "unfolding" the imaginary glass box surrounding the subject and "flattening it out." This permits all six principal plan views to be arranged so they are adjacent to one another. Once they are positioned in this manner, details can be projected from one view into another. This process makes it possible to derive any missing detail in one view by transferring information from at least two other views.

You can see an example of this process in **Figure 1.5.2**. Here, projection is being used to fill in the details of a missing front plan view for the cab of our example locomotive.

1.6: A Sense of Scale

There is one last subject to discuss in this overview of the blueprinting process. As you are probably aware, just about everything involved with modeling revolves around <u>scale</u>. In most cases, the model to be built will be some fraction of the size of its "real world" counterpart. As a result, plans for building a model are typically drawn to a specific scale. To avoid confusion, this scale should always be indicated somewhere on the blueprints.

Working drawings for a model project should ideally be the same size as the finished model. After all, when taking measurements from your drawings, you'll be obtaining the exact dimensions of the parts to be built. The only time drawings are made to a *different* scale is when the model is very large or when the drawings are to be published or distributed in a format that limits their overall size. In any event, whether or not the blueprints are going to be the exact same size as the model, the scale of the drawings should always be specified on the plans.

See **Section 2.12** in **Chapter 2** for more details on conventions used for labeling the scale of your working drawings.

For information about how to make scale calculations for your model projects, read *Easy Project Math: A Problem-Solving Guide for the Craftsman, Hobbyist, and Do-It-Yourselfer*, part of the *Modeler's Notebook Reference Series* available from:

www.ModelersNotebook.com

The drawing area inside a computer illustration program is sometimes referred to as the pasteboard. This term originates from the traditional method of creating layouts for printing by hand using paper and paste.

In this context, the term "page" is almost a misnomer. Since most modeling plans take up a large amount of space, they are often arranged on poster-sized "sheets" rather than on pages.

For additional information regarding printing your plans on paper, see **Appendix C**.

Many computer illustration programs allow you to draw objects up to about a dozen feet across. The size is limited only by the dimensions of the program's virtual canvas or drawing area. This is more than adequate for the vast majority of modeling projects. In the event your model exceeds these limits, you may be forced to reduce your drawings in order to make them fit inside the available space. Note that CAD systems may not have these limitations.

In addition, you'll need to set up a page size before you can start drawing with an illustration program. (This is something else that may not apply to a CAD program.) Since model plans can be quite large, think of this as a sheet size instead. In fact, the need to print or plot a drawing – plus the requirement of determining the sheet size in advance – may tempt some modelers to choose a scale based on how big they wish the printout to be. While this might seem like an intuitive approach, in reality it is better to make your drawings first, *then* divide up your work to fit onto individual sheets as needed.

For example, you might simply create one giant "page" in a single drawing file and place everything on that. If you run out of room on the program's virtual canvas, try dividing the drawing up into multiple files. Whatever you choose to do, you can always make a *copy* of the finished plans and format the copy for printing or plotting on paper as needed. Simply divide the copy into chunks that fit on a specific size sheet. Then, create as many sheets (i.e. pages) as needed to contain everything you want to print.

What size sheets should you use? Since most modern engineering copiers and plotters print on giant rolls of paper, they can output anything as large as the length and width of an entire roll. As you can imagine, this should certainly be large enough to accommodate plans for just about *any* model building project. So, as you can see, there is little need to worry about choosing a scale for your computer drawings based solely on the size of the paper on which they will be printed.

If, for whatever reason, you decide your plans must be made to a different scale than the finished model, consider drawing everything full size in the computer and then make a *reduced copy* of the finished drawings. In this way, the plans can be output in more than one scale with minimal extra work. Just remember, if you do change the size of the plans in this manner, be sure to also change the scale indicated on the drawings.

1.7: Summary

In the context of model design, blueprints can take two basic forms:

- Presentation Plans
- Construction Plans known as "Working Drawings"

Multi-view drawing is the process of creating plan view blueprints of any subject. Visual perspective is a natural phenomenon that causes distortion in everything you see with your eyes. To eliminate this distortion, plan views must be drawn without any visual perspective. This allows you to take accurate measurements from the plans.

Orthographic projection is the technique used to create each plan view. Not only does this eliminate all perspective, it also allows you to "graphically calculate" a missing view from information found in other views.

You must be aware of *perspective distortion* when using photographs for reference. Objects that appear close to the camera will be enlarged while those farther away will be reduced in apparent size. Both the distance from the camera and the focal length of the lens can have a dramatic impact on the distortion present in a photo. Images taken with a *telephoto lens* are generally more suitable to use as reference for drawing blueprints.

Everything about modeling revolves around *scale*. You should always indicate the scale on any blueprints you create. In general, most plans will be made the same size as the model to be built. When this is not possible, draw your plans full size and then scale a copy to fit on a particular size sheet of paper.

What's Next?

Now you have been introduced to the concept of projection. Before you can get started drawing blueprints, however, it is important to review some conventions and standards of drafting. These will be covered in **Chapter 2**. Learning about standard drafting practices can help you make your drawings as professional and clear as possible – whether they will be created only for you or for others to enjoy as well.

Topics in This Chapter:

Chapter

Blueprinting Basics & Standard Practices

2.1: Overview

In the last chapter you saw an overview of the blueprinting process and a quick example of how orthographic projection can be used to create up to six principal plan views of any subject. This same process can also be used to fill in missing details in one view based on information contained in other views. A detailed, step-by-step example of the entire process will be presented in **Chapter 3**. Before getting to that, however, this chapter will discuss some blueprinting basics and also many standard practices or "conventions" for making professional-looking working drawings.

The process of drawing blueprints is formally known as <u>drafting</u>. If that term sounds very technical, it's probably because drafting is something normally practiced by engineers, industrial designers, and architects. As a result, most books and classes on the subject are extremely detailed and technical in nature. In contrast, this volume was created to present powerful drafting techniques in a context more suited for modelers and other skilled craftsmen. As part of that process, this chapter will introduce some of the conventions followed by professional draftsmen as they create their drawings.

Why should you bother with these standards? There are two very good reasons. First, knowing the basics will help you read and interpret blueprints created by other people. This can come in very handy when you are building a model from someone else's plans. Second, by becoming familiar with and applying some of these same standards, you will be able to make professional-looking drawings for your own projects. This will not only improve the appearance of what you produce, but it will also make it easier for others to read and understand your work.

2.2: Arranging Multi-View Drawings

As a modeler, you may need to obtain critical measurements from any one of the principal plan views. As a result, it is often a good idea to prepare working drawings of all six principal plan views. This is especially true when the subject is complex, such as the vintage steam locomotive seen in **Chapter 1**.

NOTE: Underlined terms appear in the Glossary.

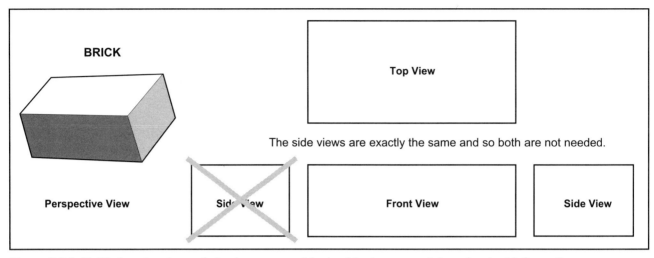

Figure 2.2.1. Multi-view drawings of simple or symmetrical subjects can contain redundant information.

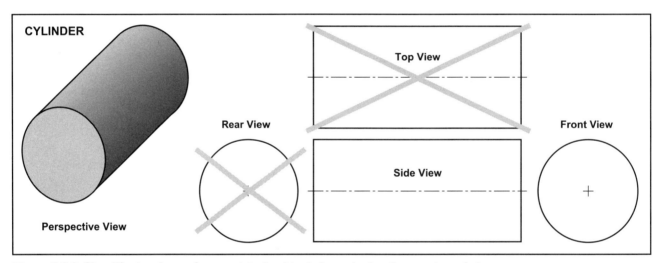

Figure 2.2.2. Simplify drawings of symmetrical subjects by reducing the number of views.

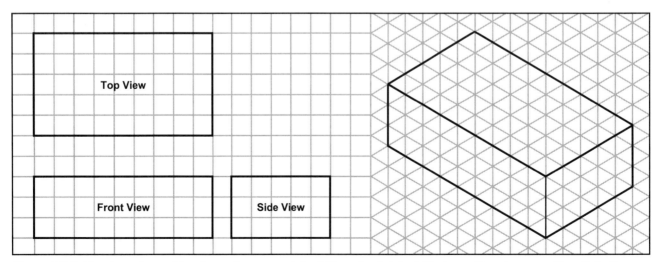

Figure 2.2.3. Create an isometric view using a special grid to get a "pictorial" view without perspective distortion.

On the other hand, when an object is symmetrical as shown in **Figure 2.2.1**, some of the plan views may simply be a mirror image of one another. In such cases, these views would contain the exact same information. By reducing the number of views shown, less space is needed to present all of the information required to recreate a simple or symmetrical structure.

In fact, a *three-view* or *four-view* drawing is often sufficient for depicting symmetrical objects. Sometimes, even fewer views are needed. As an example, **Figure 2.2.2** shows a cylinder that is symmetrical about its longitudinal centerline. Because the front and rear views of this cylinder are identical – as are the top and side views – it is really only necessary to draw a complete side view plus *either* a front view or rear view in order to adequately describe this object.

Many objects have some degree of symmetry. This is why it is common drafting practice to prepare just three views in order to describe most subjects. An optional fourth view may also be included when needed. Traditionally, this fourth view is a *three-dimensional view* prepared using a technique called isometric sketching as shown in **Figure 2.2.3**.

An isometric view is a pictorial representation of the subject that is meant to help the person viewing the drawings properly interpret what they are seeing. In keeping with the intent and purpose of orthographic projection, this view is created in such a way as to completely eliminate all visual perspective. As mentioned in **Chapter 1**, visual perspective is always present whenever you view any three-dimensional object. As a result, the concept of a three-dimensional view without true perspective may seem counterintuitive. In fact, some people may find isometric views to be confusing. Because of this, they will not be used in this book.

Yet, having a dimensional pictorial can make a set of "flattened" plan view drawings much easier to interpret. With the advent of readily available 3D modeling technology, there is really no reason not to include a true perspective view when convenient. Of course, the advantage of using an isometric pictorial is that you can obtain measurements from it. But, it can be argued, this information is already available in the plan views. Therefore, whenever a perspective view is presented in this book, it will be a *true perspective view* rather than an isometric view.

2.3: Choosing Your Views

At this point, you may be asking yourself: "So, which views should I draw?" The answer is it depends on the symmetry of your subject. For example, look at the complex and completely non-symmetrical object shown in **Figure 2.3.1**. Here, details on the left side differ from those on the right. In addition, detail exists on the top that is not present on the bottom. As a result,

Isometric sketching is a topic unto itself. Since isometric drawings present a three-dimensional or "pictorial" view without true visual perspective, they may take some getting used to.

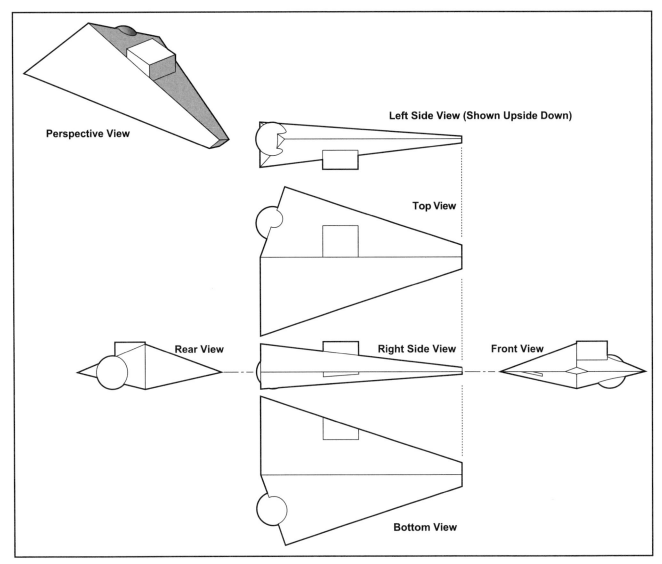

Figure 2.3.1. All six principal plan views may be needed to describe complex or non-symmetrical objects.

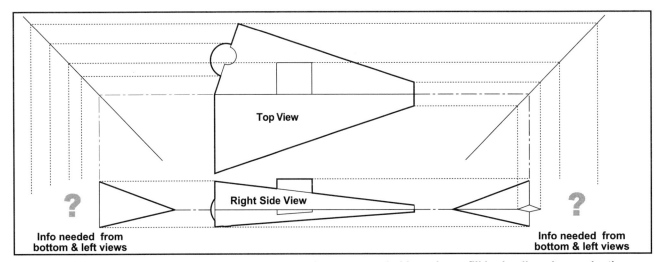

Figure 2.3.2. When the subject is asymmetrical, more views are needed in order to fill in details using projection.

for this subject, a standard three-view arrangement is simply not sufficient to completely describe it in blueprint form. In this case, all six principal plan views should be drawn.

For the purposes of this example, imagine you already had a right side view and a top plan view of the subject as shown in **Figure 2.3.2**. In that event, you would need to find the missing front and rear views. You could use the technique of orthographic projection to do this. Your options would be limited, however, because of the asymmetry in this particular subject. With only a right side view and a top plan view as a starting point, there simply is not sufficient information available to complete the front and rear plan views. As a result, only *one half* of the front or the rear view could be extrapolated from what is already present.

Why is this the case? As you will see in **Chapter 3**, the technique of projection is used to locate a point in any plan view using information from *two other views*. A detail in the front view, for example, can be derived from information found in the top view and side view (or the bottom view and side view). Since the example subject has details that appear in the top view but not the bottom view – as well as details that appear in the left view but not the right view – critical information needed to create the front and rear views requires *four* other views for reference rather than just two.

In this case, in order to draw the complete front and rear views, you would need a complete left side view, right side view, bottom view, and top view. Only with *all four* views present would you have sufficient information to generate the missing front and rear plan views of this subject using projection.

This is a good example of why having all six principal plan views can be very helpful. When it is not practical to draw all six views, carefully choose only those views that are absolutely necessary. If several different views contain the same basic information, choose the one that is easiest to interpret. For example, if two views are otherwise identical but one has more hidden lines than the other, choose the view with fewer hidden lines and thus omit the "busier" view.

This aspect of drafting is a bit subjective. Simply remember the intent is to make your drawings as clear as possible. If the completed plans are not self-explanatory, you could probably do a better job with your presentation. See **Figure 2.3.3** and **Figure 2.3.4** for examples of proper view selection.

2.4: Standards for Arrangement of Views

Since it's often convenient to depict only those views that are absolutely needed to adequately describe a subject in plan view form, having all six principal plan views is often the exception rather than the rule. For modelers,

When preparing blueprints of your subject, it is best to map out all six principal plan views. You can later consolidate things by making a copy of the drawing and removing any views you don't really need.

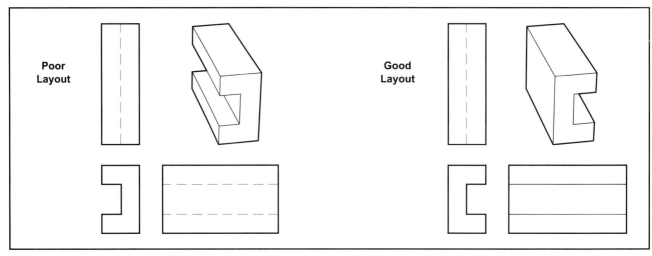

Figure 2.3.3. Make each drawing as clear as possible by carefully choosing the views you present.

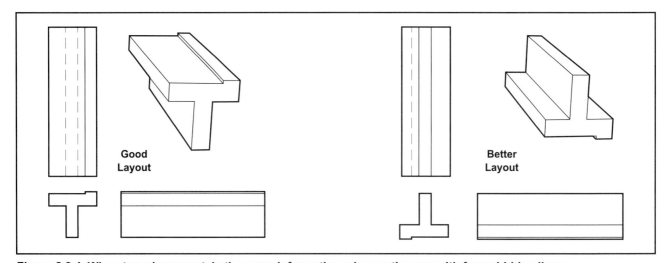

Figure 2.3.4. When two views contain the same information, choose the one with fewer hidden lines.

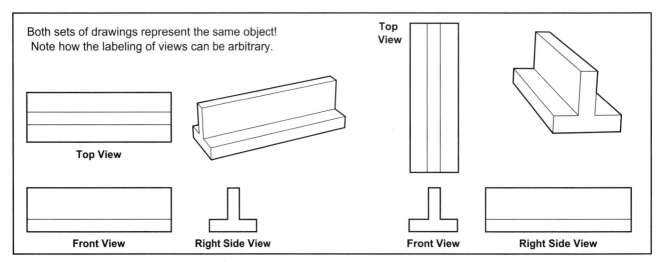

Figure 2.4.1. Use *third-angle projection* for arranging 3-view drawings according to US, Canadian, and British standards.

however, it is a good habit to prepare all six views of a subject. You may end up using only three or four of these views in your final plans, but all the information will be there if you need it. The rule here is simple: Be flexible.

Once you've decided which views to include, arrange them in a precise and organized fashion. Keep in mind, the objective of any drafting exercise is to create drawings that are both precise and *clear*. As it turns out, the manner in which you arrange your views can have a dramatic impact on the clarity of your drawings.

Fortunately, there are some guidelines that can help. For example, in the United States, Canada, and Great Britain, the accepted standard for the arrangement of views is a three-view layout similar to that shown in **Figure 2.4.1**. This standard is known as <u>third-angle projection</u>. Six-view drawings, when presented in their entirety, are typically arranged as shown in **Figure 2.4.2**. Europe and the International community have slightly different standards for arranging views, following the principle of <u>first-angle projection</u> as shown in **Figure 2.4.3**.

Third-angle projection is standard for blueprints drawn in the US, Canada, and Great Britain. First-angle projection is the standard used by the rest of the world.

If you carefully study the standards for first-angle and third-angle projection, you may notice the front view simply depicts whatever part of the object happens to be facing the front. This is not necessarily the true front of the object. In the same way, the left and right side views are arbitrarily labeled according to whatever is chosen to be the front view – whether these views represent the actual side of the object or not. In some cases, the right side view may end up representing the *left* side of the object.

To make matters worse, the standard arrangement in third-angle projection calls for the top view to appear above the front view. If an object is much longer than it is tall, this makes for a very awkward layout. Using this arrangement, you might end up making your drawing enormous just to allow

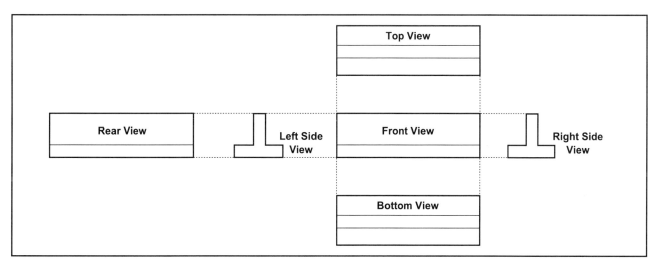

Figure 2.4.2. When using *third-angle projection*, arrange 6-view drawings as shown.

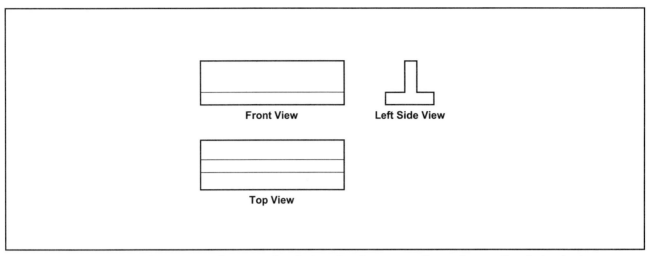

Figure 2.4.3. Use *first-angle projection* for arranging 3-view drawings according to International standards.

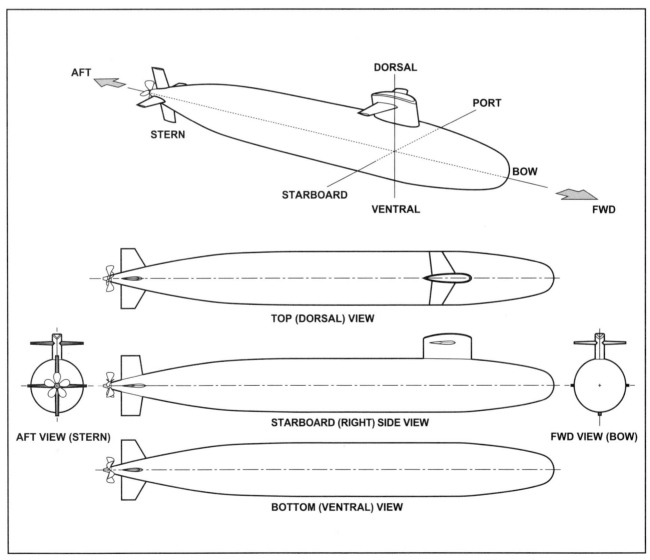

Figure 2.4.4. As an alternative, choose a more intuitive layout based on the geometry of the subject.

room for all the views. In such cases, it would be much more convenient to implement an alternate arrangement of views that does not follow the standard.

Consider the example of a model submarine like the one shown in **Figure 2.4.4**. Here the views are arranged in a *horizontal* format that conserves valuable drawing space. The subject is oriented naturally so that the front points one way and the rear points in the opposite direction. As a result, the side view becomes the "center" of the drawing rather than the front view as in the traditional arrangement. The front view is now arranged to the right of the side view and the rear view appears on the left. The top view is located above the side view and the bottom view is placed below.

Of course, you could also reverse this arrangement and have the front of the boat pointing to the *left* – it's really up to you to decide what works best. You may, however, find the arrangement shown here to be very convenient. Notice how the views in this example are oriented according to the natural geometry of the *subject* rather than some arbitrary standard.

In fact, when making drawings of a submarine – or just about any other modeling subject – it is very intuitive to label the views in this manner. In Naval parlance, for example, a boat or ship has a "bow" (front), "stern" (rear), "port side" (left side), and "starboard side" (right side). The top is known as the "dorsal" surface and the bottom is referred to as the "ventral" surface. Therefore, the front plan view represents the bow of the submarine, and the right side view becomes the starboard side of the boat. There is no room for confusion with such a layout! Because this arrangement is natural and intuitive, it will be the preferred format for arranging views used throughout this book.

2.5: Introduction to Line Types

The clarity of your drawing can be dramatically affected by the line types you use to describe the various surfaces, intersections, and hidden areas of your subject. Drafting standards dictate the use of specific line types for specific purposes. **Figure 2.5.1** provides a brief overview of several different types of lines and their respective uses. A solid black line, for example, indicates an edge or intersection. On the other hand, a dotted line is used to represent a feature below the surface that cannot be seen in a particular view and is therefore "hidden."

Keep in mind, a CAD application is specifically designed to accomodate traditional drafting practices so all the needed line types will be built into the program. On the other hand, computer illustration programs were not designed for draftsmen, so they often lack some of these lines types. For example, notice the *break line* shown in **Figure 2.5.1**. This is just a "squiggly" line that is traditionally drawn by hand with a pen on drafting paper.

You can arrange your views any way you want. Following a logical layout, however, will greatly help others who need to read and interpret your drawings.

One convention not often discussed is using thicker lines around the *perimeter* of objects. This technique is commonly employed when drawing "presentation plans" to make them look more elegant. Thicker lines can also help the viewer distinguish one part or subassembly of the subject from another. As a result, this practice can make drawings more clear. You will see this method used in most of the illustrations in this book.

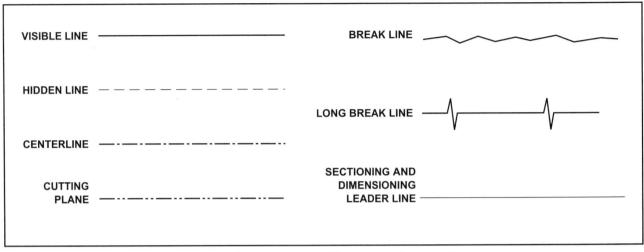

Figure 2.5.1. In order to adhere to convention, use standard line types when creating blueprints.

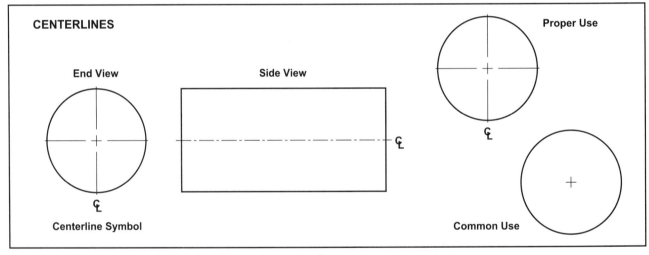

Figure 2.6.1. The centerline is one of the most important line types.

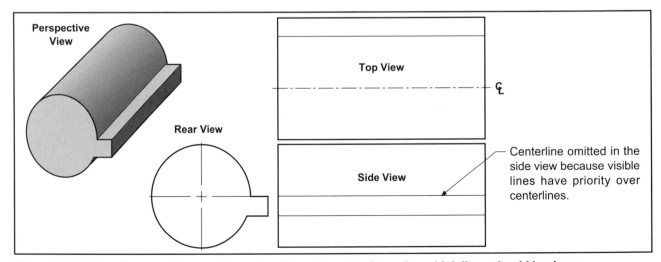

Figure 2.7.1. When lines overlap, use the *order of importance* to determine which lines should be drawn.

There is no equivalent to this type of line in a modern computer illustration program. As a result, you must draw break lines manually when using this type of program. Fortunately, this task is not difficult – just use the *Pen Tool* to draw a wavy line approximating the appearance of a proper break line.

The *long break line* is another line type that must be created from scratch when using a computer illustration program. You can use a *Multi-Segment Line Tool* to create this type of line.

2.6: Centerlines

The centerline is one of the most important types of lines you can draw when creating blueprints. Centerlines indicate a subject's axis of symmetry as illustrated in **Figure 2.6.1**. Such lines should always be drawn with a distinct dashed pattern as shown. (Note how this is a different dashed pattern than that used for indicating hidden lines.) In addition, the "CL" symbol helps clearly indicate when a line is a centerline. This symbol does not have to be included, but it is helpful to ensure clarity in a busy drawing.

Try to get in the habit of including centerlines for *all* symmetrical features in every plan view. As you will see in later chapters, this becomes very important for a number of different blueprinting and pattern-making tasks. For example, by including a centerline, you can draw just one half of an object in any view and then flip or "mirror" it to create the other half. This can save you a lot of work! Centerlines can also prove very valuable for aligning parts when it comes time to actually build your model – especially when you are making a 3D computer model.

For most objects, the axis of symmetry is simply depicted as a dashed line. On the other hand, when a subject or feature appears as a *circle* in any plan view, it is customary to mark the center of the circle with a *cross* instead, as shown in **Figure 2.6.1**. Once that is done, extend lines out from this cross in all four directions as shown. This effectively marks four key points along the edge or circumference of the circle. These points will be invaluable later when you are attempting to align parts together during assembly.

2.7: Proper Use of Line Types

When you begin using different line types in your drawings, it becomes very important to implement them properly in order to maintain readability. For example, when the centerline happens to overlap either a visible or a hidden line, the centerline should be *omitted* for clarity as shown in **Figure 2.7.1**. This concept is known as the order of importance for line types. The rules are quite simple:

It is often permissible to *omit* one half of a symmetrical subject or feature when space is limited. See **Section 2.8** for more information.

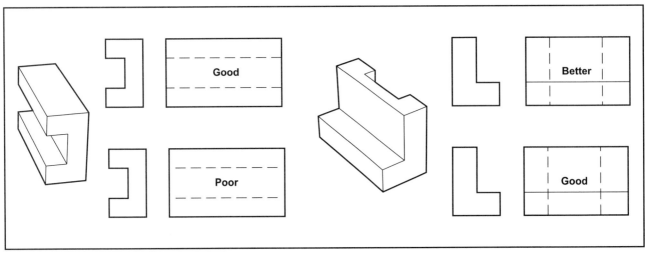

Figure 2.7.2. To make your drawings look more professional, ensure lines intersect properly.

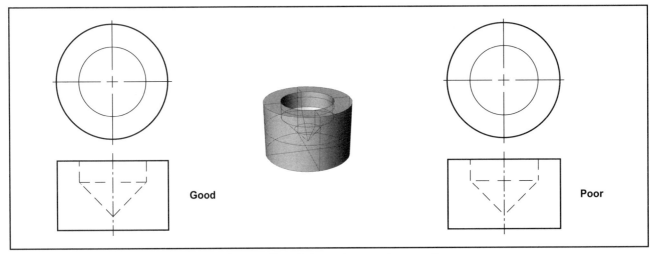

Figure 2.7.3. Make sure hidden lines and centerlines intersect properly as well.

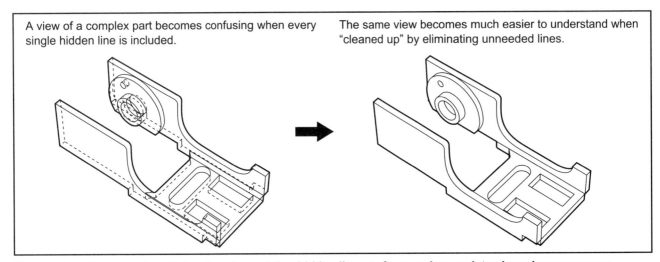

A view of a complex part becomes confusing when every single hidden line is included.

The same view becomes much easier to understand when "cleaned up" by eliminating unneeded lines.

Figure 2.8.1. Clean up "busy" drawings by omitting hidden lines to form an *incomplete view* when necessary.

- Visible lines must always be shown and therefore have priority over all other line types.
- Hidden lines are next in priority.
- Centerlines are last.

Whenever lines overlap in a view, use the "order of importance" principle to decide which lines to show and which to omit in order to maintain clarity.

There are also rules governing how lines should *intersect*. In **Figure 2.7.2** you can see some examples of properly intersecting dashed lines according to convention. Poorly rendered lines are also shown for comparison. CAD programs may handle these situations automatically. Unfortunately, when using a computer illustration program to draw dashed lines, the program will control the spacing of the dashes and they may not line up in this manner. As a result, you may not be able to get your dashed lines to appear this way without some extra effort.

Figure 2.7.3 shows the way hidden lines should ideally intersect with each other and with centerlines. Since tweaking dashed lines is not always convenient or easy when using a computer illustration program, attempting to control exactly where the dashes fall may become a frustrating exercise. As an alternative, you can always "simulate" a dashed line with a series of shorter lines for more precise control. After a while, however, you may begin to wonder if all that effort is really worthwhile. In the end, it all depends on how closely you want to follow convention.

2.8: Incomplete, Removed, and Partial Views

Sometimes an object is so complex that including every single hidden line would produce a very "busy" and confusing drawing. In this case, omit some of the hidden lines in an effort to produce a cleaner drawing. As illustrated in **Figure 2.8.1**, a view that is "cleaned up" in this manner is known as an incomplete view.

When a particular detail or feature is located so it cannot be clearly seen in *any* plan view, create a supplemental illustration known as a removed view to illustrate the part. This concept is demonstrated in **Figure 2.8.2**. Here, a detail exists on the *inside* of a part in such a way that it can only be seen using hidden lines in the side view. Since the side view contains vital information about this particular detail, illustrating it using only hidden lines would not be satisfactory. A removed view solves the problem and allows the part to be seen clearly.

A partial view can be used when space is limited and the subject is perfectly symmetrical as shown in **Figure 2.8.3**. In this case, drawing the entire view would simply be redundant. Creating a partial view provides the same

---

When drawing a line with a computer illustration program, if dashes do not appear where you want them, try cutting or *splitting* the line. (For example, in some programs, you might do this using a *Knife Tool*.) This forces the dashes to be re-aligned. You can always experiment by trimming your lines in different places until you get the results you want.

A *removed view* is labeled very much like a section view. Section views are covered in **Section 2.9** and they are also discussed in detail in **Chapter 5**.

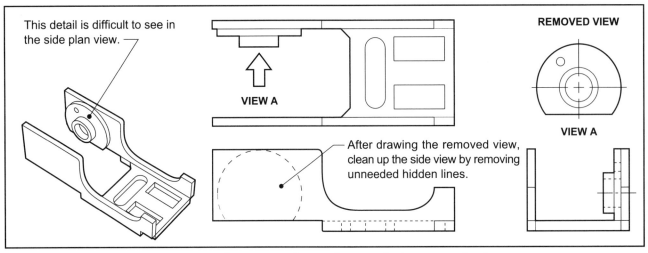

This detail is difficult to see in the side plan view.

VIEW A

REMOVED VIEW

VIEW A

After drawing the removed view, clean up the side view by removing unneeded hidden lines.

Figure 2.8.2. Create a *removed view* to illustrate an obscured part or feature more clearly.

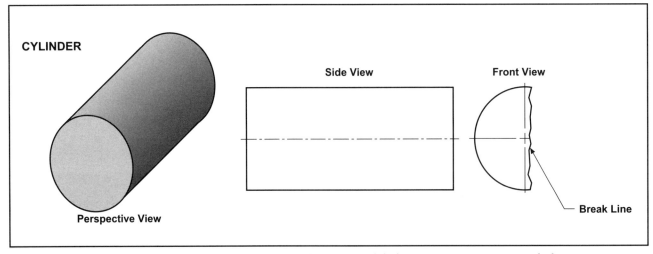

CYLINDER

Side View

Front View

Perspective View

Break Line

Figure 2.8.3. When the subject is perfectly symmetrical, use a *partial view* to save space as needed.

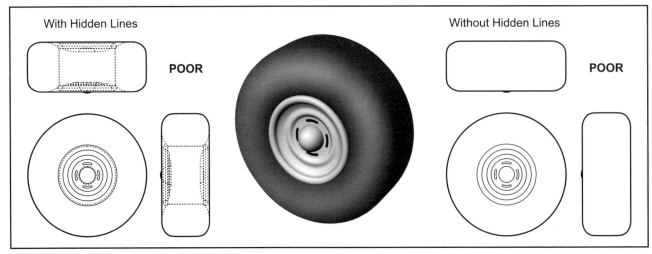

With Hidden Lines

POOR

Without Hidden Lines

POOR

Figure 2.9.1. Standard views do not provide sufficient information to recreate a structure such as this wheel.

information but saves space (and effort). A *break line* is added to indicate that a portion of the object has been omitted from the view.

2.9: Sections

While incomplete, removed or partial views can sometimes help reduce potential confusion, they may not present enough information to help you build a particular part or structure. For example, in order to create something completely from scratch, modelers need information about the cross section of the subject. For simple subjects or those that have an exposed structure, this information may already be present in the plan views. Many times, however, all or part of the subject's internal structure is completely hidden from view. In these cases, none of the plan views provide sufficient information to recreate the shape.

The solution is to create section views in order to make your drawings as clear as possible. Such views present extremely critical information about the internal structure of the subject. In many cases, it would difficult or even impossible to build a model without this information. As a result, the ability to determine cross sections is a vital skill for modelers to master.

An example of the need for a section is shown in **Figure 2.9.1.** Here, a generic wheel assembly from a vehicle has been drawn. Information about the cross section of this wheel is not visible in the top, bottom, front, or rear views because the tire is in the way. Hidden lines would therefore be used to depict the wheel in these views. This could be very confusing. Without information about the *cross section* of the wheel, you would have no basis for drawing these hidden lines anyway. In this case, hidden lines in the plan views simply do not help. But, omitting them is not very helpful either.

A *section* is a form of "cutaway" illustration that shows the outlines of parts that would otherwise be hidden from view. Do not confuse this with a *perspective* cutaway drawing that might be created to visually explain the inner workings of a subject. Such a perspective view is merely an illustration. On the other hand, a *section* is a measurable *orthographic* view that shows the true cross section in plan form.

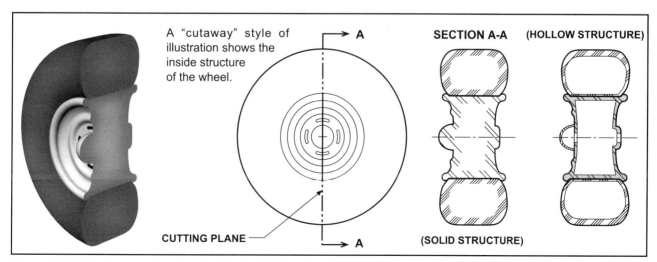

Figure 2.9.2. Create a *section* view to illustrate internal and other hidden structural details more clearly.

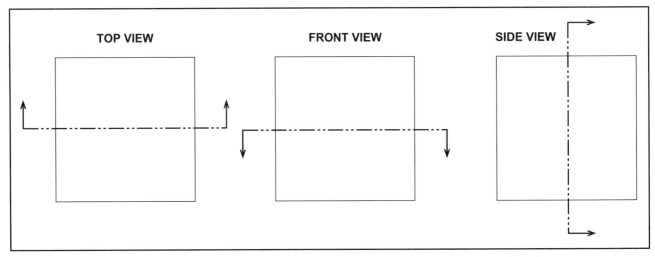

Figure 2.9.3. Choose one of three conventional orientations for the line representing a cutting plane.

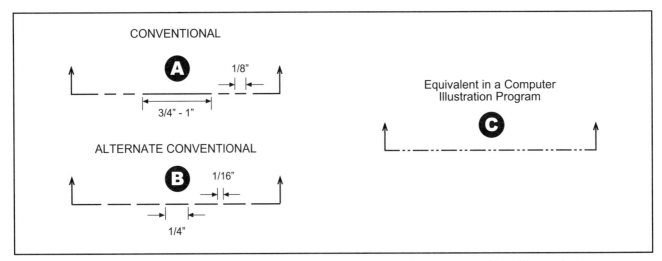

Figure 2.9.4. Formal drafting standards for cutting planes may not be easy to recreate in an illustration program.

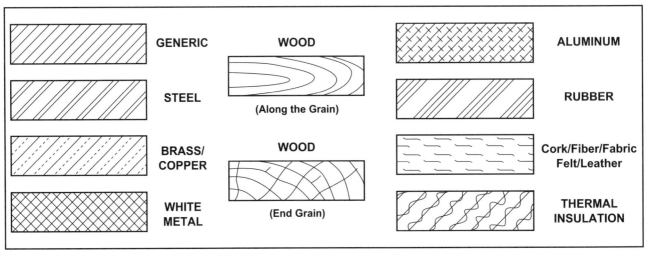

Figure 2.9.5. Use special fill patterns in section views to represent specific materials.

The solution here is to create a cross section view of the wheel. Imagine you could take a saw and cut into the object as shown in **Figure 2.9.2**. By making such a cut, the internal cross section of the wheel would become visible. In concept, this is exactly what creating a section view is like. You get to decide where and how to "slice" the object to present the needed information. In this particular example, the entire wheel assembly is cut in half right down the centerline. Once this is done, the section view will show the actual profiles needed to recreate the structure of both the wheel and the tire.

Sections might be difficult to visualize when the structure cannot be readily seen. If you know where to draw hidden lines in any of the regular plan views, you can transfer the location of these lines to the section view and then start filling in the details. In any case, the exact method of constructing the section view will depend largely on the shape and structure of the subject.

You can see some practical examples of how to do this in **Section 3.6**. In addition, all of **Chapter 5** is dedicated to this subject. The remainder of this section will be devoted to discussing drafting conventions and standards that can be used when making section views. To make such views self-explanatory, you should always indicate where you are "cutting" your subject so the viewer will understand exactly what the section view represents.

Cross sections are covered in detail in **Chapter 5**.

Cutting Planes

Draw a horizontal or vertical line in the plan view to indicate where you are "cutting" through your subject in order to create a section view. This line, called a cutting plane, should be placed at each location where a section view is available. By labeling your drawing using the format shown in **Figure 2.9.2**, the user should clearly understand what is being depicted. **Figure 2.9.3** shows how you can orient the arrows of the cutting plane line depending on the view in which it appears. These arrows indicate the direction in which you would be looking at the subject in order to see the view in question. In most cases, this is very intuitive.

Formal drafting standards for drawing lines representing cutting planes are demonstrated by both **Part A** and **Part B** of **Figure 2.9.4**. These standards were designed during a time when people were doing drafting by hand. As previously mentioned, CAD systems typically handle such situations with ease. On the other hand, this type of line configuration is not necessarily as easy to recreate in a computer illustration program.

The orientation of the arrows in a cutting plane line is meant to improve clarity. When a drawing contains a large number of section views, however, things can get confusing.

The program used to create the example illustrations features a special line type or *stroke setting* that has long dashes and two short dots. Something like this can effectively be used to represent a cutting plane. This line type may or may not be available depending on the program you are using. If a similar line type is not available in your program, it is up to you to decide how you

An example is presented in **Chapter 5** that shows an alternative approach to labeling multiple section views.

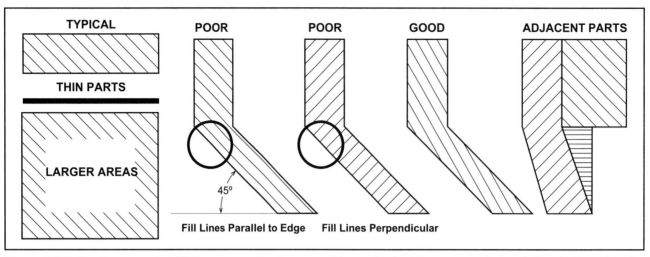

Figure 2.9.6. Configure angled fill lines according to convention and orient them properly in relation to the subject.

wish to represent your cutting planes. You can attempt to mimic the established standards or just choose any readily available line type that appears suitable.

Crosshatching

Once an object has been "sliced" to create a section view, it is customary to add a *fill pattern* that represents the material from which the object is made. While this convention may not be highly critical for modelers, feel free to add an appropriate fill if you wish to follow drafting standards. Doing this will make your section views appear more technically correct.

As an example, notice **Section A-A** in **Figure 2.9.2**. Here, the area has been filled with cross-hatched lines (a process called hatching) to indicate the assembly has been "cut" and therefore "exposed." The pattern chosen indicates the cross section of this assembly is *solid* all the way through. If this were not the case, the section view would include outlines for both the inside and outside surfaces. To illustrate this concept, an alternate version, located to the right of **Section A-A** in **Figure 2.9.2**, shows how the same section might look if the structure in question was hollow instead of solid.

In this example, the cross-hatched pattern also indicates the object is made up of two different materials. The tire is made of rubber while the wheel is made from steel. As you can see, the cross-hatching is different for each area. This demonstrates how fill patterns can be used to distinguish between rubber or wood parts and also between metal or plastic parts. Just keep in mind, this level of detail may not be necessary. If you don't need to be this specific in your drawings, you may opt to use a "generic" fill pattern instead.

Figure 2.9.5 shows some examples of conventional fill patterns that might be used when drawing plans for models. The first pattern shown represents *iron*, but it is also commonly used as a *generic* fill when specific materials

Objects created in a computer illustration program are made from lines known as *curves* that are either "open" or "closed." A closed curve forms a complete path from the starting point back to the same point. These objects can be filled with just about any desired color or pattern. The *fill setting* determines what appears inside the object.

are not being depicted. You may choose to simplify things by using this pattern for all parts. This presents a problem, however, when several parts with the same fill pattern adjoin each other. When this happens, vary the line spacing or direction so the parts do not appear to "blend" together.

Drafting standards provide guidelines to help clarify your drawings when objects with a cross-hatched fill abut against one another. **Figure 2.9.6** shows some of the conventions that govern how fills should be modified in your section views. For example, the lines that make up a crosshatched fill pattern typically run at a 45-degree angle. It is customary that these lines be neither parallel nor perpendicular to the edge of the outline being filled.

You should also keep the lines running *in the same direction* for all areas that make up a *single part*. When two or more portions of an assembly are adjacent, however, applying the same fill to everything might create confusion. When this occurs, *reverse* the direction of the lines in one or more areas to make it easier to distinguish between different parts.

In addition, when the cross section of a particular part is quite thin, it is customary to simply fill the shape with *solid black* instead of cross-hatching. On the other hand, when the area to be filled is large, hatch only the *outer edges* of the shape as shown.

Options

You don't always have to draw a full cross section view. If your subject is symmetrical, you may be able to get by with a <u>half section</u> instead. The example wheel in **Figure 2.9.2** could just as easily have been depicted by drawing a section from the centerline upward or from the centerline downward and omitting the rest of the structure. In some cases, even less than a half section is required. In these situations, you can draw a <u>partial section</u>.

There are all sorts of additional standards and conventions regarding the creation of section views. These are most useful to industrial designers and engineers interested in documenting parts for the purposes of manufacturing. If you would like to learn more about the conventions of creating sections, check out any book dedicated to drafting or engineering graphics.

2.10: Conventional Revolution

Sometimes, drawing objects as they would truly appear in a certain view can cause less-than-desirable results. An example of this situation is illustrated in **Figure 2.10.1**. Here, only one blade of a three-bladed propeller is drawn in such a way that it can be measured in the side plan view. The remaining blade is oriented so that it is not parallel to the plan view. As a result, no useful information about this other blade can be obtained from this view.

Parts such as bolts, nuts, washers, bearings, gear teeth, dowels, and pins should *not* be filled with cross-hatched lines. Fill these parts with solid white or a <u>tint</u> of black instead. A fill of 20% black, for example, is considered a "tint" of black.

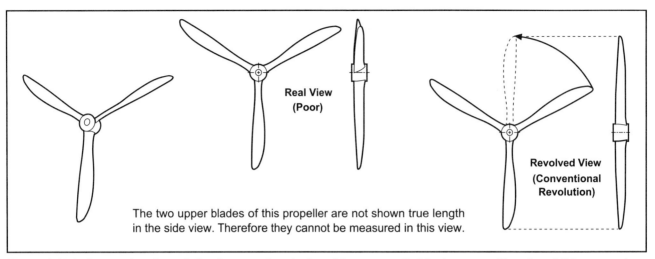

Real View (Poor)

The two upper blades of this propeller are not shown true length in the side view. Therefore they cannot be measured in this view.

Revolved View (Conventional Revolution)

Figure 2.10.1. Conventional revolution is a practice designed to ensure all objects appear "true length" in every view.

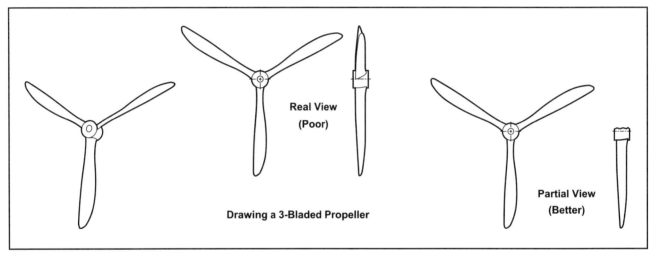

Real View (Poor)

Drawing a 3-Bladed Propeller

Partial View (Better)

Figure 2.10.2. A *partial view* may be more self-explanatory than trying to use conventional revolution.

	ENGLISH (Portrait Orientation)	METRIC (Landscape Orientation)
Portrait	ANSI "A" 8.5 X 11 (Letter)	A4 297 X 210
	ANSI "B" 11 X 17 (Tabloid)	A3 420 X 297
	ANSI "C" 18 X 24	A2 594 X 420
Landscape	ANSI "D" 24 X 36	A1 841 X 594
		A0 1189 X 841
	(Dimensions in Inches)	(Dimensions in mm)

Figure 2.11.1. Standard page or "sheet" sizes are often used when printing or "plotting" blueprints on paper.

In such cases it is conventional practice to *rotate* the object in order to improve the clarity of the plan view. This practice is called <u>conventional revolution</u>. In the case of the example propeller, you might leave the lower blade as is and then rotate one of the upper blades to create a "revolved view" as shown. This allows *two* blades to appear parallel to the plan view at the same time rather than just one. In this event, you could then obtain measurements from both blades in the same view.

Unfortunately, employing conventional revolution in this manner results in a side view of the propeller that does not truly represent the subject. This "revolved view" is an "idealized" representation rather than a true picture of what the propeller looks like from the side. While this might seem confusing at first, simply remember this technique was developed to ensure measurements can be taken from the drawings. When something appears at an odd angle in a particular view, conventional revolution can be used to solve the dilemma quickly and easily.

Deciding when and how to rotate objects, however, can be subjective and often depends greatly on the subject being drawn. Since the resulting view is not a true representation of the subject, this may confuse people who are trying to interpret the drawings. To avoid potential confusion, conventional revolution will not be used in this book unless absolutely necessary.

In the case of the example propeller, you may be able to more clearly illustrate this subject by making a *partial view* and breaking the drawing near the centerline of the prop shaft as shown in **Figure 2.10.2**. Such a view might be more self-explanatory than attempting to use conventional revolution.

A much more useful application of revolution is rotating features or lines that do not appear parallel to a particular plan view so you can accurately measure them. This technique will be demonstrated in **Chapter 4** and in **Chapter 6**.

2.11: Page Layout and Title Blocks

Page layout was discussed in **Chapter 1, Section 1.6**. A more proper term might be "sheet layout" since plans are often so large they must be printed on poster-sized sheets. In the past, when drawings were done using traditional methods, standard sheet sizes were adopted for copying and distributing paper copies of plans. These are listed in **Figure 2.11.1**.

Once you've decided on a sheet size, don't forget typical working drawings or blueprints nearly always include a *border* around the entire edge of the printed area. To create such a border, simply add a large rectangle on each sheet. Keep in mind, most printers or plotters are unable to print all the way to the edge of the paper. As a result, you should always include a minimum clearance or *gap* between the edge of the paper and any border that frames your drawing. The minimum clearance is typically 1/4-inch, but 1/2-inch or even more is better.

You can make your plans look even more professional by including a <u>title block</u> in the bottom right corner of every sheet. This is a popular and useful

If you are creating your drawings to use as a template for building a 3D computer model, you probably won't need to worry about page setup, title blocks, or anything related to printing your plans on paper. Anyone who wishes to print their drawings, however, should know how to properly format them for output to a printer or plotter. See **Appendix C** for more information.

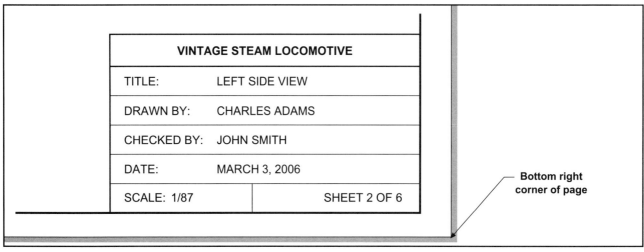

Figure 2.11.2. Add a *title block* to provide details about the subject, scale, and designer of a drawing.

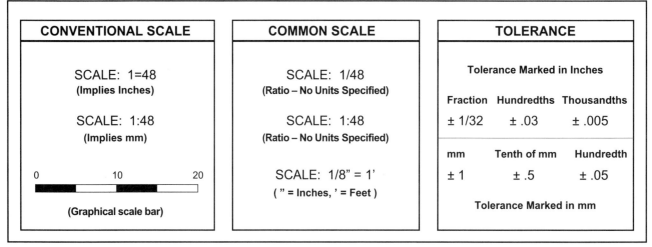

Figure 2.12.1. To avoid confusion, indicate the *scale* on every drawing. Marking *tolerance* is optional.

tradition for designers and engineers who prepare working drawings. Formats vary, but an example of a typical title block is shown in **Figure 2.11.2**. Keep in mind, this format is an example only and is not set in stone. In other words, you should feel free to modify it as you see fit.

2.12: Indicating Scale

Scale was also discussed back in **Section 1.6**. Nearly everything about modeling revolves around *scale*. Drawings, however, can be made to any scale or can even be drawn "true size," meaning they are not scaled at all. To avoid confusion, always specify the scale of the drawings you are preparing.

Figure 2.12.1 illustrates some of the ways you can label the scale of your drawings. If the objects appearing on a single sheet are all drawn to the same scale, this should be indicated in or near the title block in the lower right hand corner as previously shown in **Figure 2.11.2**. To maintain clarity, when some objects on any sheet are drawn to a *different* scale than the others, you should indicate the specific scale near the object(s) in question.

2.13: Marking Tolerances

When building a physical model of something, you might have to work very hard to achieve tolerances measured in the hundredths of an inch. Yet, with the advent of computerized drawing, it is now possible to draw your plans with an accuracy of about ten-thousandths of an inch. As a result, such parts are far more precise than is practical since they would fit together so tightly you might not be able to actually assemble them. This is an excellent example of the importance of taking tolerance into account when designing and building physical models.

Because the proper fit of parts requires some degree of tolerance, your plans should ideally take this into account when laying out components. As a rule, avoid drawing parts that fit tightly against each other with zero clearance. Instead, allow some "buffer" space around the parts. This gives you some "wiggle room" to allow for a proper fit. Adding gaps in this manner might look odd when you are drawing the parts, but it will make a major difference when it comes time to actually assemble them.

How much space should you allow? The choice is really up to you, but a margin of about 0.01inch is probably a good idea – even for machine-cut parts. If your components are going to be made by hand, you might need even more leeway because there will always be some variation between what you planned to make and what actually gets built.

Tolerance is even more critical when you are making patterns for parts that will be created by a computerized machining service such as laser cutting. These machines can create parts that are accurate to the thousandths of an inch. "Buffer space" around such parts is more precisely controlled, but it is still very much needed. In addition, you must take into account the thickness of the cutting bit or laser beam when making patterns for the parts to be cut. Just as a saw blade might make a groove of a certain width when cutting into a piece of wood, the bit of a CNC router or the beam of a laser cutter will take up a certain amount of space while making the cut.

Volume 3 of this series will discuss how to make drawings and patterns for parts that will be manufactured by "computer numeric control" devices such as CNC routers and laser cutters.

Another common mistake some modelers make when laying out parts is assuming the thickness of the material they have chosen is a known factor that does not change. In reality, raw materials are manufactured within a certain tolerance, and this can differ from one material to the next. As a result, *all* materials will vary, and some more than others. Wood, for example, often has quite a bit more variation than plastic or metal. Therefore, do not

Some materials are *deliberately* mislabeled due to convention. Common building lumber is an excellent example. A "2 X 4" wood "stick" or "stud" is actually closer to 1.5 X 3.5 inches in size. If you were unaware of this fact, your drawings would be wrong!

Cast acrylic will have more variation than extruded acrylic.

assume a piece of material labeled as being a certain size or thickness is precisely dimensioned as marked.

Acrylic sheet is a good example of a raw material that may not be the exact size indicated on the label. A sheet of 1/8-inch acrylic may actually be just 0.118 inches thick. Even this figure may vary since acrylic sheets can be manufactured using two distinctly different methods (cast and extruded), and each method has its own manufacturing tolerances. Because of this, the dimensions will differ slightly from sheet to sheet. In addition, thicker sheets of material usually have a greater variance from the labeled size while thinner sheets are often much closer to their labeled size.

If you are working with materials that do not have exact specifications, you may need to *approximate* certain dimensions in your drawing to allow for proper fit. When you know in advance that a part is subject to variation in size or thickness within a certain specified range, consider marking this tolerance on your drawing. See **Figure 2.12.1** for examples of conventional methods for marking tolerance.

2.14: Dimensioning

Overview

To be technically correct, "working drawings" of any subject should be *dimensioned* drawings. Since plans are generally drawn the same size as the finished model, some modelers may think including detailed dimensions is not really necessary. After all, if the parts are drawn actual size, all you need to do is measure or trace your templates directly off the plans, right? Regardless, including key dimensions is still a very good practice.

Conventions regarding the dimensioning of working drawings are very thorough and complex. These standards apply mainly to engineers, draftsmen and industrial designers. Many of these practices are based on published standards such as those compiled by the *American National Standards Institute* (ANSI) and the *International Standards Organization* (ISO). Depending on the industry and application, other standards and traditions may also affect the way a professional draftsman labels and dimensions his or her drawings.

A detailed overview of some of the more common practices is presented here in an effort to help you prepare the most self-explanatory drawings possible. As you review all these rules, you will see how most dimensioning standards are extremely precise and particular. As a result, strict adherence to these practices can add quite a bit of work to the process of making your drawings.

Fortunately, CAD programs have built-in tools for adding dimensions to a drawing, and these tools often do much of the work for you by creating labels that are pre-formatted according to convention. In addition, each dimension created in a CAD program is treated as an *object* that can quickly and easily be created, edited, and deleted as needed. As a result, dimensioning when using one of these programs will often be quite easy.

On the other hand, many illustration programs have no such features. In this case, you may have to create your dimensions manually. This can be quite a bit more work. There are three different approaches to doing this:

1. Draw all dimensioning elements manually and ensure each meets appropriate standards; This requires the most work.
2. To save time and effort, ignore or bypass certain conventions, thereby creating dimensioning in the most convenient manner possible.
3. Create a "library" of pre-drawn dimensioning elements such as arrowheads and add these to your drawing each time they are needed.

This section will introduce standard dimensioning practices as well as some practical techniques that can be used to add dimensions to your drawings if you are using a computer illustration program. As you will see, however, proper dimensioning without special tools made for that purpose can be somewhat labor intensive.

Terminology

Any discussion about dimensioning will include some of the many proprietary terms associated with this subject:

- Dimensioning is the process of adding dimensions to a blueprint in order to create a proper working drawing.
- Dimensioned drawings are those that include detailed dimensions.
- Dimension lines are drawn as thin lines with arrows at each end.
- Dimension numbers are labels placed in the center of dimension lines to specify the exact dimension being represented; These numbers are typically 1/8 inch in height.
- Arrowheads are placed on either end of dimension lines; They are typically as wide as dimension numbers are tall, with a height 1/3 the *width* of a dimension number; For 1/8-inch tall dimension numbers, the arrowheads would then be 1/8-inch long by about 1 millimeter tall.
- Extension lines are drawn from the edge of a part or feature outward as shown in **Figure 2.14.1**; These lines permit the dimension lines and numbers to be located away from the object in order to increase clarity.
- Leader lines shown in **Figure 2.14.1** are thin lines that connect a note(s) about an object to the area or feature in question; Leader lines should begin next to either the *first* or *last* word in the note rather than in the middle; A leader line pointing to a feature ends in an *arrowhead* while a leader line pointing to a surface or area ends in a *dot*.
- Centerlines are thin lines drawn to indicate the exact center of round objects and holes.

To learn more about dimensioning standards, visit the ANSI website at *www.ANSI.org* and search for documents with the word "dimensioning" in the title.

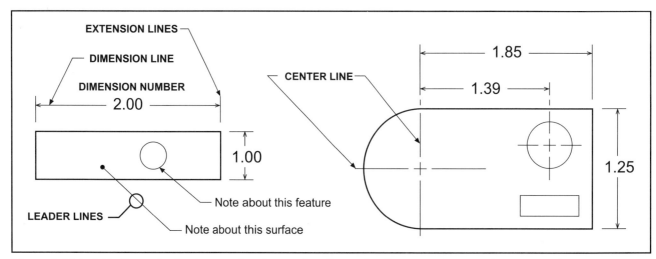

Figure 2.14.1. Add *dimensioning* to your drawings using dimension lines, numbers, and notes with leader lines.

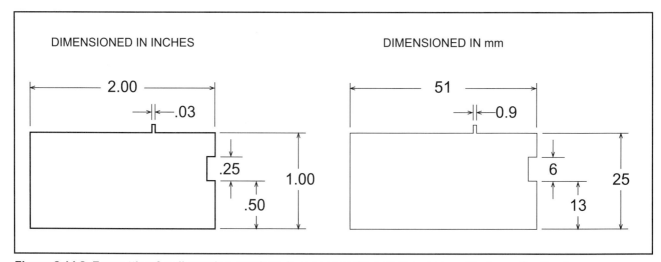

Figure 2.14.2. Formatting for dimension numbers is very specific and depends on the type of units chosen.

FRACTION		DECIMAL	FRACTION		DECIMAL
1/64	=	.015625	1/4	=	.25
1/32	=	.03	3/8	=	.375
1/16	=	.06	1/2	=	.50
3/32	=	.09375	5/8	=	.625
1/8	=	.125	3/4	=	.75
3/16	=	.1875	7/8	=	.875

Figure 2.14.3. Convert decimal inch measurements to fractional inches and vice versa.

Units and Symbols

Dimensioning on a drawing would be useless without knowing the units of measurement. Yet, it is conventional to omit the units from all dimension numbers! There is actually some logic to this method for it is designed to keep the drawing as clean and uncluttered as possible. Keep in mind, according to convention, the *scale* is always supposed to be indicated somewhere on the drawing. If dimensions are to be included as well, the units of measurement should be noted in the same location as the scale. This is often done in the title block in the bottom right corner of each sheet.

See **Section 2.11** and **Section 2.12** for more information about specifying scale on your drawing.

No matter what units you choose, in order to be technically correct, dimension numbers should be formatted in a very specific fashion according to convention. Choose either metric or English measurements and mark your drawings accordingly in either inches or millimeters. Examples of standards for dimensioning units are shown in **Figure 2.14.2**.

As you will see, it is preferable to label inches according to a *decimal* system rather than by using fractions. The reason is quite simple. Fractions are harder to add, subtract, multiply, and divide. By using decimal inches, you can just punch the numbers into a calculator when needed. Of course, this makes things more difficult when you need to translate dimensions on your drawing into practical measurements using a standard ruler. The solution is to use a ruler graduated in decimal inches or convert the decimal values back into fractions as needed. A table of common fractions used with inch measurements and their decimal equivalents is shown in **Figure 2.14.3**.

Always round metric measurements to the nearest millimeter since this is the smallest practical unit of measurement available on any metric ruler. If you must specify a fraction of a millimeter, add a *leading zero*. On the other hand, inches should always be rounded to the nearest *hundredth* of an inch

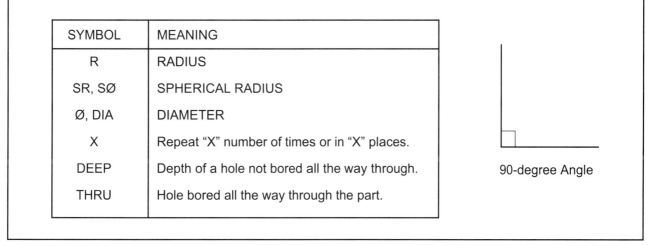

SYMBOL	MEANING
R	RADIUS
SR, SØ	SPHERICAL RADIUS
Ø, DIA	DIAMETER
X	Repeat "X" number of times or in "X" places.
DEEP	Depth of a hole not bored all the way through.
THRU	Hole bored all the way through the part.

90-degree Angle

Figure 2.14.4. Use special symbols as needed when dimensioning objects.

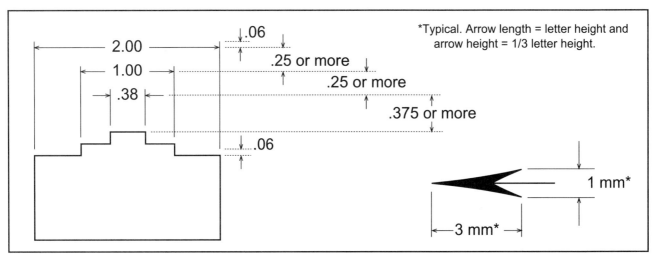

Figure 2.14.5. To conform with convention, arrange dimension labels carefully.

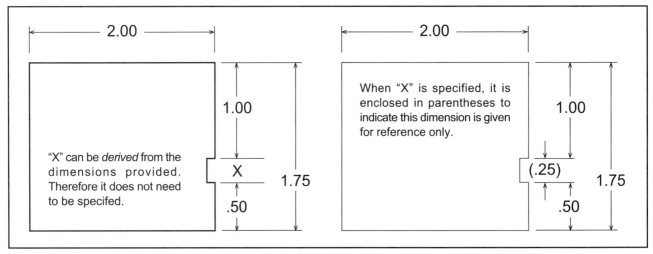

Figure 2.14.6. Omit certain measurements when they can easily be *derived* from available information.

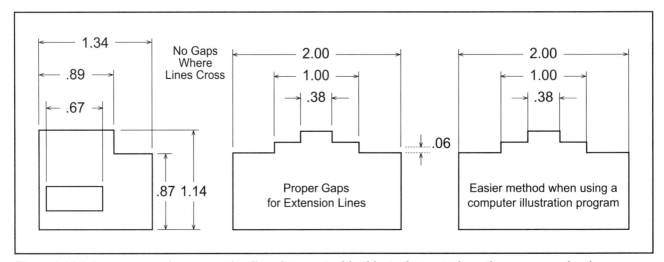

Figure 2.14.7. Leave *gaps* where extension lines intersect with objects, but not where they cross each other.

or *two decimal places*. When specifying inch measurements, however, do *not* use leading zeros.

Special symbols are often associated with dimensions on a drawing. Some of the more common symbols are listed in **Figure 2.14.4**.

Placement

Figure 2.14.5 shows some examples of well-organized dimension labels. The standards can be very particular when it comes to just how these labels are to be formatted. Engineers and professional draftsmen are required to strictly adhere to these standards and conventions as part of their job. On the other hand, modelers may simply wish to make their plans as clear as possible. To make your drawings appear more professional, consider following these types of dimensioning conventions as much as possible.

The basic idea in all this is to avoid "clutter" and potential confusion by keeping dimension lines and numbers from overlapping or appearing too close to each other. One way to accomplish this is to "stack" the dimension labels and allow for proper spacing so they are as clear as possible. Start with the smaller dimensions and work your way up to the larger ones in a "tiered" fashion as shown. The clearances illustrated in the example correspond to a typical letter height of 1/8 inch. If your letters are larger, increase these clearances accordingly.

When stacking dimensions in this way, it is customary to omit certain figures if they can be easily underived from other values. This saves space by minimizing the number of dimension labels needed in the drawing. An example of this convention is shown in **Figure 2.14.6**. As a modeler, however, you might want all relevant dimensions handy at all times. To do this while remaining strictly within convention, add parentheses around the derived dimension as shown to indicate it is provided only for reference.

When drawing extension lines, do not permit *gaps* to occur where these lines cross each other or where they cross lines that are part of the object being dimensioned. On the other hand, extension lines should be drawn so there *is* a gap between the end of the extension line and the feature being dimensioned as shown in **Figure 2.14.7**.

This is done automatically in most CAD applications that have dimensioning tools. When using a computer illustration program, however, this convention may get in the way of efficiency. Without special tools to precisely locate the ends of dimension lines and arrows, you must place these items manually. The easiest way to do this is to *overlap* the extension line with the edge of the object or feature as shown. This violates convention, but ensures extension lines are precisely aligned. If you want your dimensioning to follow the

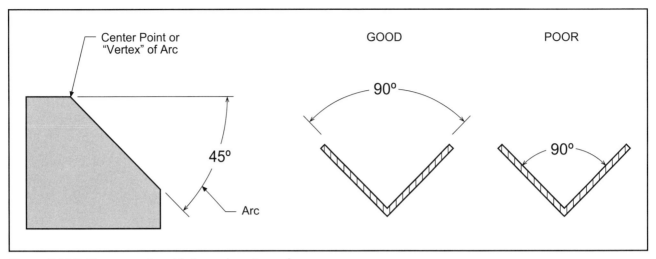

Figure 2.14.8. Use an *arc* to add dimensions to angles.

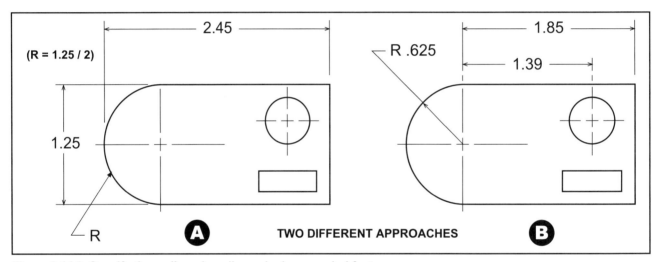

Figure 2.14.9. Specify the *radius* when dimensioning rounded features.

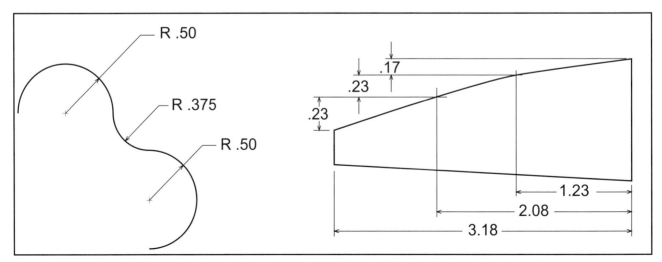

Figure 2.14.10. Specify the radius for *regular* curves, but define coordinates for *irregular* curves.

standard formatting, place your lines this way and then shorten them to create a proper gap. Or, to speed things along, simply leave them as is.

Dimensioning Angles and Curves

When dimensioning drawings, angles are a special case. Angle dimensions are always labeled in <u>degrees</u>. Rather than drawing a dimension line, an <u>arc</u> is used instead. The center point or <u>vertex</u> of the arc is the same as the vertex of the angle as shown in **Figure 2.14.8**. To keep the drawing uncluttered, convention dictates that the dimension number be placed *outside* the angle rather than inside.

Rounded features are typically dimensioned by noting either the <u>diameter</u> of circular features or the <u>radius</u> of semi-circular portions. To accomplish this, the *center point* must always be defined for such features. Without a center point, the diameter can sometimes be measured, but the radius often cannot. As a result, try to get in the habit of plotting the exact center point of all round features.

The process of marking the center point of circles as well as the vertex of curves and arcs is shown in **Figure 2.14.9**. If a round or cylindrical part is less than a full circle, the *radius* of the curved part should be dimensioned instead of the diameter. A special symbol – shown in **Figure 2.14.4** – is now used to indicate diameter measurements. It may be easier, however, to use the older standard of adding the letters "DIA" after the number. Use the letter "R" in front of the number to specify the value shown represents a radius rather than the diameter.

When parts have rounded ends, you can choose between two different approaches to dimensioning. The simplest method is to show the overall dimensions of the part and then indicate that a radius exists on the rounded end(s) as shown in **Part A** of **Figure 2.14.9**. This means the person reading the plans will need to *derive* the radius, but all information needed to do so will be present.

Another approach is to measure the distance between the center point of the semi-circular end and any other feature as shown in **Part B** of **Figure 2.14.9**. Be sure to specify the exact radius of the rounded end(s). With this approach, all relevant measurements are specified, and nothing needs to be derived.

You can also specify a radius for any part that has a curved surface made up of smooth arcs as shown in **Figure 2.14.10**. On the other hand, when a part is made up of *irregular* curves, this method is not suitable. In such cases, all you can do is plot a series of points or "coordinates" along the edges of the object. Then, note the dimensions between these points as shown.

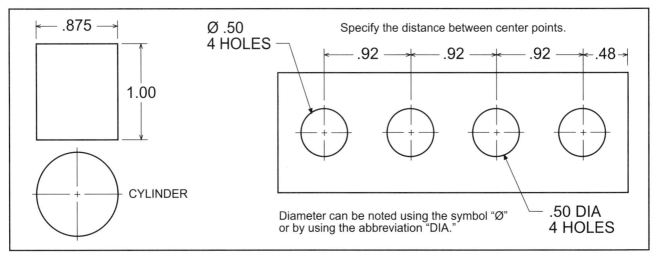

Figure 2.14.11. Dimension cylinders and holes as shown.

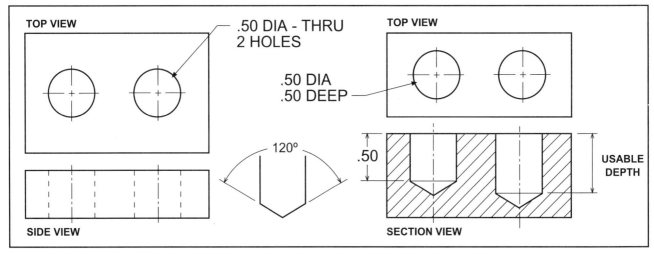

Figure 2.14.12. Holes can be bored all the way through or only partially through a surface.

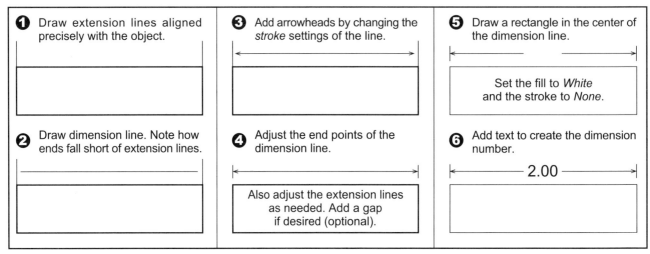

Figure 2.14.13. Dimensioning with a computer illustration program is a multi-step process.

Dimensioning Round Parts

When dimensioning items such as cylinders, label them according to the diameter rather than the radius since the diameter is much easier to measure. Rather than note the diameter in the end view, however, use a height dimension in the view where the cylinder appears as a rectangle or trapezoid. An example of a dimensioned cylinder is shown in **Figure 2.14.11**.

Holes are a special case and these require labeling that is very clear and self-explanatory. To locate holes precisely, provide distances between the hole(s) and an edge, feature, or surface "landmark" that can be easily and accurately measured. Holes in an object may be <u>bored</u> either partially through or all the way through a part. These holes can be labeled in different ways as shown in **Figure 2.14.11** and **Figure 2.14.12**.

<u>Through holes</u> are easily labeled in the view where the hole appears as a circle by adding the abbreviated term "THRU" to the diameter dimension. Holes that do not go all the way through the material can be specified either by labeling the depth of the hole in a *section* view or by specifying a dimension with the term "DEEP" added.

Note the depth indicated should be the <u>usable depth</u> of the hole rather than the <u>true depth</u>. Most drill bits have tips that are angled at 120 degrees, making the bottom of the hole cone-shaped as shown in **Figure 2.14.12**. The usable depth does not include the cone-shaped space occupied by the tip of the drill bit when it bottoms out in the hole.

Dimensioning Other Features

There are a variety of other dimensioning standards. Many are designed for use in preparing working drawings of parts that are to be *machined*. These can include standards for features such as:

- Boring
- Counterboring
- Countersinking
- Chamfering
- Keyseats
- Knurling
- Necks
- Reaming
- Spotfacing
- Tapers
- Undercuts

Since many modeling applications may not make use of such features, they will not be covered here. If you would like to know more about how to label

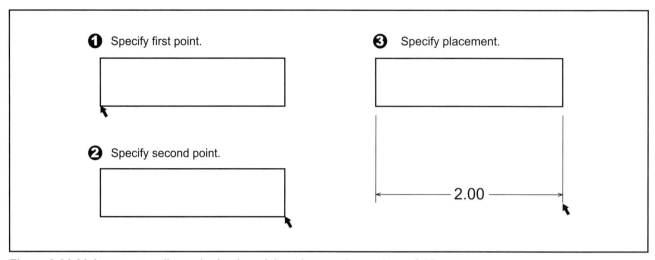

Figure 2.14.14. In contrast, dimensioning is quick and easy when using a CAD program.

parts that include these kinds of features, check out a drafting textbook or other reference text on dimensioning.

Techniques

A step-by-step example of how to create dimension lines, arrows, dimension numbers, and extension lines using a typical computer illustration program is shown in **Figure 2.14.13**:

1. Create two extension lines to mark each end of the dimension line.
2. Draw a dimension line that connects both extension lines; Add arrowheads to each end by modifying the *stroke* setting of the line; As an alternative, copy and paste a ready-made arrowhead symbol and place it at each end of the line.
3. Adjust the endpoints of the dimension line so the arrowheads are positioned correctly; Adjust the length of the extension lines to create a gap between the extension lines and the feature being dimensioned (optional).
4. Draw a rectangle over the center portion of the dimension line large enough to "punch a hole" in the line to make room for the dimension number text; Set the *fill* of this rectangle to "White" and the *stroke* to "None;" *Group* this rectangle with the dimension line drawn in **Step 2** to prevent it from being selected by itself; You want this rectangle to move and be resized along with the dimension line.
5. Add numbers inside the newly created "gap" in the dimension line to indicate the desired dimension; Select the *Text Tool* and place the mouse over the point in the drawing where you wish the numbers to appear, then click with the mouse and start typing; Set the typeface and style of the text as needed; Finish by *grouping* the dimension line with the numbers to complete the dimensioning process.

According to convention, choose a *point size* for your dimension numbers that generates characters approximately 1/8 inch in height. This value, however, is somewhat arbitrary. Feel free to choose whatever size and style of lettering you wish. In addition, the example shown assumes the program being used offers *stroke* options that include "arrowheads" on one or both ends of the line. With this option, you can draw your line, select it, and then alter the stroke settings so the arrowheads will appear automatically.

Keep in mind, when arrowheads are created in a computer illustration program by setting the stroke options of a line, you can sometimes get unexpected results. For example, some programs automatically place the arrowhead so the tip extends *beyond* the end of the line. This is most inconvenient because it means your dimension lines will have to be made *shorter* on either end to allow room for the arrowheads. To compensate for this, first draw the line full length and set the stroke option to add arrowheads. Then, select the end point of the line and move it as needed.

If you can't add arrowheads to the ends of your lines, you must draw each one individually. Each arrowhead should be properly laid out according to drafting standards. An example is illustrated in **Figure 2.14.5**. Keep in mind, you can create your arrowheads in advance and store them along with other commonly used symbols in a special template file. In this case, simply copy and paste these symbols into your drawings as needed.

Older versions of the illustration program *Deneba Canvas* (Version 3.x) include built-in dimensioning tools that function very much like those in a CAD program. This makes *Canvas* an ideal choice for modelers who wish to prepare blueprints for their projects using an older Macintosh system.

As already mentioned, the process of creating dimension lines and labels is much easier if you are using a CAD program. An example of this process is shown in **Figure 2.14.14**. All you need to do is select the dimensioning tool and mark the locations for the start and end points of the feature being dimensioned. Finish by telling the program where to place the dimension label. That's it! As you can see, this is much quicker and easier than creating all the dimensioning elements from scratch.

CAD programs may have different tools for creating horizontal, vertical, and angular dimensions. Simply choose the right tool for the task at hand. Once created, you can then edit the dimension label as needed. You may also be able to resize, reposition, or delete the dimension – all at a click of a mouse. This is because all the components that make up a dimension (dimension line, dimension number, and extension lines) are treated as a single object.

2.15: Summary

This is one of the longer chapters in this volume, but it contains important information for anyone who wants to draw their own blueprints. Conventional standards and practices dictate how many of the details in a typical set of plans should appear. So far, you have learned the following:

- Six principal plan views can completely describe any subject; Simple or symmetrical subjects may require fewer views while complex subjects will require more.
- Views are typically arranged according to the drafting conventions of *third angle projection* in the US or *first angle projection* in Europe and the International community.
- You can also arrange your views in an intuitive fashion based on the geometry of the subject.
- Use different line types to make your drawing as clear as possible.
- *Centerlines* should be included for any symmetrical features to aid in alignment.
- When lines overlap, use the established *order of importance* to decide what to show.
- To create the cleanest and most professional drawing possible, make sure all your lines intersect properly.
- *Incomplete views* are cleaned up by removing some hidden lines; This makes these views easier to interpret.
- *Partial views* can be used to save space when depicting symmetrical subjects.
- *Removed views* show details that would be very hard to see in any regular plan view.
- *Conventional revolution* can be used to adjust the orientation of an object so it can be measured in a particular view where it would otherwise appear at an odd angle.
- *Title blocks* can be used to organize and label your drawings.
- *Scale* should always be indicated on every drawing while marking *tolerance* is optional.
- When creating proper working drawings, it is critical to include detailed *dimensions*; Many conventions exist that govern how you should specify these dimensions in your drawings.

While drafting conventions might seem quite detailed and complex at first glance, you can now see how these rules could prove very valuable as you start creating your own blueprints. By following established practices, your plans can appear very professional and they will be much easier for others to read and interpret.

This chapter contains more than enough information to get you started. To learn even more, be sure to check out a good book on drafting or engineering graphics.

What's Next?

With the completion of this chapter, along with the introduction to blueprinting in **Chapter 1**, you have now covered all the basics you need to know in order to get started drawing. In the next chapter, you will see exactly how to lay out orthographic plan views step by step. By the time you finish working through this material, you should be ready to start creating your very own blueprints from scratch.

Topics in This Chapter:

Chapter

Laying Out Plan Views

3.1: Overview

Now that you have reviewed some important drafting standards and conventions, it's time to get to work! The principles outlined in this chapter will help you lay out your plans to produce blueprints of just about any subject. This will conclude **Section 1** of this volume.

From these drawings you will then be able to make *measurements* in order to proceed to the next step – creating accurate templates and construction patterns for your project. In **Section 2**, you will see how to make these patterns from information contained in the principal plan views.

3.2: Getting Started

As discussed in **Chapter 1**, orthographic projection makes it possible to take information from two existing views and derive missing details in a third view. This is truly the secret to creating blueprints. By starting with basic information about your subject such as key dimensions, you can begin assembling your drawing like pieces of a puzzle. Using the principles of projection to find the missing details, your plans can be filled in one piece at a time. Once all the details are in place, a complete picture of your subject will emerge in plan view form.

Figure 3.2.1 shows a typical set of "presentation" blueprints. This illustrates the overall concept of using projection to transfer details from one view to another. Because this process is very deliberate and precise, it can seem somewhat tedious. Rest assured, however, it always works. To see exactly how it can be done, take a look at the following exercise. This example will demonstrate how to create presentation blueprints for a model airplane. It will walk you through the entire process step by step.

In order to create plan view drawings of any subject, you must have a starting point. Ideally, this might include detailed dimensions of your subject. With that kind of information you can create accurate blueprints with the least amount of effort. When you lack such reference, however, the process of making blueprints can become more difficult. Nevertheless, it is still possible

NOTE: Underlined terms appear in the Glossary.

The drafting concepts illustrated in this chapter apply no matter what computer drawing program you use (CAD or other). The specific tips and techniques outlined here, however, are geared toward drawing with a *computer illustration program* since this is the easiest method available for most modelers.

For a step-by-step guide that will get you up and running quickly, be sure to read *How To Draw Anything With a Computer: A Quick-Start Guide for the Craftsman, Hobbyist, and Do-It-Yourselfer*, part of the *Modeler's Notebook Reference Series* available from:

www.ModelersNotebook.com

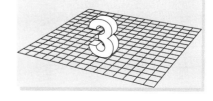

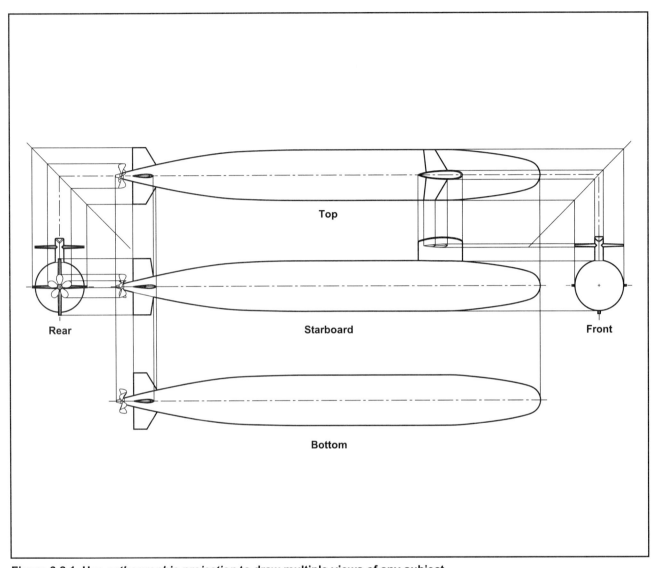

Figure 3.2.1. Use *orthographic projection* to draw multiple views of any subject.

Think of the blueprinting process as a problem-solving exercise. In this way, it can be very similar to working on a picture puzzle. Like a puzzle, you can use existing information to derive or <u>resolve</u> the missing pieces of a blueprint.

to create accurate plans for a subject – even when you do not have detailed measurements from which to work. The techniques presented in this chapter will show you how to draw your plans using both known dimensions and photographic reference.

If you recall the discussion of projection in **Chapter 1**, at least two existing plan views are required to generate missing details in a third view. Therefore, to get started, you need sufficient information up front to draw at least two different plan views of your subject. Once you get the ball rolling, you can begin plotting or "resolving" the remaining plan views. One at a time, the details needed to make each view will fall into place. By the time you are done, you will have sufficient information to begin building your project.

Rather than simply reading about all the many steps needed to make plan view drawings, in this chapter you will see "hands on" how to make blueprints by walking through the process of creating actual plans. For the purposes of this example, the goal will be to draw blueprints that depict the overall form of a model airplane. These "presentation" drawings will show what the subject looks like in plan view form. You can then use this information to create more detailed plans that depict every structural detail of the model.

To keep this example as simple as possible, however, let's start with the basics and attempt to draw just the overall shape of the airplane. By the time you are done, you will have an excellent understanding of how to use orthographic projection in your own projects.

3.3: Using Photos as Templates

Before you can begin drawing, it is very helpful to have a guide or template. (It is possible to create your own blueprints using nothing but a series of measurements, but this may be more difficult for some subjects. It is also less intuitive.) If you can find an existing blueprint or 3-view drawing of the subject, this will make an excellent starting point, and it can save you much time and effort. On the other hand, if you cannot find any existing drawings to use for reference, you will have to start from scratch.

Without detailed measurements available, you will need at *minimum* a suitable side view photo to use for reference in order to draw a subject such as the airplane in this example. If you can find good reference images of other views, that's better still. Just keep in mind, for any photo to be of value as a template, it should be as close to a perfect orthographic view as possible.

Distortion in Photographs

If you recall the discussion in **Chapter 1**, the term "orthographic view" basically means "flattened view." This describes the concept of removing all *visual perspective* from a drawing. Unfortunately, both your eye and the camera see perspective in everything. As a result, no photo can ever represent a true orthographic view of something. The best you can do is control certain factors while taking the photo in order to minimize perspective distortion.

An example of a possible template image for the subject airplane is shown in **Figure 3.3.1**. (This is not actually a photograph – it is merely meant to illustrate what a reference photo might look like.) How can you tell if this image is suitable for use as a template? The only way to know for sure is to *analyze* it to determine how the subject is oriented in relation to the camera.

Do you remember the old adage "Photos don't lie"? Well, this is not necessarily true. In fact, photographs can sometimes be extremely misleading when you are using them as templates for drawing blueprints. Because they can contain a great deal of perspective distortion that can fool your eye in

If you would like to practice drawing these blueprints as you read through this exercise, scan the reference image shown in **Figure 3.3.1** into your computer to use as a template. See **Appendix B** for detailed information on how to create and work with scanned image templates.

Figure 3.3.1. To create blueprints for a plane, a starting point such as this side perspective template image is needed.

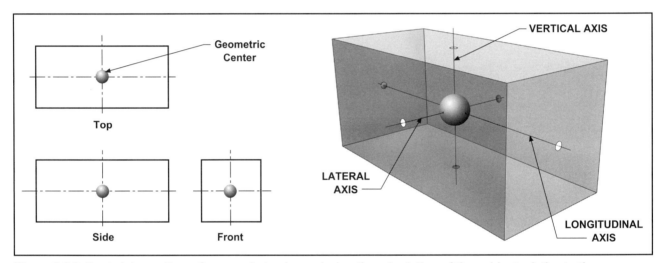

Figure 3.3.2. Begin interpreting reference photos by analyzing the orientation of the subject relative to the camera.

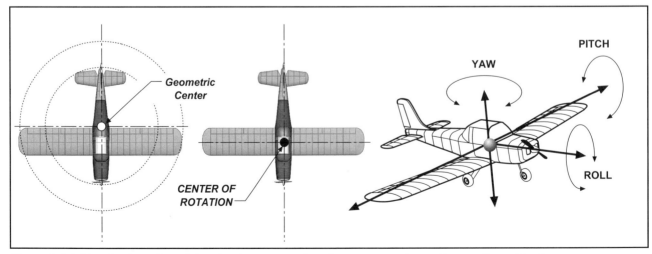

Figure 3.3.3. Terminology describing the three axes of motion can vary depending on the subject.

many different ways, relying on photos can lead to all sorts of problems when you are trying to figure out the proportions and details of a subject.

For example, in addition to issues caused by the placement and/or setup of the camera, the shape of a subject can also have a dramatic impact on the degree of distortion in a photo. To understand how this might affect your project, imagine for a moment you are drawing plans for a simple sphere. With this particular shape, you could take a photo from just about any angle and get the exact same results. Visual perspective would still be present in all the photos, but would not alter the apparent shape of the sphere. As a result, such a shape could be considered somewhat "immune" to the effects of perspective distortion in reference images.

Unfortunately, this is not the case with most subjects. In fact, the majority of objects will be prone to perspective distortion in one way or another. The actual amount of distortion can vary quite a bit depending on how "compact" or symmetrical the shape appears to be. For example, a *cube* might exhibit little distortion while a long, rectangular *box* might appear more distorted.

In general, the potential for perspective distortion becomes greater as a feature is located farther away from the true <u>geometric center</u> of an object. Armed with this knowledge, you can attempt to control many of the factors that lead to perspective distortion when taking your own reference photographs. Even when this is not possible, you will be able to use this knowledge to analyze available photos to determine where and how the subject has been distorted.

Refer to **Chapter 1, Section 1.5** for additional discussion of visual perspective.

Orientation of a Subject

All this begins with looking at exactly how the object is oriented in relation to the camera. For example, imagine replacing your subject with a simple box like the one shown in **Figure 3.3.2**. This box has a <u>geometric center</u> and three axes of alignment:

- <u>Lateral axis</u>
- <u>Longitudinal axis</u>
- <u>Vertical axis</u>

The box can be rotated around any one of these axes of alignment. As a result, you might think of them as potential <u>axes of motion</u>. Understanding the axes of motion can be a huge help when determining where and how an object may be distorted in any photograph taken of it.

The labels for each axis of motion may be different depending on the type of subject. When dealing with subjects that are not vehicles, for example, these axes are commonly labeled x, y, and z.

To avoid confusion, try to use the correct terminology for describing the axes of motion for your particular subject. This terminology can vary quite a bit depending on the subject. In the case of an airplane, these axes result in motion called "pitch," "roll," and "yaw" as shown in **Figure 3.3.3**.

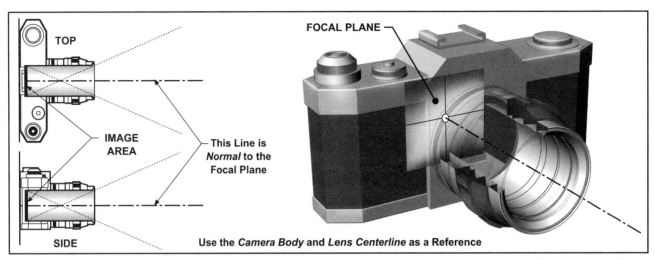

Figure 3.3.4. The camera "sees" by focusing light onto a *focal plane*; Orientation of this plane affects perspective.

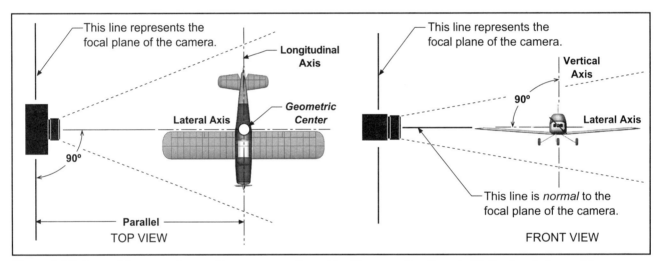

Figure 3.3.5. To avoid perspective problems, ensure the subject is correctly aligned with the focal plane of the camera.

An aircraft can *pitch* up and down, *roll* from side to side, and experience *yaw* or "sideways slipping" to the left or to the right. "Yaw" is simply a measure of where the nose of the aircraft is pointing.

In addition, the aircraft rotates laterally about an axis that runs *through the wings*. This <u>axis of rotation</u> is not necessarily the same as a lateral axis running through the true geometric center. The vertical axis of the plane may also pass through this center of rotation. As a result, the plane might "roll" about its true geometric center, but "pitch" and "yaw" around a different point. Remember this whenever you are gauging the orientation of a plane.

Many subjects must be precisely oriented in relation to the camera to keep visual perspective from playing havoc with the appearance of certain features. Looking again at our example airplane, notice how the wingtips are located far from the center of rotation. As the plane *rolls* about its longitudinal centerline, the tip of each wing moves a great distance compared with the center area of the wing. As a result, even one degree of rotation can cause the wingtip to move up or down quite a bit.

In addition, the body of the plane or *fuselage* is quite long. This places the tail at a much greater distance from the center of rotation than the nose. As a result, if the plane were to *spin* or "yaw" about its vertical axis, the tail could swing left or right over a considerable distance compared with the nose. At the same time, the tail can also move up or down quite a bit as the plane *rotates* or "pitches" about the lateral axis.

Orientation Relative to the Camera

Now that you've seen how objects can be oriented in three-dimensional space, let's discuss the camera for just a moment. A camera takes a photo by allowing light to focus on a frame of light-sensitive film – or, in the case of a digital camera, on a light-sensitive electronic device called a CCD (Charge-Coupled Device). The film or CCD is positioned so it lies precisely on the <u>focal plane</u> of the camera as illustrated in **Figure 3.3.4**.

Whenever you are taking reference photographs, there are two important factors that can help you approximate an orthographic view as closely as possible. First, in order to minimize perspective distortion, the subject should be precisely oriented relative to the focal plane of the camera. Second, the camera should be positioned at a proper distance from the subject and fitted with an appropriate lens (try to use a *telephoto lens* whenever possible).

In the case of our example airplane, a side view photo can only approximate an orthographic plan view under very specific conditions. First, the camera will have to be focused on the *geometric center* of the aircraft. Second, the plane will need to be precisely aligned relative to the focal plane of the camera as follows:

- The *longitudinal axis* of the plane should be *parallel* with the focal plane of the camera.
- The *lateral axis* running through the true geometric center should be <u>normal</u> to the focal plane of the camera; This will result in the vertical axis being *parallel* with the focal plane.

Figure 3.3.5 illustrates the proper alignment of this particular subject in order to take a side view template photo with minimal distortion. As long as the subject is oriented in this manner, distortion resulting from the position and orientation of the aircraft will be minimized.

Interpreting Existing Images

Of course, it will seldom be possible to obtain an existing photo where the subject is in such precise alignment. In most cases, you will need to analyze available reference photos carefully to determine where and how the subject may be misaligned in relation to the camera. Once you are able to properly

The *center of rotation* may or may not be the same as the *geometric center* of an object. In the case of our example airplane, the center of rotation is quite a bit farther forward than the true geometric center of the shape.

The camera should be focused on the *geometric center* of the subject.

A line that is "normal" to a plane is perpendicular to its surface.

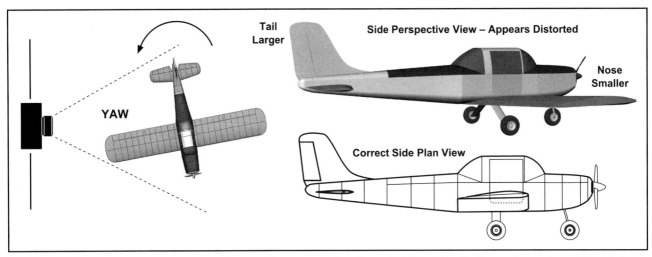

Figure 3.3.6. Note how the orientation of the subject can affect the suitability of a photograph used as a template.

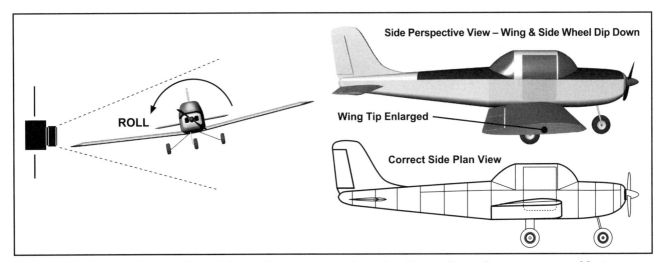

Figure 3.3.7. Even a minor rotation relative to the camera can have drastic results on the appearance of features.

interpret such photos, you will know which features appear distorted. As a result, you will be able to compensate for this in your drawings.

Getting back to our example airplane, take a look once again at the side view template image shown in **Figure 3.3.1**. What are the key parts of the structure that might appear distorted in this photo? If you remember that parts located far away from the center of rotation can easily be distorted, this points to both the long fuselage and large wings as potential trouble spots when taking pictures of this subject. In fact, because the wingtips are so much closer to the camera than anything else, they appear grossly exaggerated. As a result, the wings should be ignored altogether in this image.

Looking at the fuselage, you may notice how rotation about the lateral axis (or "pitch" in aviation parlance) does not affect the usefulness of the photo at all since any misalignment can easily be adjusted simply by rotating the image. On the other hand, rotation about the vertical axis (called "yaw") will cause the fuselage to appear slightly *shorter* than it really is. For example, if the nose points to the left, the tail will swing closer to the camera while the nose gets farther away. This causes the tail to become enlarged while the nose is reduced in apparent size as illustrated in **Figure 3.3.6**.

In addition, if the airplane rotates about the longitudinal axis (or "rolls"), the wingtips, horizontal stabilizers, and outboard landing gear will all move up or down relative to the camera. **Figure 3.3.7** illustrates how the roll attitude of the aircraft can affect the accuracy of the template photo. As you can see, the distance of each feature from the center of rotation will determine the amount of movement as the subject rotates.

3.4: Tracing the Template Photo

Once you have located a suitable template photo, start tracing key features to block out a view of your subject. Since it is very unlikely your photo will be just the right size, simply trace it as is. Then, make a copy of the traced outline and scale the copy up or down as needed.

How exactly can you trace the photo? Start by *scanning* the image so it can be manipulated with a computer program. Once scanned, import the image into your drawing program. Both CAD and computer illustration programs have the capability of working with scanned images so they can be traced. Computer illustration programs, however, are very effective for this task because of their powerful curve creation tools.

Drawings created with a computer are known as <u>vector-based art</u>. All CAD and computer illustration programs generate this type of artwork. Vector-based drawings are *object-oriented*, meaning each line and object is treated as a separate entity. Because of this, all the objects in a drawing can be freely rearranged as needed. Drawing files are also very compact in terms of the disk space required to store them. In fact, they can sometimes take up as little space as a word processing document.

In contrast, scanned photos are <u>bitmap images</u>. In order to view or alter these photos, an <u>image editing program</u> must be installed on your computer. The entire image is a single entity composed of tiny segments called <u>pixels</u>. When an image gets scanned, it is divided into thousands of such pixels. Both the color and light/dark values of each pixel are recorded. This information is then assembled into an <u>image file</u>. As a result, the file size of bitmap images can be quite large. This means they can take up lot of disk space.

Even though drawing programs work with vector-based line art, nearly all such programs can also open bitmap images. This permits you to integrate such images into the artwork created with an illustration program. This feature is very valuable if you want to trace all or part of a photograph.

If you convert your bitmap image to <u>grayscale</u>, much less memory will be required to work with it. This can speed up the performance of your drawing program when you are tracing large bitmap images.

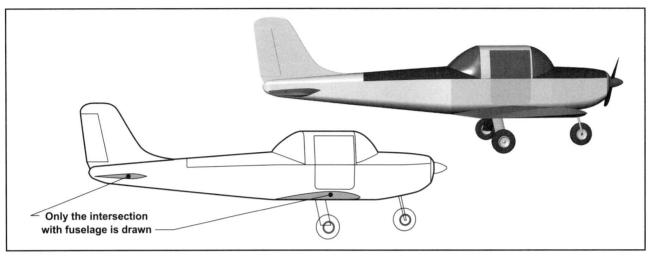

Figure 3.4.1. Extract as much information as possible when tracing the template image.

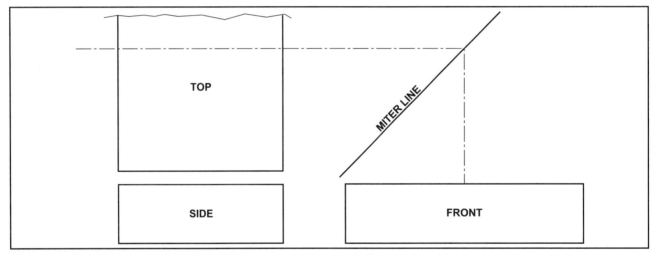

Figure 3.5.1. Begin by creating blocks that represent the overall dimensions of each view.

Appendix B provides more information on how to scan and manipulate images for use as templates in your drawings.

Use either the "Import" or "Place" command to insert a bitmap image into your drawing.

Keep in mind, drawing programs are not designed to manipulate or *edit* scanned images. This means you should set the size, color, and resolution of your scanned photo using an image editing program *before* you import it into the drawing program.

Once you have your photo sized and formatted properly, open your drawing program and create a new document. Then, create a new <u>layer</u> in this document. You could, for example, call this layer "TEMPLATES" or "IMAGES." Whatever you decide, make sure it is placed *beneath* the main drawing layer.

Once the layer is ready, import the image into the drawing. As an alternative, you can also use "Copy" and "Paste" to copy the image from your photo editing program and paste it into the drawing. Make sure the image is placed on the layer you just created. Once the image is in position, lock the image layer to keep the photo from being selected or moved accidentally.

Now, switch to the main drawing layer. Begin sketching out the form of the aircraft using the *Pen Tool*, *Line Tool*, and/or *Multi-Segment Line Tool*. Draw as many features as you possibly can. Once you are done, select all the lines and group them together.

While tracing the photo, be sure to draw any and all details you might need in order to adjust the geometry of the subject in the next step. At the same time, consider omitting some items that are grossly distorted. **Figure 3.4.1** shows an example of how you might trace a side view template photo of the example airplane. Note how the outlines of the wing and horizontal tail surfaces are omitted. These parts of the plane are badly distorted in the reference image and so they should not be used for reference. Instead, the approximate shape of the wing's cross section is determined where it intersects with the fuselage. The same thing is done for the horizontal tail surface.

Save your template drawing. You can leave this drawing open while you move on to the next step.

3.5: Blocking Out Overall Dimensions

Fortunately, it is relatively easy to obtain basic dimensions of many different aircraft subjects. For the purposes of this example, assume certain information is readily available such as the wingspan, overall length, and overall height of the subject. Use the following figures:

Wingspan:	39.0 feet
Overall length:	27.5 feet
Overall height:	9.5 feet (including the vertical tail)

First and foremost, be sure to establish the scale of your drawings before doing anything else. If, for example, you wanted to build a model in 1/10 scale, divide the dimensions of the real airplane by 10. For the purpose of this exercise, a scale of 1/10 is very convenient simply because the math will be easy.

With these figures in hand, draw some boxes that define the overall dimensions of the airplane. Lay out these boxes in your drawing according to the arrangement of views you have chosen. If you want to strictly follow drafting standards, use either third-angle projection or first-angle projection. Or, if you prefer a more intuitive arrangement, place the right side view in the middle of the drawing with the top view above and the front and rear views on either side as shown in **Figure 3.5.1**.

Make the first box 2.75 feet long by 0.95 feet tall (the dimensions of the "real" subject divided by 10). This box will represent the *side plan view*.

The *Pen Tool* is preferred when tracing an image because it allows you to draw smoothly flowing lines. This tool creates what are known as Bézier curves. These are common to all illustration programs. It is very easy to draw and manipulate these curves.

Features that are hidden or partially obscured such as the landing gear struts can be *extrapolated* to show where they actually intersect with the fuselage. Do this by tracing over what is visible and then extend these lines until they end in approximately the right location. Use your best judgment.

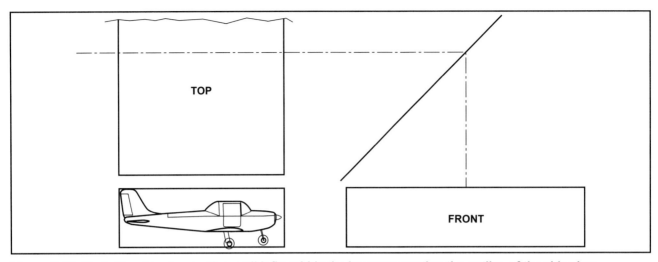

Figure 3.5.2. Scale the side view tracing until it fits within the box representing the outline of the side view.

To create a box outline for the front view of the aircraft, clone the side view box and drag the copy to the right while holding down the "Shift" key. By using a modifier key in this fashion, the copy will be forced to move in a straight line horizontally. This is an easy way to establish the correct height of the box in the front view while keeping everything in precise alignment between views. With the copy still selected, access the *Object Info* settings and change the width to match the scaled wingspan of 3.9 feet.

Divide the box outline in the front view in half to determine its centerline. This will be the location of the longitudinal centerline of the airplane. There are several different ways to divide an object using a computer illustration program. If you are fortunate, the program will indicate the center of each side of the box automatically whenever you select it. If not, you can use *Object Info* to get the exact width of the box. Then, do the following:

1. Draw a smaller box of any height and width.
2. Use the *Object Info* control to set the width of this smaller box to be exactly *one half* the width of the larger box (the height, however, does not matter at this point).
3. *Lock* the larger box representing the outline of the front view.
4. Select both boxes and use the "Align" command to align the left and bottom edges.
5. Don't forget to unlock everything when you are done.

Locking the larger box prevents it from being shifted out of position by the "Align" command. At this point, the right edge of the smaller box should fall on the exact centerline of the larger box. You can now use this as a template to position a vertical centerline directly over this point. If you really want to get precise, try the following:

1. Draw a vertical line.
2. Set the stroke of the line to dash-dot-dash to represent a centerline.
3. Select the smaller box and *Lock* it.
4. Select both the vertical line and the smaller box and use the "Align" command to align the *right* edges.
5. Don't forget to unlock everything when you are done.

Now, it's time to create a box that represents the outline of the top view. This box will be 2.75 feet long by 3.9 feet wide (these measurements represent the length of the fuselage and the width of the wings or "wingspan"). Mark the centerline of this box and arrange all the boxes you have drawn as shown in **Figure 3.5.1**. Extend the centerlines of the boxes representing the top view and front view until they cross. Then, draw a <u>miter line</u> from this exact point that extends both upward and downward at a perfect 45-degree angle.

This arrangement will be critical to the process of projection that you will use to map out details in each view. Remember, the miter line must be angled at precisely 45 degrees. You can draw this line by holding down the "Shift" key to constrain the line. If that does not work, draw a horizontal or vertical line and then use the "Rotate" command with numeric option to rotate the line exactly 45 degrees.

Now, open your side view template drawing. Or, if your template drawing is already open, switch to this drawing and select the traced outline of the side view of the aircraft. Copy this tracing (the lines only – *not* the scanned image) and close your template drawing. Then, go back to your main drawing file and paste the traced figure into the drawing. Once that is done, move the traced figure so it is positioned directly over the box representing the side view of the aircraft.

Finally, *resize* the tracing until it fits within the outline of the box representing the side view as shown in **Figure 3.5.2**. There are two ways to do this:

Method 1

1. *Lock* the box to prevent it from being accidentally selected or moved.
2. *Group* all the lines that make up the side view tracing.
3. Grab one of the selection handles of the group and then stretch it until it fits; Be sure to hold down the "Shift" key to maintain the aspect ratio!

Method 2

1. *Group* all the lines that make up the side view tracing
2. Select the group and access the *Object Info* control to obtain the exact length of the group.

Aligning your template to the box representing the true dimensions is a highly critical step. Any mistakes made here can have profound consequences. You might end up redoing much of your work later on. To prevent this from happening, become familiar with the concept of visual perspective and how it creates distortion in reference images. This will help you align your drawing properly from the beginning.

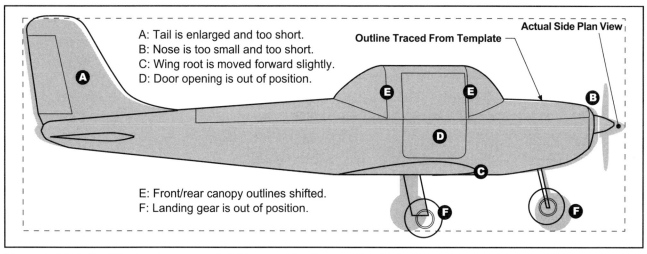

A: Tail is enlarged and too short.
B: Nose is too small and too short.
C: Wing root is moved forward slightly.
D: Door opening is out of position.

Outline Traced From Template

Actual Side Plan View

E: Front/rear canopy outlines shifted.
F: Landing gear is out of position.

Figure 3.6.1. Adjust the tracing as needed to correct for perspective distortion.

3. Select the box outline of the side view and access the *Object Info* control to obtain the exact length of the box.
4. Determine the correct percentage of enlargement/reduction needed to make the traced figure match the length of the box outline in the side view.
5. Select the traced figure and use the "Scale" command with numeric option to enlarge or reduce it by the appropriate percentage.

3.6: Adjusting the Traced Image

As previously mentioned, no matter how close your template photo is to a perfect plan view, factors such as the orientation of the subject along with the distance from the camera and the focal length of the lens can all have a dramatic affect on how its features will appear. In this example, the subject airplane was not perfectly parallel to the focal plane of the camera when the reference "photograph" was taken. As a result, some features were distorted. The question to answer when tracing a template image like this is: "Exactly what needs to be adjusted?"

The answer will, of course, vary from one photo to another. This example, however, will walk you through the process step by step so you can get a feel for how it all works. **Figure 3.6.1** shows a magnified portion of the side view tracing after it has been correctly aligned within the box representing the overall side view. The tracing has been positioned as accurately as possible within this area. Unfortunately, it does not fit perfectly. The reason is perspective distortion. The box represents a perfect orthographic view, but perspective distortion is present in the traced image since it was present in the original photograph. Now you can see exactly how this distortion has affected the accuracy of the side view template.

To illustrate this, an orthographic or "true" side plan silhouette is also shown in **Figure 3.6.1**. This silhouette has been placed underneath the traced outline, thereby creating an overlay. It should be obvious just how much the traced side view drawing is "off" compared to the true orthographic view.

You can see, for example, how the length of the drawing does not match the silhouette. This is because the subject was rotated about the vertical axis when the template photo was taken. As a result, the tail was closer to the camera while the nose was pushed farther away. This caused the plane to appear a bit too short in the side view.

In addition, because the tail section shifted toward the camera, it became enlarged. In a similar fashion, the tip of the nose was farther away from the camera so it was reduced in size. As you can see, distortions like this can have a substantial impact on the accuracy of your drawing when you are relying on photographs as your primary reference. In this particular case, when you scale the tracing to fit the known length of the airplane, the traced outline is too short. If you did not know exactly why this was the case, you would be unable to fix the problem without resorting to guessing. This might cause your finished drawings to differ substantially from the actual subject.

Fortunately, there is a workable solution. The first step is being aware of what is happening in the template photo. Now that you know the tracing is too short, you can make adjustments to compensate. In order to do this, leave the *height* of the tracing as it is, but "stretch" the nose and tail until the overall side view length is correct.

The only way to do this accurately, however, is to obtain detailed dimensions of the subject and use them as a guide to make sure all the parts remain in correct proportion relative to one another. If you just stretch the entire side view, for example, you would be increasing the length of every part of the airplane. Instead, what is needed here is to make the nose slightly longer and then make the tail (and, perhaps, the tail boom) slightly longer. This should be done without changing the position and dimensions of the cockpit area.

As you can see, it would be very helpful to know the actual distance from the tail of the aircraft to the rear window and also the correct distance from the propeller to the windshield. Without these measurements from the "real" subject, you will be forced to *guess* just how much you should stretch the nose and tail in order to compensate for the distortion in the side view.

There are also a few more details to be corrected. Because the tail was closer to the camera than it ideally should have been when the template image was made, the vertical stabilizer (i.e. the large tail fin) is too large. You must reduce it somewhat to make it the correct size. The only way to do that accurately is to know the exact height of the tail fin on the subject. Fortunately, in this case that is known to be exactly 9.5 feet.

Being forced to guess about dimensions and proportions can make it much harder to complete accurate plans for a subject. Depending on the circumstances, your options for finding the missing information may be limited. One solution is to create a *mockup* based on your "best guess" and then compare the results to the actual subject.

The fastest, easiest way to build a mockup is by using a 3D modeling program. This process will be covered in detail in **Volume 2** of this series.

That takes care of adjusting the shape of the fuselage in the side view. Now, what about the wings? Since the wing tip was much closer to the camera than the rest of the wing when the template image was made, it is badly distorted. As a result, you should ignore the wing altogether in this view.

In fact, the only information you can rely on in this particular image is the shape of the wing where it meets the fuselage (an area known as the "wing root"). In this case, the shape appears correct since it is the same distance from the camera as the rest of the fuselage. Because the plane was turning away from the camera when the photo was taken, however, the wing root was shifted slightly forward.

Trace the approximate shape of the wing in this location and shift the outline back slightly. This will be critical for aligning the wings later on. Repeat this same process where the horizontal tail surface meets the fuselage in the rear of the plane.

With your template for the side view nearly "fixed," tweak the remaining details of the aircraft such as the windshield, side doors, and landing gear struts. Keep in mind, any of these details can be shifted, exaggerated, reduced, or distorted due to perspective distortion. Therefore, whenever possible, use actual dimensions from the subject to accurately place each feature.

A prime example is the door opening. This was also shifted slightly forward due to the yaw of the aircraft. So, as you can see, it will be necessary to adjust the placement of these kinds of features until you are reasonably certain the entire side view is accurate. As you can imagine, this may take some careful study of the subject. The more familiar you are with your subject and how it is built, the easier this process will be.

By the way, don't forget to note the angle of the landing gear strut. From studying the subject, you will see this detail is actually perpendicular to the fuselage in the side view. In the template image, however, it angles forward instead. So, what part of the strut should you adjust? In this case, the portion of the landing gear closest to the camera is the most exaggerated. This means the very bottom of the strut is out of position in the tracing. The area where the strut meets the fuselage is more likely to be in the correct position relative to the side plan view since it is closer to the center line of the fuselage. Therefore, adjust the angle of the strut by moving the *bottom* until it is oriented vertically as shown.

Keep in mind, you should not judge the *height* of landing gear from the photo alone. Just as with the wings, when the plane *rolls*, the landing gear moves up or down relative to the fuselage. Even a rotation of just a few degrees can cause significant vertical movement. The exact amount will depend upon the length of the strut and the angle at which it juts out from the fuselage.

If you had the correct dimensions for the strut on the actual plane, this would be an easy fix. Without this information, you are forced to guess once again. Since the subject was banking toward the camera when the photo was taken, the right landing gear rotated *downward*. Therefore, the gear is too low in the side view photo. Move the bottom of the gear up slightly to compensate for this effect. Since you know the correct overall height of the plane, it should not be too difficult to shift the landing gear into the correct position.

3.7: Projecting Points From One View to Another

Now that the side view has been sketched out, you have an excellent starting point for drawing blueprints of this aircraft. Next, begin working on the top and front views. Again, you need a starting point for each view. This will depend entirely on the subject you are drawing, as well as how much information you have to work with. In this case, for example, you already know the length of the wingspan as this was blocked out in **Section 3.5**.

To avoid making any mistakes on your drawing, make sure you understand what each dimension truly represents. In this example, the wingspan is defined as the distance in the top view from wing tip to wing tip. But, note how the wings angle *upward*. Known as "dihedral," this is a common feature of airplane wings.

Since the wings are positioned at an angle relative to each other, the actual length of each wing is somewhat *longer* than what appears in the top view. Therefore, knowing the wingspan by itself is not sufficient to start drawing the wings in the front view. The dihedral angle is also needed to determine the correct location and placement of each wing.

For the purposes of this example, assume the dihedral is a known quantity and is exactly 4 degrees. This angle, combined with the wingspan figure, gives you enough information to draw the wing accurately in the front view.

How can you do this? Start by dividing the wingspan in half. Then, you can begin mapping out a *triangle* to help define the correct shape of the wing in the front view. The dihedral angle provides the "missing link" needed to complete this triangle as shown in **Figure 3.7.1**.

This is an excellent example of how math – including algebra, geometry, and trigonometry – can be extremely helpful when making blueprints. Once you have determined the structure in question can be mapped out using a triangle, it's relatively quick and easy to employ mathematical formulas in order to calculate the exact lengths involved.

Of course, math is not absolutely necessary to solve these types of problems. Fortunately, there are also some simple graphical techniques, and those will be illustrated here. During this process, you will determine where to place

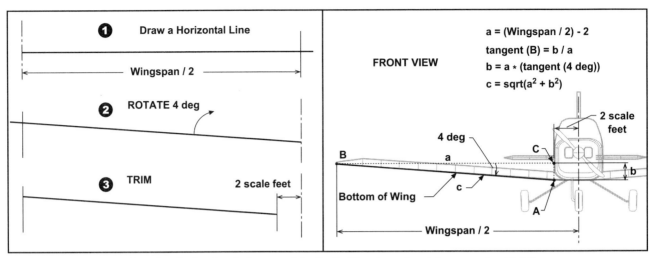

Figure 3.7.1. Map out the wing in the front view graphically (left) or by using trigonometry (right).

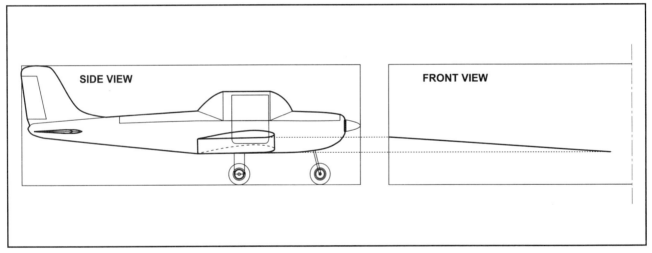

Figure 3.7.2. Project details between the front and side views in order to plot the correct position of the wing.

the wings and also how high the wingtips are elevated relative to the center area or "root" of the wing. All this can be plotted in the *front view* using the following information:

- Known wingspan.
- Dihedral angle.
- Width of the fuselage in the top view.
- Location of the wing root transferred from the side view.

In this way, you will see how it is often necessary to jump from one view to another while figuring out the details that make up your drawing.

To get started drawing the wing, think for a moment about what you need to know. Where should the wing root be located relative to the fuselage? In this case, the answer is easy since the bottom of the wing is flush with the bottom of the fuselage. Were this not the case, you would need to locate the exact vertical position of the wing root in the side view based on your tracing of the template and then project that information into the front view.

Now, working in the front view, draw a line outward from the centerline *past* the outer edge of the box representing the total width of the plane as shown in **Figure 3.7.1**. Next, select this line and rotate it 4 degrees clockwise to match the established dihedral angle of the wing. Make sure the inboard end of this line is located at the centerline of the plane.

If you study the shape of the subject carefully, however, you will notice that the wing does not actually begin at the centerline of the plane. Rather, it begins at the outer edge of the fuselage and extends outward to the wing tip. In order to correctly position the wing in the front view, you need to know the width of the fuselage where it meets the wing root.

If you are fortunate, dimensions of the fuselage will be available to use as a guide. If not, you'll have to approximate the width of the fuselage relative to the total wingspan. This can be done in the top view and that information can then be transferred to the front view using projection. For the purposes of this example, assume the fuselage is about 4 feet wide in this location.

Mark out a distance of 2 scale feet or 2.4 inches from the centerline and create a reference mark. This will be where the bottom of the wing meets the fuselage in the front view. Trim the line representing the wing here and at the other end so the wing is depicted at the correct overall width as shown.

Where did the value "2.4 inches" come from? Since 2 feet is equal to 24 inches, divide this number by 10 because the model is 1/10 scale.

You have now successfully begun the process of plotting the shape of the wing in the front view. This becomes a starting point for everything that gets drawn in that view. Next, copy the angled line and flip the copy to create a mirror image representing the other wing. The very last step is to reposition both lines so they are in the correct vertical location. To do this, transfer the position of the *wing root* from the side view as shown in **Figure 3.7.2**.

As you have just seen, you can locate or "plot" the location of any feature in one view by using information from another view. This is the process of orthographic projection in a nutshell! The easiest way to make this work is to transfer information between adjacent views. An adjacent view is one that is located side-by-side with, directly over, or directly underneath another view. In this case, the side and top views are adjacent, and the side and front views are also adjacent. To project the location of the top and bottom of the wing into the front view, simply draw horizontal lines from the side view into the front view. These are called construction lines.

Here are some tips for drawing construction lines. First, zoom in as far as necessary to precisely place the starting point. Using the *Line Tool*, click and hold the mouse to begin drawing. Hold down the "Shift" key to constrain the

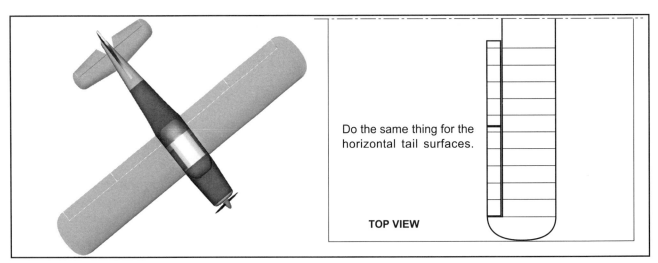

Do the same thing for the horizontal tail surfaces.

TOP VIEW

Figure 3.8.1. Use reference images to extrapolate the correct shape and details of the wing in the top view.

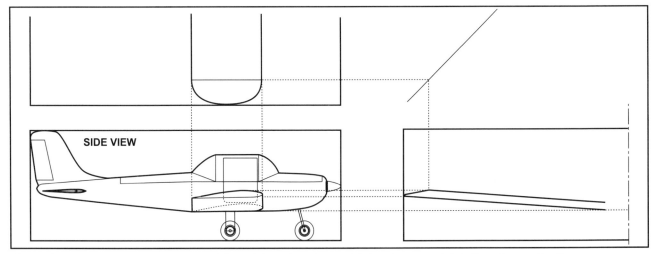

SIDE VIEW

Figure 3.8.2. Flesh out the proper position of the wing along with its shape and details using projection.

You can change the color of a construction line by changing the *stroke* setting of the line. For example, a 10% tint of either cyan or magenta works quite well.

line so it is perfectly straight and then continue dragging until you reach the desired location. (If you are zoomed in, the screen should automatically scroll as you drag the mouse.) You can also use the "Shift" key to make lines that are perfectly vertical. In some programs, this trick also allows you to draw lines at a perfect 45-degree angle.

When projecting points from one view to another, you'll be creating dozens and sometimes hundreds of construction lines. As a result, it is best to put them on a separate layer and choose a color other than black. For example, you can create a new layer called "CONSTR LINES" and place all your construction lines on that layer.

To ensure all your lines are organized properly, always make sure the correct layer is active while you draw. It is not necessary, however, to constantly switch back and forth between layers. An easy approach is to draw all your lines on the main drawing layer. Then, periodically select and move groups of lines to the "CONSTR LINES" layer as you go. This will help keep things nice and neat with a minimum of effort.

3.8: Filling in Details in Adjacent Views

Now that you've established a starting point for the wing position in the front view, it's time to start drawing the rest of the wing. To determine the correct shape, you will need some reference photos. The best source would be a top-down view of the airplane such as that shown in **Figure 3.8.1**. Without this, you will have to make your best guess as to the correct shape of the wing. Use the outline shown in the reference image of the top view, along with the position of the wing root in the side view, to locate the front and rear edges of the wing as shown in **Figure 3.8.2**.

The exact same method works for drawing the horizontal stabilizer in the tail section of the aircraft. With reference images as a guide, plot the shape in the top view. Then, use information in the side view to determine the proper fore-aft position, as well as the correct vertical position of the assembly. Finally, transfer all this information to the front view. (Details on how to do this will be discussed in just a moment.)

Now, it's time to start blocking out the shape of the fuselage. Begin by drawing it in the top plan view. How wide should it be? Once again, reference photos or measurements can help. The best source would be a front or rear view of the airplane along with a top-down view. Without this information, you will have to make your best guess as to the correct shape of the fuselage.

If you are fortunate, some dimensions will be available to use as a guide. This will make the whole process much easier. As previously noted, assume the fuselage of the "real" subject is 4 feet wide at its widest point. Note how this point is located where the fuselage meets the wings. The shape then tapers towards the nose and towards the tail. Using this information, attempt to draw one half of the fuselage in the top plan view as shown in **Figure 3.8.3**. Use as many reference images as you can find to guide you. Once completed, copy and flip this outline to create the other half of the fuselage.

To proceed from here you'll need to be able to project points from the top view into the front view and vice versa. This will be necessary in order to plot the *cross section* of the fuselage so you can determine the shape and location of features such as the windshield and the cowl. Only after the correct cross section has been determined will you have sufficient information to draw in these sorts of details.

If you look closely at the illustration shown in **Figure 3.8.4**, you will see how the outline of the windshield can be plotted where it meets the fuselage by using information in the side, front, and top views. The key here is selecting

See the documentation that came with your program for information on how to create layers and move objects from one layer to another.

One of the biggest advantages to drawing with a computer is that you can create just one part of a symmetrical structure and then "flip" or "mirror" it to create the remaining parts. This can save a tremendous amount of time and effort while drawing.

The front and top views are *non-adjacent* views.

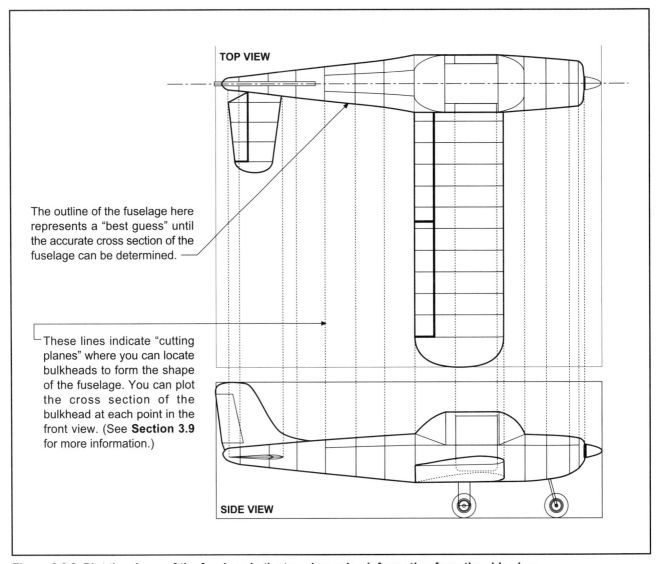

TOP VIEW

The outline of the fuselage here represents a "best guess" until the accurate cross section of the fuselage can be determined.

These lines indicate "cutting planes" where you can locate bulkheads to form the shape of the fuselage. You can plot the cross section of the bulkhead at each point in the front view. (See **Section 3.9** for more information.)

SIDE VIEW

Figure 3.8.3. Plot the shape of the fuselage in the top view using information from the side view.

The precise method for plotting the windshield and cowl will be covered in **Section 3.9**.

a series of points and then plotting their location in all views at the same time. For example, you can obtain information about the *vertical position* of any point from the side view. But, if you simply project this information by drawing a horizontal construction line, you will not know where to end the line in the front view. This means you also need to know the *lateral position* of the point (i.e. the distance from the centerline of the fuselage). This can be found in the top view. So, as you can see, each point must be plotted in more than one view in order to determine its exact position in all three dimensions.

So far, you have used projection to transfer points from one adjacent view to another. This is the easiest technique of all to master. The projected construction lines are drawn vertically or horizontally using the *Line Tool*. By dragging the mouse and holding down the "Shift" key, you can constrain the lines so they are always perfectly straight.

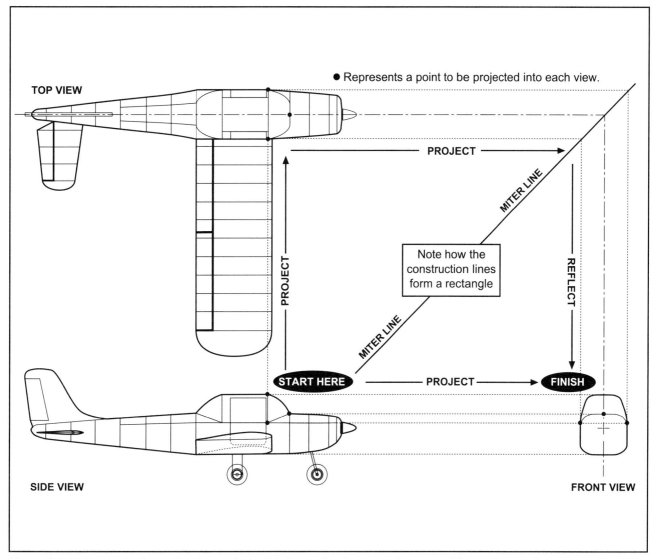

Figure 3.8.4. Create the front view by projecting information between the top and front views using a *miter line*.

The true power of projection becomes apparent, however, when you use information in two different views to map or plot a point in a third view. Unfortunately, since the top view is not adjacent to the front view, transferring information between these views will not be quite as easy as drawing a straight line. When views are not adjacent, construction lines must be *reflected*. This is the case for both the top and front views of our example airplane.

The secret to mapping points between non-adjacent views is a special device called a *miter line*. This line is drawn at exactly 45 degrees relative to the X-axis. Depending on the program you are using, you may be able to draw a perfect miter line with the *Line Tool* by holding down the "Shift" key while dragging with the mouse. Not only does this constrain lines to a perfect horizontal or vertical orientation, it often works for 45-degree lines as well. If, for some reason, this trick does not work in your program, simply draw a

Points cannot be projected to a non-adjacent view using a simple straight line. These points can be plotted instead by *reflecting* construction lines from a 45-degree *miter line*.

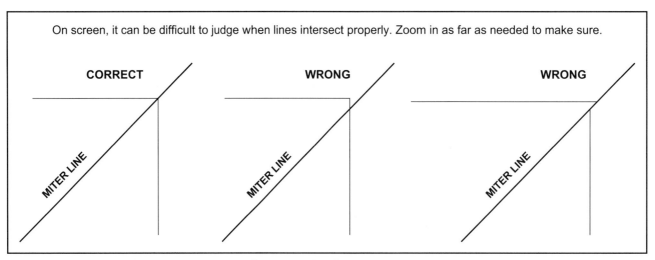

On screen, it can be difficult to judge when lines intersect properly. Zoom in as far as needed to make sure.

CORRECT   WRONG   WRONG

MITER LINE   MITER LINE   MITER LINE

Figure 3.8.5. To maintain accuracy, ensure all construction lines intersect properly.

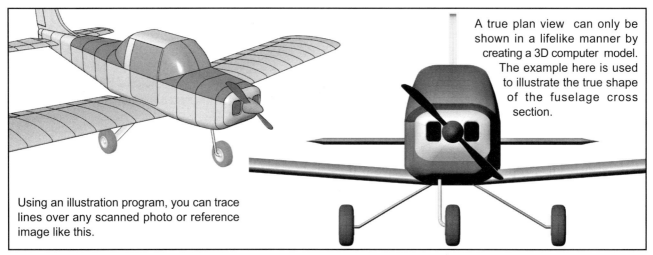

A true plan view can only be shown in a lifelike manner by creating a 3D computer model. The example here is used to illustrate the true shape of the fuselage cross section.

Using an illustration program, you can trace lines over any scanned photo or reference image like this.

Figure 3.9.1. Sketch lines on top of reference images as needed to help visualize the shape of the cross section.

horizontal line (holding down the "Shift" key while dragging with the mouse) and then rotate this line exactly 45 degrees.

Once the miter line is in place, you can project any point between the top and front views. To project from the top view into the front view, start by drawing a construction line from a point in the top view to the miter line. Then, *reflect* this construction line down into the front view as shown in **Figure 3.8.4**. Note how these construction lines form a rectangle when they connect a point in all three views. As a shortcut, you can simply draw a rectangle instead of individual line segments and then adjust all four corners of this rectangle so they are precisely aligned as needed. This will ensure your points are always located precisely in each view.

Keep in mind, when drawing construction lines from a point in any view to the miter line, you may not be able to "snap" to the miter line unless your program allows you to create <u>custom *Guides*</u>. If your program permits this, move all your miter lines to the *Guides* layer. If you are unable to snap to the miter line while drawing, be sure to zoom in as much as needed to ensure the construction line and the miter line meet at the correct point. This simple concept is key to making projection work between non-adjacent views.

Figure 3.8.5 shows an example of a properly "reflected" construction line. If you are off here, a projected point will fall in the wrong place. Just remember, it is not always possible to determine whether lines are intersecting properly simply by looking at the screen under normal magnification. Two lines may appear to overlap when, in fact, they do not actually touch. Therefore, always be sure to zoom in as far as necessary to ensure the lines really do meet in the right place.

3.9: Determining Cross Sections

With the side view nearly complete and the top view now started, the next step is to determine the <u>cross section</u> of the fuselage. This is the shape of the center part of the plane as it appears in the front and rear plan views. Understanding how your subject looks in all three dimensions will be very valuable during this process. You will need to know exactly how the lines "flow" across and along the length of the shape. To better visualize this, it may be helpful to sketch some lines on top of your reference images to help map out the true shape of the subject. An example of this method is illustrated in **Figure 3.9.1**.

As you have already seen, using an illustration program gives you the advantage of being able to easily make tracings on top of scanned photos just like this. You can bring a scan into a drawing file and then sketch lines on it to help you visualize the form. Simply create a separate layer to hold the scanned image and place this layer *below* the main drawing layer. Once set up, lock this layer to prevent the image from being accidentally selected while you draw.

To help illustrate the shape of our example fuselage, both a perspective view and a true orthographic plan view rendering are presented in **Figure 3.9.1**. Since perspective is always present in any photograph, the only way to see a true orthographic view portrayed in such a lifelike fashion is to build a 3D computer model. While making such a model is beyond the scope of this volume, the rendering shown here is presented to help you visualize the process of mapping out the cross section of the example airplane fuselage. Hopefully, by knowing where you are going with this exercise, you will have an easier time achieving the end result.

Without actual measurements or drawings of the correct cross section of the fuselage to use as a reference, the best you can do is make an educated guess.

To ensure lines meet in the right place, draw all your lines with a *minimum* line width. This will be the "hairline" setting in some programs. Using the thinnest possible lines will prevent the width of the line from interfering with your ability to judge how well the end points line up. Once all your lines are drawn properly, increase the line width of select lines as needed.

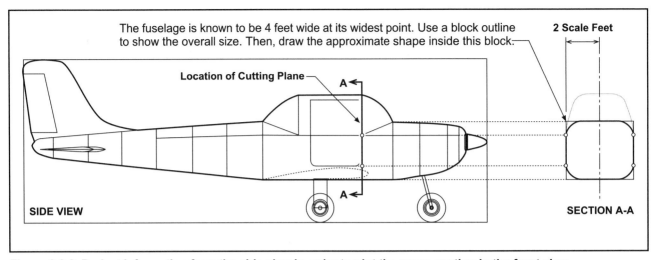

The fuselage is known to be 4 feet wide at its widest point. Use a block outline to show the overall size. Then, draw the approximate shape inside this block.

2 Scale Feet

Location of Cutting Plane

A

A

SIDE VIEW

SECTION A-A

Figure 3.9.2. Project information from the side view in order to plot the cross section in the front view.

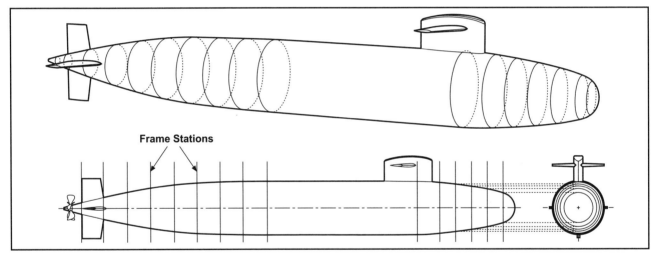

Frame Stations

Figure 3.9.3. Create a constant-cross-section shape by *scaling* the cross section profile at specified intervals.

If this is the case, begin by transferring some key points from the side and top views into the front view and then sketch out the shapes from there. Study the form carefully to get clues that will help you plot key details.

If you look closely, for example, you may notice the outline of the fuselage when viewed in either the front or rear plan view is the cross section *at its widest point*. Therefore, start by plotting the outline of the cross section where it is widest and work from there. In this case, the fuselage is widest where it intersects the wings. It then tapers fore and aft from this point.

The cross section is represented by a vertical line in the side view. This line is known as a <u>cutting plane</u>. Imagine this plane "slicing through" the fuselage wherever the vertical line is drawn in the side view. It's up to you to determine what the cross section looks like at this point. To do this, pick a series of key points along the cutting plane in the side view and transfer these points into the front view using projection.

What points should you pick? In this case, note how the side of the fuselage is flat while both the top and bottom portions are curved. Therefore, a good place to start will be determining where the shape of the fuselage transitions from a flat to a curved shape. If you look closely at all the reference images shown so far, you will see that the bottom of the side window and the bottom of the front side door appear to be the approximate points of transition. Therefore, find these points on the cutting plane in the side view and project them into the front view.

Fortunately, you already know the correct width of the fuselage (4 feet at the widest point). Use this information to block out the overall shape in the front view by drawing a rectangle 4 feet wide. Make this rectangle the overall height of the fuselage as measured in the side view, but not including the windows and canopy.

Now, draw the flat sides of the fuselage in the front view. These sides will simply be vertical lines in this view. The location of these lines will be 2 scale feet on either side of the centerline. The top and bottom of each line will be determined by information transferred from the side view as illustrated in **Figure 3.9.2**. Once you have the flat sides of the fuselage drawn in the front view, you can approximate the curves needed to form the rest of the shape as shown.

With the proper cross section determined, you now have sufficient information to draw the entire fuselage in both the front and rear views. If you are lucky, the cross section will be *uniform* throughout the structure. An example of a subject with a uniform cross section is the submarine shown in **Figure 3.9.3**.

This is the easiest type of structure to map out in 2D since the cross section is evenly scaled along the entire length of the vessel. In this event, you could plot the <u>bulkhead</u> profiles in either the front or rear view using just one other view as a guide. For instance, you could transfer the vertical location (top and bottom) of each bulkhead from the side view and then draw the outlines in the front and rear views as shown.

Unfortunately, many modeling subjects may not have such a uniform cross section. When the cross section is non-uniform, information from two other views will be needed in order to plot the correct shape in the front or the rear view.

Fortunately, the fuselage of the example airplane is fairly uniform in shape. As a result, the main cross section profile can simply be scaled at various points as needed. Start by drawing *cutting planes* at regular intervals down the entire length of the structure as illustrated in **Figure 3.9.4**.

Chapter 5 discusses the concepts and techniques of creating cross sections in more detail, including the use of cutting planes.

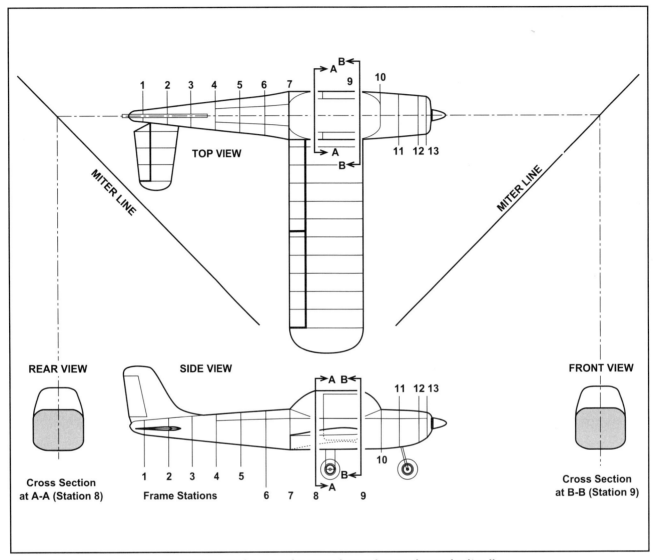

Figure 3.9.4. Number all frame stations and set up the rear view using a mirrored miter line.

Once again, these cutting planes are represented by vertical lines drawn in the side view and also in the top view as shown. If you plot the cross section of the fuselage where each cutting plane "cuts" through it, you will end up with bulkhead templates at each of these points.

In Naval parlance, the position of each cutting plane marks the location of a <u>frame station</u> (or, simply, a "station"). This marks the point along a vessel where either a bulkhead or a <u>transverse frame</u> is positioned. Frame stations are therefore the most logical locations for marking cutting planes when drawing blueprints. This is a critical part of the process of creating construction patterns for any model.

Be sure to number all the frame stations. As an example, you might begin at the rear of the fuselage and label the first cutting plane **Station 1**. All frame stations from this point forward could then be numbered sequentially.

Keep in mind, the widest part of the fuselage will mark the "dividing line" between the bulkhead outlines to be drawn in the front view and those that will appear in the rear view. In this example, the widest part of the fuselage lies between **Station 8** and **Station 9**. Cutting planes labeled "**A-A**" and "**B-B**" are placed at both these points. The arrowheads on the cutting planes point in the direction you would be looking at the subject to see the view in question. Since the cross section at "**A-A**" appears in the rear plan view, you would see this outline when looking at the aircraft from behind. In a similar fashion, the cross section at "**B-B**" appears in the front plan view. You would therefore see this outline when looking at the aircraft from the front.

Cutting planes "**A-A**" and "**B-B**" are actually identical in this case. Each one represents the outline of the fuselage at the widest and tallest point. You could therefore use either of these outlines as the starting point for drawing the front and rear plan views of the fuselage. In this case, all bulkhead outlines numbered "**9**" and higher will be drawn in the *front view* while all bulkhead outlines corresponding with frame stations numbered "**8**" and lower will be drawn in the *rear view*.

You may have noticed, however, that a rear view has not actually been created for our example airplane just yet. This can easily be remedied by adding a *miter line* that is a mirror image of the one drawn for mapping out the front view as shown in **Figure 3.9.4**. Once this miter line is in place, it marks the centerline of the rear plan view. Use this to accurately position the cross section outline for **Station 8** in the rear view.

Now that you've created a starting point in the front and rear views, proceed with plotting the outlines of all the remaining bulkheads. The easiest way to do this is to simply copy the main or *primary* cross section and scale it. Just remember, this trick only works when the cross section is perfectly uniform.

It is very important to align each bulkhead precisely as you do this. Fortunately, you can employ a few "tricks" to take advantage of an illustration program's powerful drawing capabilities in order to make this process as easy as possible. Start with the primary cross section drawn at both **Station 8** and **Station 9** and use it as a template. These outlines can then be duplicated and scaled as many times as needed to create the remaining cross sections. Each copy, however, must be scaled precisely and lined up correctly.

To scale each outline, you will need to know exactly how wide and how tall to make it. Since many of the bulkheads are about the same size, it will be difficult to illustrate this process in our example unless a bulkhead is chosen that is significantly smaller than the main cross section. Therefore, the following procedure will be used to create an example bulkhead for **Station 12**. Keep in mind, the exact same process can also be used to draw all the other bulkheads.

A *bulkhead* actually marks the dividing line between watertight compartments on a ship. All other stations in between these bulkheads represent the position of *transverse frames*. With airplanes, however, all such frames are simply called "bulkheads."

Station numbering conventions may vary. The example shown may not strictly conform to established standards. Instead, it is intended merely to be easy to use and intuitive.

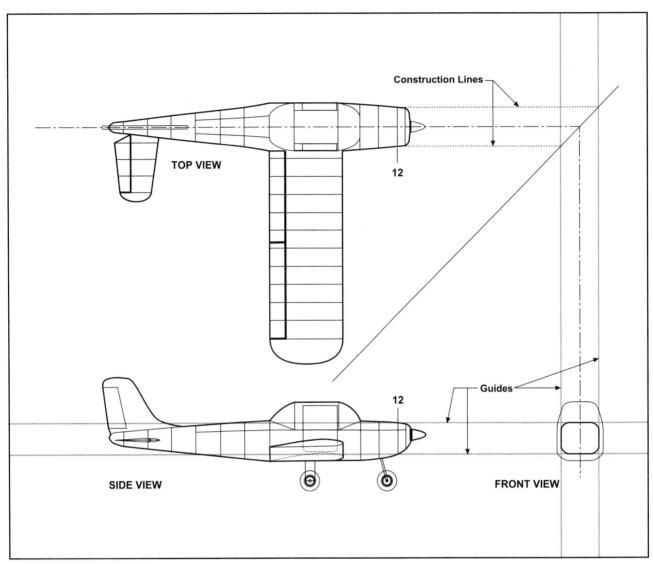

Figure 3.9.5. *Guides* can help you quickly and easily block out the proper size and alignment of each bulkhead outline.

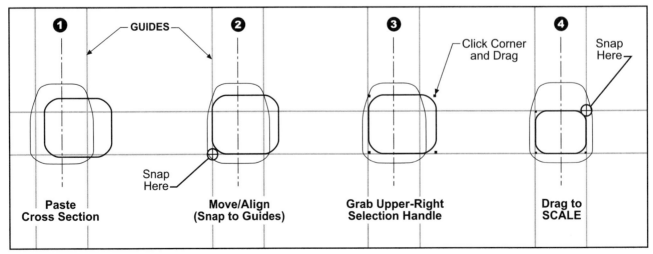

Figure 3.9.6. Copy and scale the main cross section to create additional cross section outlines at each frame station.

Use projection and reflection from the side and top views to determine the correct height and width of each cross section as follows:

1. In the side view, create a horizontal *Guide* and align it with the *top* of the fuselage at **Station 12**.
2. Create another horizontal *Guide* and align it with the *bottom* of the fuselage at **Station 12**.
3. In the top view, draw a construction line starting at the rightmost side of the fuselage at **Station 12** and project it to the miter line; Next, create a vertical *Guide* and align it so the construction line is reflected down into the front view.
4. In the top view, draw a construction line starting at the leftmost side of the fuselage at **Station 12** and project it to the miter line. Now:
   a. Create a vertical *Guide* and align it so the construction line is reflected down into the front view.
   b. At this point, the *Guides* you have just created should outline a "box" in the front view as shown in **Figure 3.9.5**; These *Guides* will help you precisely position a scaled copy of the cross section in the next step.
5. Make a copy (using either "Duplicate" or "Clone") of the primary cross section:
   a. After copying this outline, prepare to scale it in order to make a new bulkhead for **Station 12**.
   b. *Group* the copy of the cross section outline so the control points are locked; This allows you to reposition and/or scale the entire outline simply by dragging one of its four selection handles.
6. With the cross section outline still selected:
   a. Move it into position in the front view.
   b. Place the outline so the bottom-left corner of its bounding box snaps to the bottom-left corner of the "box" formed by the *Guides* as shown in **Figure 3.9.6**; You will need "Snap to Guides" turned on for this to work.
7. Click the upper-right selection handle of the cross section outline:
   a. Hold down the mouse button and drag it to scale the outline; Do not hold down the "Shift" key to constrain the motion, but allow the outline to *stretch* as needed.
   b. Drag the selection handle until it snaps to the upper-right corner of the "box" formed by the *Guides* as shown.

Repeat this process at each frame station to plot the outline of all the remaining bulkheads. Rather than continuing to paste and scale the primary cross section outline each time, simply clone the previous bulkhead outline and use that

Since you already created your vertical and horizontal *Guides* the first time, simply move them to their new positions for each additional frame station. This is quicker than creating new *Guides* each time and results in less clutter in your drawing.

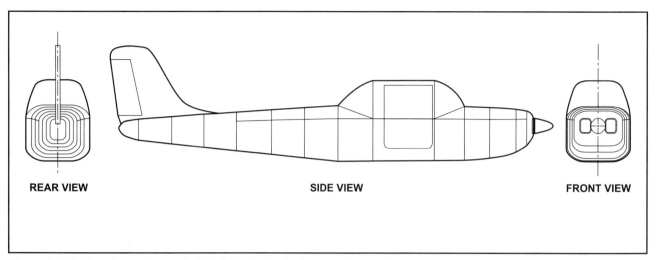

Figure 3.9.7. Plot the outlines of all bulkheads in the front and rear views in order to complete the fuselage plan.

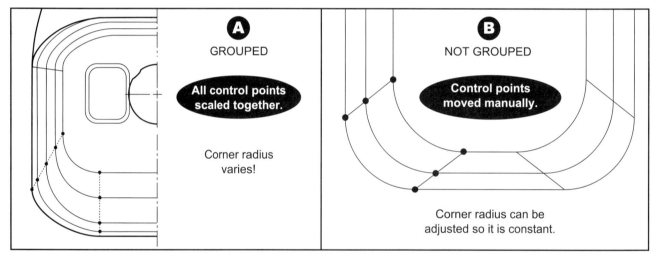

Figure 3.9.8. *Grouping* **determines how the points that make up each outline are scaled.**

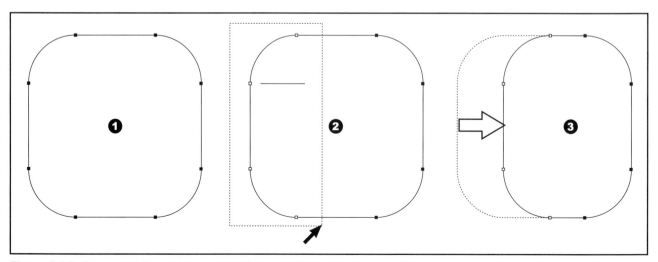

Figure 3.9.9. To control the radius, select all the control points in *two corners* **and move them at the same time.**

instead. Repeat until you have drawn all the bulkheads at all the frame stations. When you are finished, you should have complete front and rear profiles for the entire fuselage as shown in **Figure 3.9.7**.

The technique just demonstrated is fairly quick and easy. There are times, however, when it may not be the best approach. Here, grouping the points that make up a bulkhead and then scaling them all together subtly alters the shape of the curve that makes up each corner of the cross section outline.

If you look closely at the magnified view shown in **Part A** of **Figure 3.9.8**, you can see how the radius of the corners becomes *smaller* each time you scale down the outline. For our example airplane, this is perfectly acceptable since that is exactly how the fuselage is supposed to be shaped. For other subjects, however, this may not be appropriate.

In some cases, it may be necessary to maintain the exact same corner radius for each bulkhead. An example of this approach is illustrated in **Part B** of **Figure 3.9.8**. You can accomplish this by modifying the way you scale the cross section outlines. Rather than grouping the outline to scale all control points at once, select and move the individual control points instead. This is tedious and requires more work, but it results in precise control over the exact shape. If you use this method, the radius of the curve can remain the same for all scaled bulkheads.

The procedure for scaling by altering the individual control points is illustrated in **Figure 3.9.9**. If necessary, *ungroup* the object to make sure the individual control points are accessible. Using the *Arrow Tool*, draw a selection handle or "lasso" around all the control points that form two corners. It is important to select all control points in two adjacent corners at the same time. This makes adjusting the points quick and easy.

With the points in two corners now selected, drag them with the mouse or use the arrow keys on your keyboard to move them. If using the mouse, hold down the "Shift" key to constrain the motion vertically or horizontally. In this manner, you can quickly and easily adjust the outline so it is scaled without changing the radius of the corners.

With the fuselage cross section mapped out, you now have sufficient information to draw in more details. You can, for example, begin plotting the outline of the windshield where it meets the fuselage. To do this, plot a series of key points in the side view and transfer these points to the front view and then into the top view.

First, find the vertical location of a point on the windshield in the *side* view. Project this point into the front view by drawing a horizontal line. Note where this line intersects the appropriate cross section outline in the front view as illustrated in **Figure 3.9.10**.

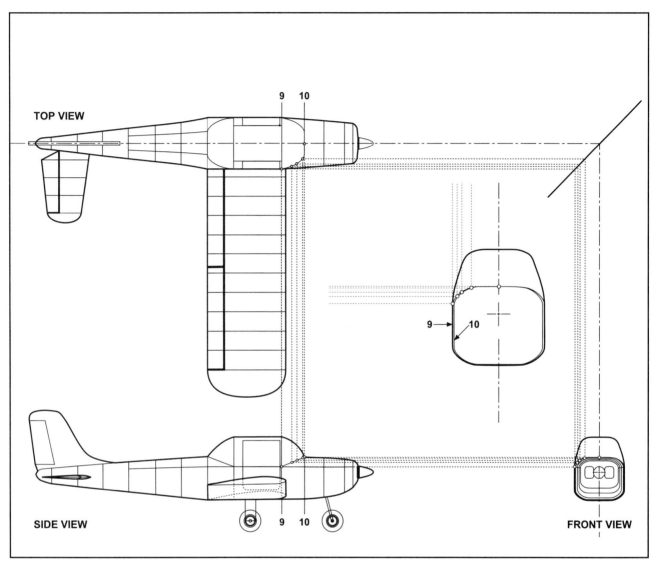

Figure 3.9.10. To draw the windshield, project from the side view into the front view and then back to the top view.

Keep in mind, when the drawing is full of closely spaced objects, things can start to get confusing. You must make sure your construction line intersects with just the right cross section outline for each point being projected. Be sure to use station numbering to keep track of what is going on. There is also a special trick you can use to make this process go more smoothly:

1.   Select the relevant cross section outline in the front view.
2.   Access the *stroke* settings and change the line color to bright red.
3.   Draw your construction line and find the intersection.
4.   When you are finished projecting the point, select the cross section outline and change the line color back to black.

With this method, when you draw each construction line, you will easily be able to tell which cross section outline is the correct "target" as your line is projected into the front view.

You can now finish by projecting each point from the front and side views into the top view. Find the location where the projected construction lines meet in the top view. This will be the location of the desired point on the windshield. When you have plotted a sufficient number of these points, connect them to draw the shape of the windshield in the top view.

3.10: Mapping Out a Subject's Geometry

At this point, the shape and position of the landing gear struts have already been mapped out in the side view. If you recall, this shape was corrected to compensate for visual distortion encountered in the template photo. Now, it's time to finish mapping out this feature in the other views. To do this, you will need to know an important fact about the subject – the exact angle between the struts. If you know this angle, drawing the landing gear will be easy. On the other hand, if you don't know the exact angle, you will have to make an educated guess.

Fortunately, when creating these kinds of features, designers often choose from among several commonly used angles:

- 90 degrees
- 60 degrees
- 45 degrees
- 30 degrees
- 22.5 degrees (i.e. 1/2 of 45 degrees)
- 15 degrees

Most angles used in construction come from this list of commonly used values, are multiples thereof, or are otherwise rounded to the nearest five degrees. Any other choice would be considered an <u>odd angle</u>. It is up to you to decide which angle is appropriate for any given situation.

Based on the reference photos available for our example airplane, assume the landing gear side struts are positioned at a 30-degree angle relative to the horizontal plane (i.e. the ground). This means the angle between the struts will be 120 degrees. The correct value can be found by drawing the struts at a 30-degree angle in the front view and then measuring the angle between them. It can also be derived by using basic *trigonometry*. This is even more precise than employing graphical methods.

As you can see, each strut forms part of a *right triangle* as shown in **Figure 3.10.1**. Triangles are often encountered when making blueprints of a subject. Thus, understanding basic geometry and trigonometry can be tremendously helpful. You can use mathematical formulas to quickly determine angles and distances rather than being forced to measure everything and take a chance on making mistakes.

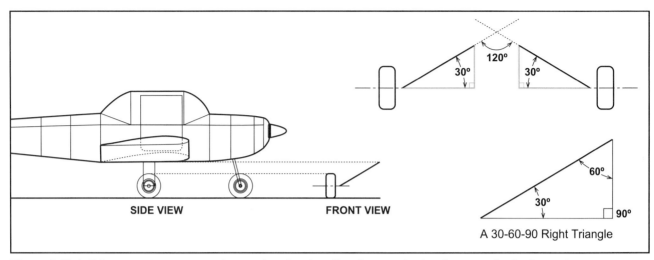

Figure 3.10.1. Trigonometry can come in very handy when figuring out the landing gear in the front view.

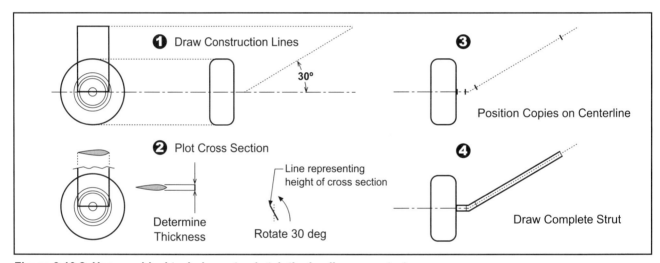

Figure 3.10.2. Use graphical techniques to sketch the landing gear strut.

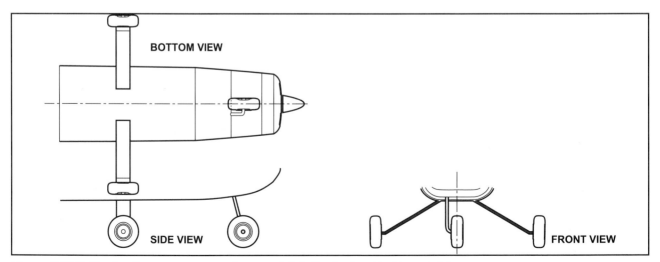

Figure 3.10.3. The landing gear can now be completely fleshed out in blueprint form.

With the correct angle for the landing gear decided, draw the struts in the front view. Find the position of the top and bottom of the gear by projecting from the side view as illustrated in **Figure 3.10.1**. Also, mark the centerline of the wheel in the front view as shown in **Figure 3.10.2**. Then, create a new line that is rotated 30 degrees relative to the ground as shown. This represents the centerline of the landing gear strut.

Using reference images as a guide, assume this strut has an airfoil shape. You need to know the thickness of this part before you can draw it. Without an exact figure, however, you can only make an educated guess. Use this information to finish drawing the strut as shown.

This takes care of the side gear. Now, all that remains is the front or nose gear. The wheel for the nose gear will be identical to that of the left side gear. The strut itself, however, is quite different. You will need some reference images to determine the proper shape.

In this case, the nose strut is merely a metal tube that will be represented by a bent piece of wire on the model. You can use projection to map out exactly where the strut meets the fuselage and also how the nose gear is assembled. Finished drawings for the landing gear are presented for reference in **Figure 3.10.3**. A bottom view is included as well so you can see exactly how the gear is drawn in all plan views.

3.11: Wrapping Up

A complete set of plan view drawings for our example airplane appears in **Figure 3.11.1**. Refer to these drawings to see how any portion of this aircraft is drawn in plan view form.

In this exercise, you have successfully used the techniques of orthographic projection to map out the basic form of a model airplane. You have drawn the fuselage, wings, tail, cockpit, and landing gear in the side, top, front and rear views. If you have never drawn blueprints before, this is quite an accomplishment. Give yourself a good pat on the back!

But, you are not quite finished. Any features that remain can be mapped out in exactly the same way as what you have already seen. The propeller or "prop," for example, is an important feature that still needs to be created. Unfortunately, because the surface of the prop "twists" along its length, it is a difficult shape to draw in plan view form.

For this type of challenge, you may want to use some 3D "power tools" to make things easier. A 3D program can easily generate true orthographic plan view renderings. In this way, the prop would be drawn precisely without having to tediously map out every inch of it using projection. In fact, some 3D modeling programs can actually make your 2D drawings for you.

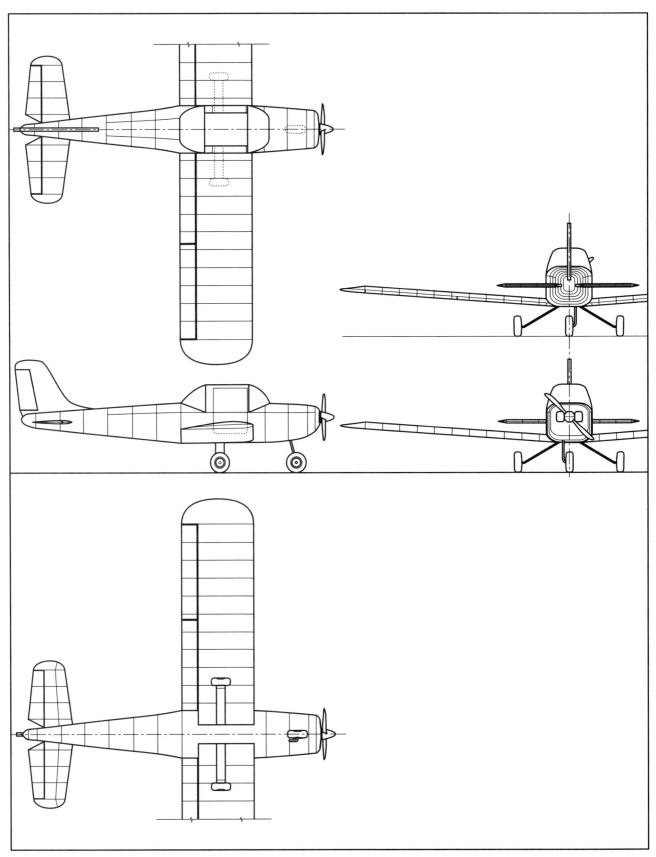

Figure 3.11.1. Completed plan view drawings of the example airplane.

3.12: Summary

Orthographic projection is the secret to making blueprints. This process enables you to take information from two existing views and derive missing details in a third view. By starting with basic information about your subject such as the overall dimensions, you can use the principles of projection to fill in the details – one piece at a time:

- A *starting point* is needed to create plan view drawings of any subject.
- Since two existing views are required to generate a missing third view, you must have sufficient information up front to draw at least two different views of your subject.
- It is best to use an existing blueprint as a starting point; Only if such a reference is not available should you consider tracing photographs.
- If you choose to trace a photo to use as a template, be aware all photographs contain *perspective distortion* that must be accounted for and corrected.
- Block out the overall dimensions of your subject and arrange these blocks in a precise fashion suitable for using orthographic projection.
- If necessary, you may trace a template image to use as a guide; Place the resulting drawing in one of the blocks, then scale it to fit.
- Adjust the traced outline to compensate for perspective distortion.
- Use projection to transfer information from one view to another until all the crucial details of your drawing have been filled in.
- Projection between adjacent views is easy while projection between non-adjacent views requires the use of a *miter line*.
- Most shapes can be plotted graphically, but knowing basic geometry and trigonometry can be very helpful when making blueprints.

Congratulations! You have now covered the basic concepts and principles needed to start creating your very own blueprints. Just keep in mind, such drawings are merely a starting point for the modeler who wishes to build something from scratch. Once you have your plan views, you still need to extract information from them in order to make templates and construction patterns for your project. These patterns will be used to build the actual components of your model.

What's Next?

The remaining chapters in this book will focus on techniques needed to make construction patterns. First, you will learn how to properly read your plans and determine how to plot the correct shape and dimensions of parts that do not appear *true size* in a plan view. Finally, you will see how to derive accurate construction information for many of the geometric shapes you may encounter during the model-making process.

Section 2
Making Construction Patterns

Topics in This Chapter:

Chapter

Pattern-Making Basics

4.1: Overview

Although it might seem tedious and time consuming for complex subjects, using orthographic projection to create plan view drawings is a fairly straightforward process. Where the real work often begins is turning those drawings into useable construction patterns and templates from which you can actually build your model's structure. This chapter will introduce some important techniques that can be used to do just that.

4.2: Lines Shown "True Length"

One of the most important skills to master in the process of making construction patterns is knowing how to properly read and interpret your drawings. No concept is more important to this process than the notion of <u>parallelism</u>. When a line or feature is *parallel* to a principal plan view, it can be measured directly from the plans. On the other hand, if a line or feature is not parallel – meaning it lies *at an angle* relative to a principal plan view – it cannot be accurately measured.

The ease with which you can make construction patterns and templates from your drawings will depend largely on your ability to distinguish between those features that are parallel to a plan view and those that are not. This idea is best illustrated by a practical example. **Figure 4.2.1** shows a wooden block that has been cut so its front face is at an angle (i.e. sloping). It is easy to see how the six principal plan views for such a block can be drawn using orthographic projection.

Each surface of the block – except for the sloping side – is *parallel* to one of the principal plan views. When a surface is parallel to a plan view, its dimensions can be measured in that view. The side of the block, for example, can be measured in the side plan view. In the same way, the top of the block can be measured in the top plan view. Lines denoting the outlines of these surfaces are said to be <u>true length</u>. This is extremely useful to know because any feature that is shown true length in your plans can be measured directly from the drawings.

NOTE: Underlined terms appear in the Glossary.

If any line, surface, or feature does not appear *true length* in a particular view, it should not be measured in that view. Since the object would appear *compressed*, such measurements would be completely useless.

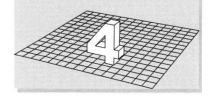

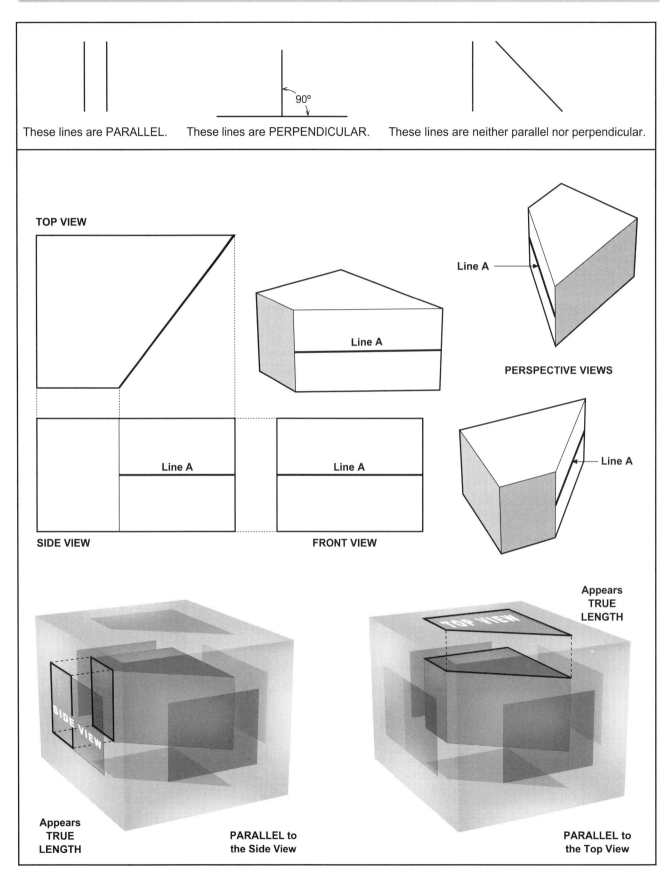

These lines are PARALLEL.   These lines are PERPENDICULAR.   These lines are neither parallel nor perpendicular.

90°

TOP VIEW

Line A

PERSPECTIVE VIEWS

Line A

SIDE VIEW

Line A

FRONT VIEW

Line A

Line A

Appears
TRUE
LENGTH

Appears
TRUE
LENGTH

SIDE VIEW

TOP VIEW

PARALLEL to
the Side View

PARALLEL to
the Top View

Figure 4.2.1. This example block has an angled face that is not parallel with any principal plan view.

Knowing this certainly makes things easier when it comes time to make construction patterns and templates. After all, you need correct measurements for all the parts of your model before you can start building it. Being able to correctly read and interpret your drawings will make this process much easier.

So, what happens when a feature is *not* parallel to a plan view? Any line or surface that lies at an angle relative to a principal plan view is said to be foreshortened. Such a line or feature does not appear true length and so it cannot be measured *in that particular view*. In the case of our example block, the sloping side is not parallel to any principal plan view. Because of this, you must be very careful when trying to determine the dimensions of this area. This is a good example of why you should not take measurements directly from the drawings unless you know for sure exactly which parts appear true length and which do not.

Line "A" in **Figure 4.2.1** indicates the length of the sloping face of the example block. If you held this block in your hand, it would be very easy to measure the length of this line using a ruler or measuring tape. When working with two-dimensional blueprints, however, it is not always that easy. If you need to know the length of a line or feature that does not appear true length, you'll have to extract measurements from the drawings. Doing so, however, may require using some special techniques.

The same example block is illustrated once again in **Figure 4.2.2**. Here you can see how the angled face becomes *compressed* when it is projected into either the front or the side plan view. As a result, **Line "A"** appears *foreshortened* in both views. This means you cannot measure its length in either view. If you attempt to do so, your measurement will be *shorter* than the true length of the surface.

To further illustrate this concept, look at the plan view drawings of our example block shown in **Figure 4.2.3**. In order to properly read and interpret these drawings, you should be able to determine what is shown true length and what is not simply by looking at them. If the concept of true length is not yet intuitive, study this figure carefully until it makes sense. In this case, while the *sloping face* is not parallel to any principal plan view, the *edges* of this face are indeed parallel. These edges appear as *lines* in the drawings. In the top view, the edge of the sloping face is shown true length. Even though you cannot actually see **Line "A"** in this particular view, it is parallel to the *edge* of the sloping surface and is therefore the same length as this edge. As a result, you can measure the length of **Line "A"** in the top view.

Notice what happens, however, when you position the top view over the side view and then compare the dimensions of the sloping side of our example block in both views. It is easy to see how **Line "A"** now becomes *foreshortened* in the side view. The same thing happens when you position

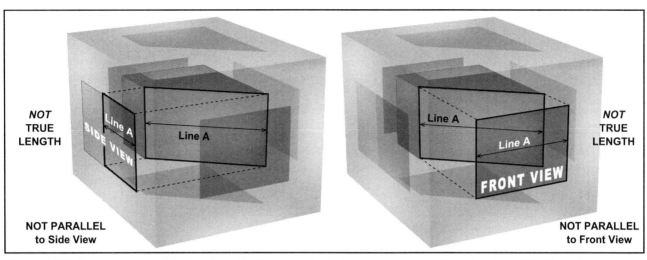

Figure 4.2.2. Any part of an object *not* parallel to a principal plan view appears "foreshortened" in that view.

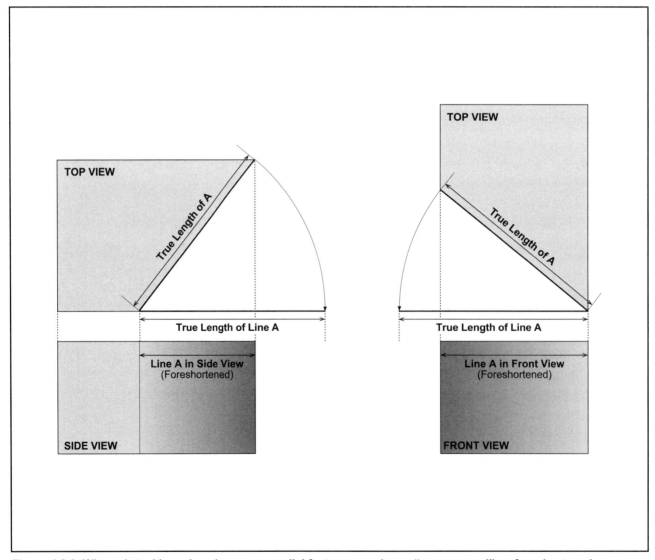

Figure 4.2.3. When plotted in a plan view, non-parallel features are drawn "compressed" or *foreshortened*.

the top view over the front view. **Line "A"** is true length in the top view but is foreshortened in the front view. As a result, in order to extract accurate dimensions from these drawings, you should measure the length of the sloping side of the block *only in the top or bottom views*. It should *not* be measured in either the front or the side view.

But, what happens when the shapes involved are not quite so simple? Chances are, many of the objects in your drawings will be more complex than what you have seen so far. In these cases you still must be able to tell at a glance which features appear true length and which do not. As an example, look at the subject shown in **Figure 4.2.4**. This structure is dome-shaped with radial lines or "ribs" that extend out from the center to the edges. When viewed from the top, you can see the exact orientation of these ribs.

If you visualize this object inside an imaginary glass box where the sides of the box represent the plan views, it should be easy to determine which ribs are parallel to any particular plan view and which are not. In this case, concentrate on the top view where the ribs appear as straight lines. Only the horizontal and vertical lines represent ribs that will be parallel to a plan view. In contrast, those ribs arrayed at an *angle* in the top view will *not* be parallel to the plan views.

The actual width of any rib (i.e. the distance from the center of the object to the outer edge) can be measured in the top plan view. You can also measure the angle between the ribs in this view. If you look at the side view, however, only two ribs will appear true length while the remaining ribs will appear foreshortened. As a result, only measure the width of a rib in the side view when it is *parallel* to that view. In addition, the shape of each rib is defined by the *outer curved edge*. This also can only be obtained from the *side* view.

All the techniques demonstrated in this and later chapters will revolve around the idea of *true length*. Thus, it is very important to understand this concept thoroughly. To demonstrate how all this relates to a modeling project, imagine for a moment you are actually building a model of this particular object. The model can be made by cutting out a *circle* to act as a base with twelve radial ribs fleshing out the form. Foam can be inserted between the ribs and sanded to shape, using the edges of the ribs as a guide to obtain the correct profile.

Or, if you wanted to build a 3D model of this shape, you could extract a *profile* from the side view and then rotate this in a full circle. The model could then be "sliced" into pieces like a pie. All the information needed to do this is readily available in the side and top views.

To make construction patterns for either project, start by extracting the needed measurements and profiles from the plan view drawings as illustrated in **Figure 4.2.5**. In order to do that, you must be able to tell at a glance which

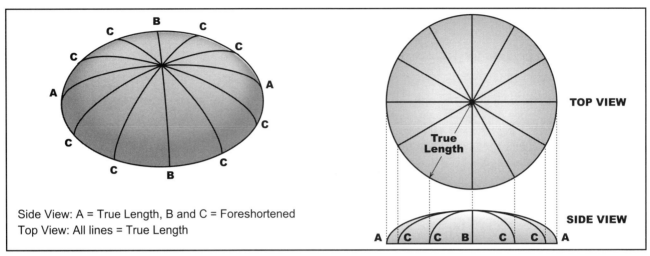

Figure 4.2.4. Lines on a circular object may be foreshortened.

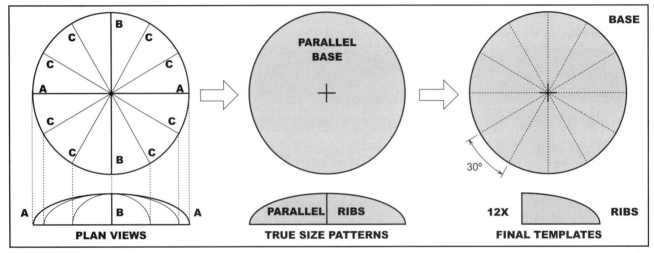

Figure 4.2.5. Create construction patterns by extracting true-length measurements from the plan views.

features to measure and in what views you should measure them. In this case, you can obtain the outline for the circular base directly from the top plan view. This view also provides the correct location of each rib and the angles between them. (Don't forget to mark the exact center point of the circle as well.) A pattern for each of the ribs can be extracted from any side view. You must pick the correct rib, however, or your patterns will not be accurate. In this case, choose one of the ribs that is *parallel* to the side view and base your template on that. Here, only the ribs marked "**A**" are parallel to the side view as shown.

So far, you have seen how lines and features can appear true length or foreshortened in any view. The techniques presented here and in the remaining chapters will make use of these concepts to help you extract accurate measurements from your drawings. Such measurements will be needed to make construction patterns and templates for your projects. To assist you in this process, some special definitions and rules have been developed. Before those can be introduced, however, an important new concept needs to be discussed first.

4.3: Planes of Projection

According to the theory of orthographic projection, an imaginary glass box can be placed around a subject, and the six principal plan views projected onto the sides of this box. Each side of the box is therefore a *plane of projection*. A plane is simply a flat surface existing somewhere in three-dimensional space. When you are making a drawing on a piece of paper, for example, the paper itself can be considered a plane. Since the paper is typically laid flat on a working surface, you might think of it as a *horizontal plane*.

Yet, all six views are not always required to completely describe a subject in plan view form. In fact, three views are all that is needed for many subjects. It is these three "primary" views that form the basis of multi-view drawing. They show the subject's height, width, and depth. These are the vital dimensions needed to recreate the object. To map out these vital dimensions, you need, at minimum, a front, top, and side view.

If you think about it for a moment, both the front and rear views exist on opposite sides of the same imaginary glass box. Since these sides are parallel to one another, this means the plane of projection that yields the front view is parallel to the plane of projection that yields the rear view. In the same way, the plane of projection for the top view is parallel to the plane of projection for the bottom view. The same goes for the left and right side views.

Now, imagine you could combine the planes of projection for the front and rear views into a single plane. This plane could then be repositioned along the length of the subject as needed to create projections for either the front or the rear view. If you do the same thing for the remaining views, the six planes of projection can be reduced to just three planes. These are known as the three principal planes of projection as shown in **Figure 4.3.1**.

With this idea in mind, all six plan views can now be created by projecting the subject onto the three principal planes of projection. These planes are labeled as follows:

- Frontal plane (projects the front and rear views); The frontal plane is also known as the vertical plane.
- Horizontal plane (projects the top and bottom views).
- Profile plane (projects the left and right side views).

For the remainder of this book, whenever a line is said to be parallel to a particular plan view, it will no longer be necessary to refer to the specific

Orthographic projection was introduced in **Chapter 1** and demonstrated in detail in **Chapter 3**. The basis of projection is an imaginary, six-sided "glass box" surrounding the subject. Each of the six principal plan views can be projected onto one of the sides of this box.

By the traditional definition, a *profile* is an outline that appears in a *side view*. This is due to the fact profiles are extracted by passing the *profile plane* through an object. As a result, in order to be technically correct, outlines in any other view may not be referred to as profiles.

This restriction, however, can become an issue when you begin to discuss 3D modeling. In that context, profiles are 2D lines used to build 3D shapes. These lines can appear in any plan view. Therefore, the term "profile" as used in this book will not be restricted to its traditional definition.

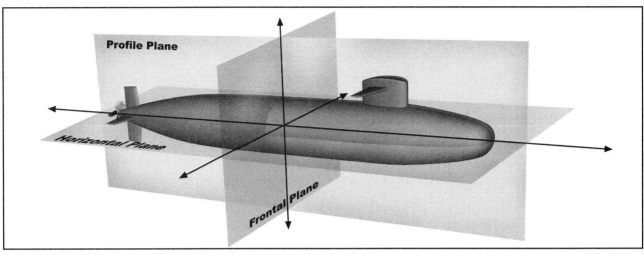

Figure 4.3.1. Define the height, width, and depth of any object using the three "principal planes of projection."

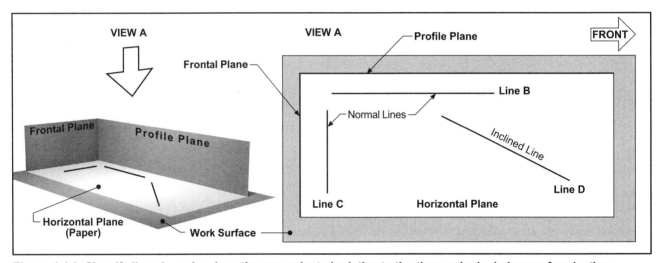

Figure 4.4.1. Classify lines based on how they are oriented relative to the three principal planes of projection.

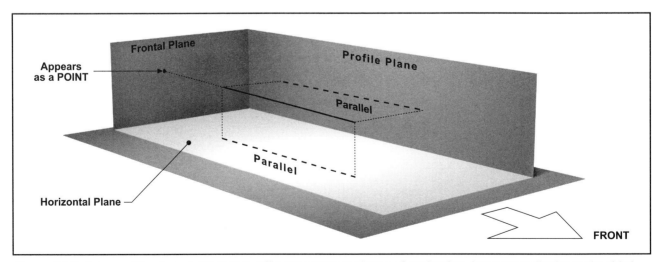

Figure 4.4.2. A *normal* line is parallel to *two* different principal planes of projection, but perpendicular to the third.

view (i.e. front view, rear view, etc.). Instead, the line may be referenced as being parallel to a particular *plane of projection.*

Why is this further definition necessary? As you will see throughout this chapter, many of the techniques for making construction patterns require you to find the true length of lines that are not parallel to any plan view. Making the most of these techniques requires a basic understanding of the principal planes of projection. This knowledge will also be required in order to introduce some new terms and definitions related to the true length of non-parallel lines and features.

4.4: Normal, Inclined, and Oblique Lines

In any orthographic plan view, lines can be represented in one of three ways:

- True length
- Foreshortened
- As a *point*

When making construction patterns from your blueprints, you should be able to recognize the lines that can be directly measured in the drawings. As part of this process, it is very helpful to properly classify the different lines in your plan views. According to the principles of orthographic projection, these lines can be placed in one of three categories:

- Normal
- Inclined
- Oblique

To understand the differences between the three classifications, imagine you are drawing a series of lines on a hypothetical *horizontal plane* represented by a piece of paper as shown in **Figure 4.4.1**. Now, imagine your piece of paper is placed on a "work surface" so that the *profile plane* forms a "wall" bordering the top edge while the *frontal plane* forms a "wall" bordering the left side of the paper. This exercise will help you become familiar with the principal planes of projection. It will also help you understand exactly how lines can be oriented in relation to them.

Since any hypothetical lines drawn on this piece of paper will be confined to the horizontal plane, they can exist in only *two dimensions*. For example, you might draw a horizontal line (left to right), a vertical line (top to bottom), or an angled line. First, look at what happens if you draw a horizontal line. In **Figure 4.4.1** you can see how any line similar to **Line "B"** is drawn parallel to the *profile plane*. Since such a line exists on the piece of paper, it is also parallel to the *horizontal plane*. Such a line is therefore parallel to two different planes of projection at the same time.

Remember how one plane of projection can be used to create two different principal plan views? This is why a line parallel to a *single* plane of projection will be parallel to *two* different plan views.

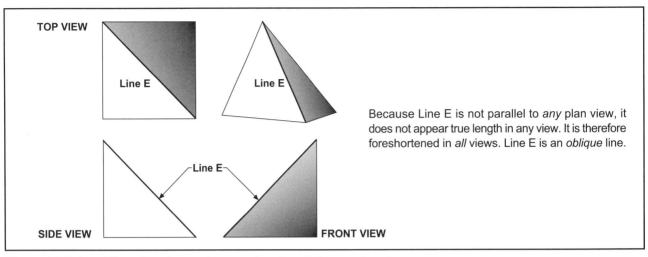

Because Line E is not parallel to *any* plan view, it does not appear true length in any view. It is therefore foreshortened in *all* views. Line E is an *oblique* line.

Figure 4.4.3. An *oblique line* does not appear true length in *any* plan view.

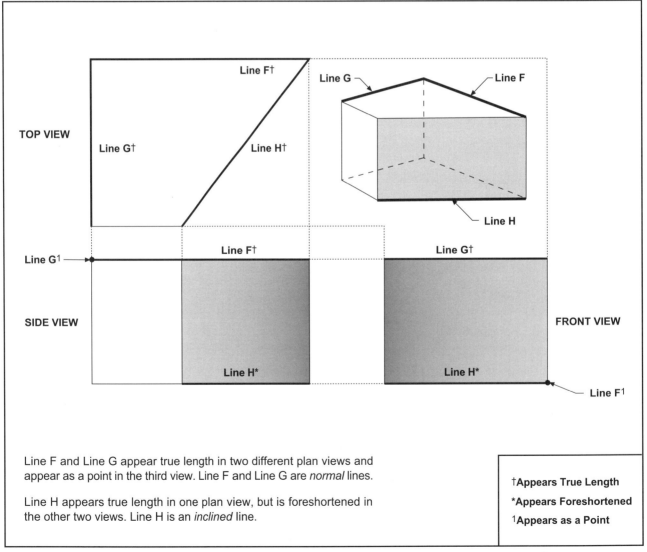

Line F and Line G appear true length in two different plan views and appear as a point in the third view. Line F and Line G are *normal* lines.

Line H appears true length in one plan view, but is foreshortened in the other two views. Line H is an *inclined* line.

†Appears True Length

*Appears Foreshortened

[1]Appears as a Point

Figure 4.4.4. Measure normal and inclined lines only in those view(s) where they appear true length.

Also, note how any line drawn on the paper that is parallel with the profile plane will also be *perpendicular* to the frontal plane. When a line is parallel to two principal planes of projection, but perpendicular to the third, that line is said to be a <u>normal line</u>. Because normal lines are parallel to two different planes of projection, they appear true length in *four* different plan views at the same time. This makes a normal line the easiest type of line to measure.

This concept is further demonstrated in **Figure 4.4.2**. Here, a horizontal line is depicted as "floating" in three-dimensional space so you can more easily see how it can be parallel to two different principal planes of projection at the same time. Note, however, what happens when the line is projected into the *frontal plane*. Since the horizontal line is *perpendicular* to this plane, it appears as a *point* in the frontal plane. This concept might be confusing at first, but it is important to understand.

Note that a vertical line drawn on our example piece of paper would also be considered a normal line. This is illustrated by **Line "C"** in **Figure 4.4.1**. The only difference here is the orientation relative to the principal planes of projection. This vertical line is parallel to both the frontal plane and the horizontal plane, but perpendicular to the profile plane. Such a line would therefore appear true length in the top, bottom, front, and rear views, but would appear as a *point* in both the left and right side views.

As you can see, knowing when a line is normal can help you figure out which view to choose if you want to measure it. But, what happens when a line is *not* normal? Any line that is not parallel to two different principal planes of projection is called a <u>non-normal line</u>. As you can imagine, such lines are not nearly as easy to measure.

There are two different types of non-normal lines:

- Inclined
- Oblique

You can see an example of an <u>inclined line</u> by looking at **Line "D"** in **Figure 4.4.1**. Imagine drawing such an angled line across the hypothetical piece of paper in this example. This line would be parallel with the horizontal plane since it is drawn on the paper, but it would not be parallel with either the frontal or profile planes. As a result, this line is not a normal line.

In this case, however, since it is parallel with the horizontal plane, you can accurately measure the length of the inclined line in either the top or the bottom view. The line will appear true length in these two views, but it will be *foreshortened* in all other views.

Inclined lines are slightly more difficult to manage than normal lines since you must be certain the line appears true length in a particular view before

When making templates and construction patterns, being able to recognize the difference between normal, inclined, and oblique lines can be a very valuable skill.

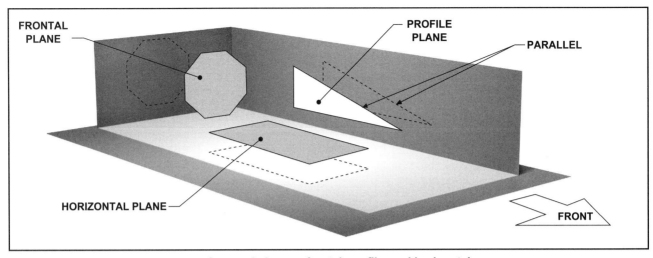

FRONTAL PLANE

PROFILE PLANE

PARALLEL

HORIZONTAL PLANE

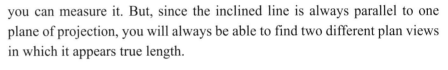

FRONT

Figure 4.5.1. There are three types of *normal planes* – frontal, profile, and horizontal.

you can measure it. But, since the inclined line is always parallel to one plane of projection, you will always be able to find two different plan views in which it appears true length.

Unfortunately, there is another type of line that *never* appears true length in *any* plan view. Look at the pyramid-shaped block shown in **Figure 4.4.3**. Unlike a regular pyramid, this block has two vertical sides that are parallel to the profile and frontal planes of projection. The remaining two sides, however, are not parallel to *any* plane of projection. The intersection between these two non-parallel sides is represented by **Line "E."** Because this line is neither parallel nor perpendicular to any principal plane of projection, it does not appear true length in *any* plan view. **Line "E"** is therefore an <u>oblique line</u>.

Whenever you are dealing with surfaces or features that are not parallel to any of the principal plan views, you will end up with oblique lines. As a result, these features will appear foreshortened in all plan views. As you can imagine, this makes oblique lines the most difficult of all line types to measure. Unfortunately, this type of line will often make up a portion of the structure of your subject. For this reason, you must know how to deal with this scenario when taking measurements from your drawings.

Figure 4.4.4 depicts both normal and inclined lines where each is labeled according to whether it appears true length, foreshortened, or as a point. As mentioned previously, **Figure 4.4.3** illustrates an oblique line. Study both these figures carefully and be sure you understand the differences between the line types. It may be helpful to memorize the following three basic rules:

- When a line is *normal*, it can be measured in *four* different plan views.
- You can measure the true length of an *inclined line* in *two* plan views.
- If a line is oblique, it cannot be measured in *any* plan view.

At this point, you might be wondering what you can do to determine the length of oblique lines since they do not appear true length in any view. Fortunately, there are several techniques that can help you do this. These will be presented in **Sections 4.6** through **4.8**.

4.5: Normal, Inclined, and Oblique Planes

Flat surfaces on your subject are represented by *planes* while the edges and intersections of these surfaces are represented by *lines*. Now that you have been introduced to the concepts of normal, inclined, and oblique lines, it is time to discuss normal, inclined, and oblique planes. Remember how lines can appear true length, foreshortened, or as a point in any plan view? In a similar fashion, planes can also be represented in one of three ways:

- True size
- Foreshortened
- As an *edge*

Just as lines can be normal, inclined, or oblique relative to the principal planes of projection, planes can be *parallel*, *perpendicular*, *inclined,* or *oblique*. When a plane on your subject is parallel to a plane of projection, it appears <u>true size</u> in the corresponding plan views. For example, a plane that is parallel to the frontal plane of projection will appear true size in both the front and rear plan views.

A plane that is parallel to two principal planes of projection is considered to be a <u>normal plane</u> (also known as a <u>principal plane</u>). There are three forms of normal planes as shown in **Figure 4.5.1**:

- A <u>frontal plane</u> is parallel to the frontal plane of projection; Frontal planes appear true size in the front and rear views.
- A <u>profile plane</u> is parallel to the profile plane of projection; Profile planes appear true size in the left and right side views.
- A <u>horizontal plane</u> is parallel to the horizontal plane of projection; Horizontal planes appear true size in the top and bottom views.

As with lines, planes are not always parallel to the principal planes of projection. When this happens, things can get complicated. A plane that is not parallel to two different planes of projection is a <u>non-normal plane</u>. Just as a non-normal line can be classified into one of two different categories, so can a non-normal plane:

- An <u>inclined plane</u> is not parallel to *any* of the principal planes of projection, but is *perpendicular* to one plane of projection; This concept is illustrated in **Figure 4.5.2**.
- An <u>oblique plane</u> is neither parallel nor perpendicular to *any* of the principal planes of projection; This makes an oblique plane impractical to measure in any plan view.

> When the edge of a plane is parallel to a principal plane of projection, the edge will be drawn as a *line* that appears *true length* in the corresponding plan views.

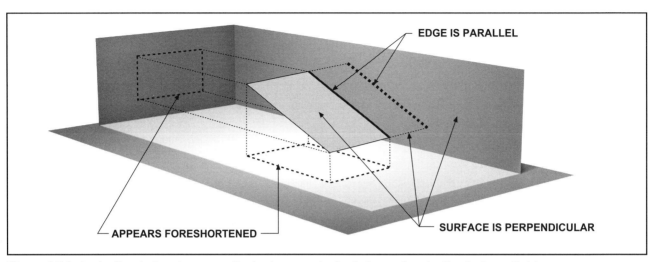

Figure 4.5.2. An *inclined plane* is perpendicular to one principal plane of projection but parallel to none.

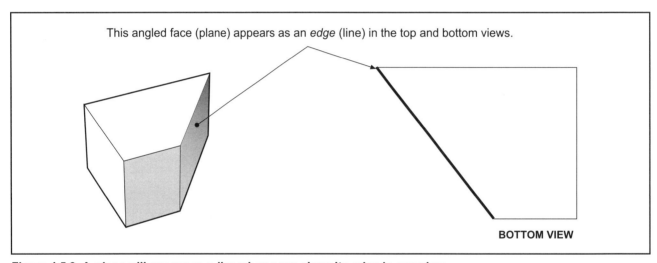

Figure 4.5.3. A *plane* will appear as a *line* when seen along its edge in any view.

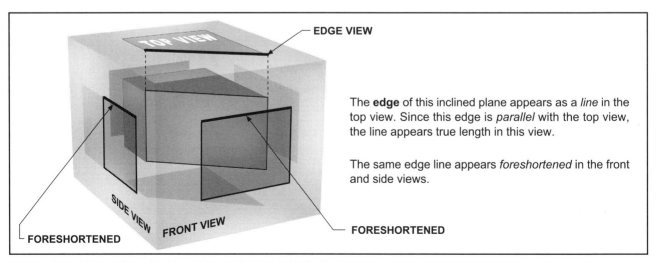

Figure 4.5.4. If the *edge* of a plane is parallel to a principal plan view, it will appear true length in that view.

Look at the sample block shown in **Figure 4.5.3**. This block has an angled face that is not parallel to any of the planes of projection. Note how the *edge* of this sloping surface appears as a *line* in the top and bottom views. This is known as the edge view of a plane and is further illustrated in **Figure 4.5.4**. Since the edges of the sloping surface are parallel to one of the principal planes of projection (in this case, the horizontal plane), this sloping surface is an *inclined plane*. As a result, you can measure its length simply by measuring the *length of its edge* in either the top or bottom view.

Now, look at the front and side views of the example block in **Figure 4.5.4**. Note how the same line representing the edge of the inclined face now appears *foreshortened*. Because this face is inclined, the edge appears true length only in the top and bottom views, but is foreshortened in all other views.

As you can see, inclined planes are not terribly challenging to master because they can always be measured in two different plan views. All you need to do is choose the view in which the edge appears true length. On the other hand, there are times when the edges of a plane are not parallel to *any* plan view. When this happens, the plane is an *oblique plane* and thus does not appear true size in *any* plan view.

Plotting the outline of oblique planes can be very challenging. Unfortunately, many of the subjects you might choose to model are likely to include surfaces represented by oblique planes. If you cannot determine the true size and shape of these planes, you will be unable to make construction patterns needed to actually build them. As a result, learning how to determine the true size of oblique planes can be critical to the process of creating templates and construction patterns from your drawings.

Special techniques are available to help you figure out the true dimensions of oblique planes. In the next few sections of this chapter, you will see some powerful methods that can be used to determine the true length of inclined and oblique lines, as well as the true size of inclined and oblique planes.

4.6: Revolution

The concept of *conventional revolution* was introduced in **Chapter 2**. This practice is designed to clarify working drawings by rotating or *revolving* elements that appear at an angle until they are perfectly parallel with a plan view. When the object in question has been revolved in this fashion, it appears true size and so it can be measured directly from the plan view.

The problem with this convention is that it often results in a plan view that does not truly represent the subject. An example of such a situation is illustrated in **Figure 4.6.1**. Here, two blades of a three-bladed propeller appear at an odd angle in the side plan view. This means you cannot measure either blade in this view. According to drafting convention, this is a poor way to represent an object such as this propeller – even though it is, in fact, the actual side view.

The solution, according to conventional practice, is to revolve the "offending" blade until it is parallel with the side view. When this is done, you can measure

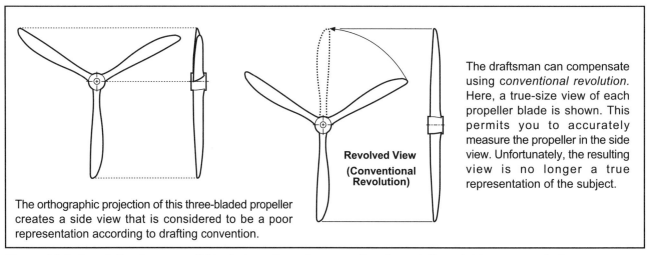

The orthographic projection of this three-bladed propeller creates a side view that is considered to be a poor representation according to drafting convention.

Revolved View (Conventional Revolution)

The draftsman can compensate using *conventional revolution.* Here, a true-size view of each propeller blade is shown. This permits you to accurately measure the propeller in the side view. Unfortunately, the resulting view is no longer a true representation of the subject.

Figure 4.6.1. *Revolution* **is a powerful technique, though** *conventional revolution* **might cause confusion.**

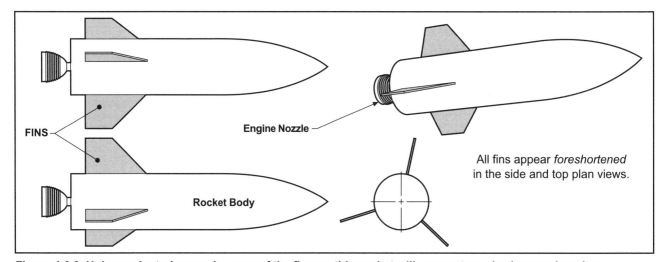

FINS

Engine Nozzle

Rocket Body

All fins appear *foreshortened* in the side and top plan views.

Figure 4.6.2. Unless oriented properly, none of the fins on this rocket will appear true size in any plan view.

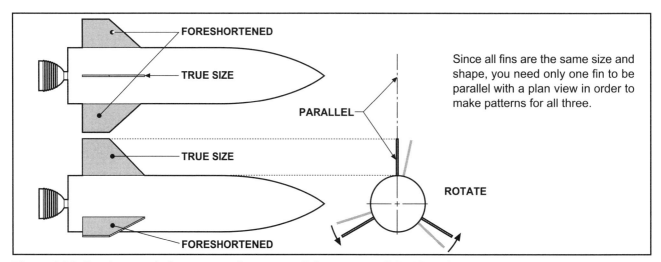

FORESHORTENED

TRUE SIZE

PARALLEL

TRUE SIZE

ROTATE

FORESHORTENED

Since all fins are the same size and shape, you need only one fin to be parallel with a plan view in order to make patterns for all three.

Figure 4.6.3. Employ *revolution* **to rotate features until they are parallel with a plan view.**

both blades in this view. Unfortunately, this might cause confusion for anyone who is not experienced at interpreting blueprints. For this reason, the practice of conventional revolution will not be promoted in this book.

This does not mean, however, that revolution itself is not a useful technique. On the contrary, it is extremely helpful for determining the true length of an oblique line or the true size of an oblique plane. In fact, revolution may be one of the most valuable techniques you can master when creating templates and construction patterns for your projects.

As an example, whenever you need to measure an oblique line or plane, you may be able to *revolve* it until it's parallel to a principal plan view. You can really see this technique start to come into play when using the advanced pattern-making techniques discussed in **Chapter 6** and **Chapter 7**.

To see just how useful revolution can be when making construction patterns, look at the example shown in **Figure 4.6.2**. Here you can see plan views of a rocket with three symmetrical "stabilizer fins" arranged about its longitudinal centerline. Unfortunately, this rocket is poorly oriented so none of the fins are parallel to the side, top, or bottom views. As a result, they do not appear true size. Because of this, you might have a hard time making construction patterns for these fins using information available in the plan views.

In this case, you might use information in the *front* view to derive the correct shape of the fins, but that could be somewhat tedious. Things would be much easier if this rocket were to be oriented more appropriately as illustrated in **Figure 4.6.3**. This is the best choice because at least one of the three fins will be parallel to a plan view. Therefore, it will appear *true size* in that view.

Revolution can be used to adjust the orientation of this example rocket – or just about any other subject. First, find the correct center of rotation. Then, *revolve* the subject about this center until it is oriented as desired.

This process is demonstrated in **Figure 4.6.3**. Here, the center of rotation is the longitudinal centerline of the rocket's body. Since the cross section of this body is circular, the center of rotation is the center point of the circle.

Once the orientation is adjusted, you can begin the process of making accurate construction patterns for the rocket. Since the body and engine nozzle are perfectly symmetrical structures, rotating them will have no effect on how these features appear in the plan views. Even more, since all three fins are the exact same size and shape, all you really need to do is get one fin in the proper position in order to obtain a suitable template for building all three. In this case, you need only pay attention to the topmost fin.

What would happen if all the fins were *not* the same size and shape? In that case, you could rotate the subject not once but *several times* to get the

Once again, you can see how important it is to mark the exact center point of all symmetrical objects.

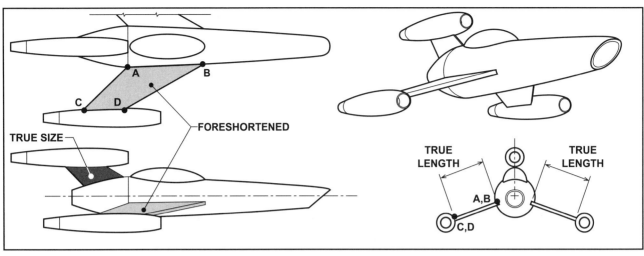

Figure 4.6.4. Plot a series of points on the feature that is to be rotated.

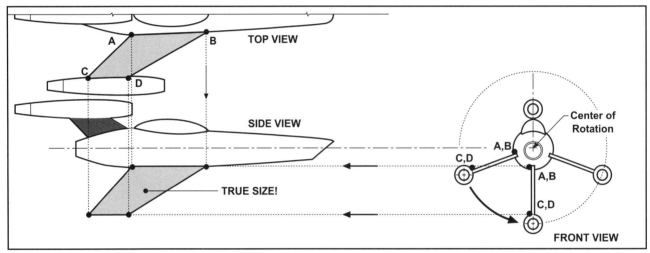

Figure 4.6.5. Revolve the assembly, then project the plotted points to map the outline of the feature.

information needed to draw each fin – one at a time. This would be easy for our example rocket since the rest of the structure is not affected by rotating it about the longitudinal centerline. Unfortunately, this might not be the case with some other subjects. In such cases, you might end up redrawing the entire subject each time you use revolution to find the true size of one of the features. That could be a lot of work!

Fortunately, you don't really need to rotate the *entire* subject when all you want to do is find the true size of just one feature. Instead, rotate only those features that need to be found true size (or true length). This is much quicker and easier than attempting to rotate the entire subject. Just be sure to rotate the feature about the correct point.

This method is illustrated in **Figure 4.6.4**. Here, a "rocket fighter" has three stabilizer fins that are not symmetrical. In this particular case, the top or *dorsal* fin is parallel to the side plan view. Therefore, it can easily be measured in this view. The other two fins, however, appear foreshortened in both the top and side views. (To find the true size of these two fins, they can be rotated into the proper position using revolution.)

In this case, the *width* of all three fins is shown true length in the front and rear views. These views therefore provide the correct locations of points "**A**," "**B**," "**C**," and "**D**" as shown. You can revolve these points in the *front* view until the fin is parallel with either the top or the side plan view. Since the dorsal fin already appears true size in the side view, it makes sense to plot the true size of the remaining fins in this same view as well.

Once all four points have been moved, project this information back to the side view as shown in **Figure 4.6.5**. This will give you the new position of points "**A**," "**B**," "**C**," and "**D**" in the side view. By connecting these points with lines you will end up with a true-size template for one of the lateral fins. The result is a construction pattern that is ready to be cut out of whatever material you choose to build the fin. Fortunately, since both lateral fins are symmetrical, you need only plot the outline of one of them. This pattern will be exactly the same for both fins.

As you can see, revolution can be a very useful way of finding the true size of oblique planes. In **Chapter 6**, you will see even more applications of this method as part of the pattern-making process. Overall, it is a very simple and practical technique. Of course, the most important part is making sure to choose the correct center of rotation. These two examples clearly illustrate why it is so important to always specify the center points of objects – as well as centerlines – when you are creating your working drawings. Doing so will make it very easy to employ revolution whenever you need it.

4.7: Auxiliary Views

Revolution is a simple and quick solution in situations like our rocket example. It is not the only approach, however, to finding the true size of a feature that appears foreshortened in a plan view. If you cannot obtain measurements directly from your plan view(s), you can also draw an *alternate* view in which the feature appears true length. This alternate view is called an <u>auxiliary view</u>.

This approach works well for inclined planes. In general, you can use either revolution or auxiliary views in these situations. Things get more complicated, however, when you need to plot the true size of an oblique plane. This can also be done using either method, but the process can be quite a bit more involved. Oblique planes will be covered in more detail in **Section 4.8**.

Since the surface of an inclined or an oblique plane is not parallel to *any* plan view, the true shape cannot be plotted in any normal view. Therefore, an *auxiliary view* is needed. Such a view is never parallel to *any* of the principal planes of projection. As a result, it cannot be projected from the imaginary glass box used to make the six normal plan views.

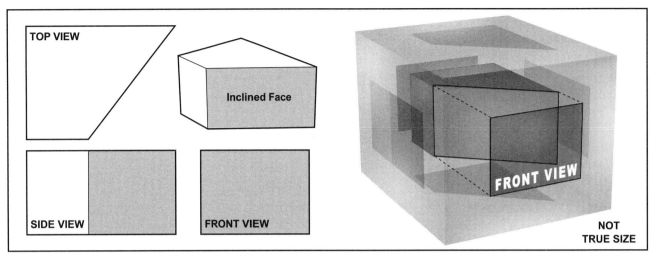

Figure 4.7.1. The true size of an inclined plane cannot be plotted in any normal view.

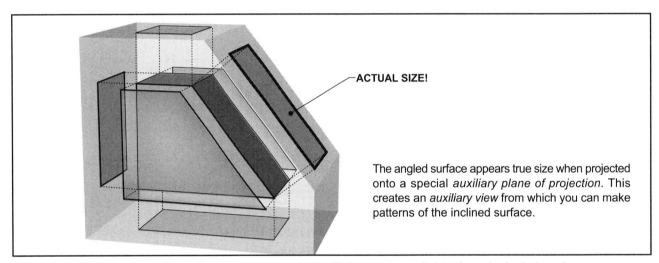

Figure 4.7.2. Create an *auxiliary view* to map out surfaces that are not parallel to the principal plan views.

To see how auxiliary views work for inclined planes, look at the example shown in **Figure 4.7.1**. This is the same example block first shown in **Section 4.2**. It has an angled face that is inclined relative to the front and side views. When this block is enclosed inside an "imaginary glass box" via orthographic projection, six principal plan views can be drawn as shown. Since these views are projected from one of the three principal planes of projection, each is said to be a <u>normal view</u>.

If you wanted to build a model of this block, you would need to create a template for each face. For the faces that are parallel to one of the principal plan views, this would be very easy. Each parallel face already appears *true size* in its accompanying view. As a result, the top, bottom, left, right, and rear faces can all be measured directly from the plan view drawings and then cut out of the desired material in order to form a model of the block.

The inclined face, however, presents a problem. If you look at this face in both the front and side views, it does not appear true size. On the other hand, as you saw in **Section 4.5**, the *edges* of the inclined face can, in fact, be measured since they are parallel to the plan views. As a result, you can plot the true size and shape of the inclined face using these edge dimensions as a guide. The process for doing this involves creating an *auxiliary view*.

The concept of orthographic projection as it has been used thus far must be modified in order to create an auxiliary view. To make illustrating this process easier, our example block will be re-oriented so the sloping side faces *upward* instead of forward. Looking at the illustration in **Figure 4.7.2**, note how the block is enclosed in a different version of our imaginary glass box than the type traditionally used for orthographic projection.

In this case, an additional side has been added to the box that is *parallel to the inclined face*. This creates an <u>auxiliary plane of projection</u>. With this auxiliary plane in place, it is possible to project the angled side of the block and create an auxiliary view that shows its true dimensions. The plan views can now be labeled as shown in **Figure 4.7.3**.

For simple objects, this method should be very straightforward. For more complex subjects, however, the process of creating an auxiliary view might seem a bit tricky. That said, producing auxiliary views is still one of the most powerful techniques you can learn. It is a very important method for making construction patterns and templates from your blueprints. Therefore, it would be to your advantage to go through this section carefully and make sure you understand the concepts clearly before moving on to the next section.

Creating a Primary Auxiliary View ("Folding Line" Approach)

In the case of our example block, the new section added to the imaginary glass box must be perfectly parallel with the inclined face in order to obtain the true dimensions of this surface. While the normal views of the block were projected from the principal planes of projection, the auxiliary view will be projected from this new, auxiliary plane. An auxiliary view created in such a way is called a <u>primary auxiliary view</u>.

To begin the process of creating the primary auxiliary view for the example block, "unfold" the imaginary glass box surrounding the subject. You can then combine all the planes of projection into a single plane. This concept is illustrated in **Figure 4.7.3**. Note how the box unfolds to produce all the normal plan views. In this case, however, the new auxiliary view is also included. Also note the "fold lines" in between each view. These will be critical to the process of mapping out the auxiliary view.

In concept, this should be fairly intuitive. The process of actually projecting the true size of the inclined face of the block in the auxiliary view, however,

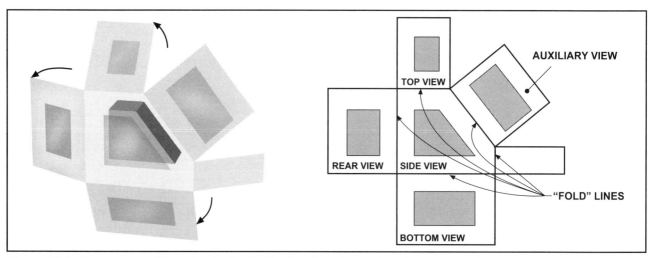

Figure 4.7.3. Create an *auxiliary view* by "unfolding" an imaginary glass box surrounding the subject.

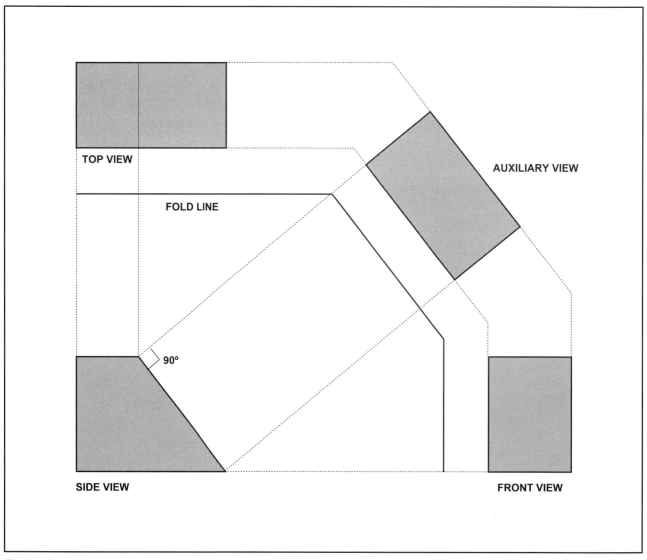

Figure 4.7.4. Lay out the auxiliary view precisely in order to accurately determine the outline in question.

is very exacting. Start by drawing construction lines extending out from the inclined face at the proper angle. These lines must be *perfectly perpendicular* to the inclined face of the block. This will be key to plotting the outline in the auxiliary view. Next, select key measurements from one of the principal plan views (i.e. the normal views) and transfer them into the new auxiliary view to begin plotting the shape.

To see the end result of this process, a finished drawing of the auxiliary view is presented in **Figure 4.7.4**. Hopefully, this will give you an idea of the information that will be needed to map out such a view.

The exact procedure for creating this auxiliary view is illustrated in **Figure 4.7.5** and **Figure 4.7.6**. First, lay out construction lines **A** and **B**. These lines will define the entire auxiliary view. This is perhaps the most

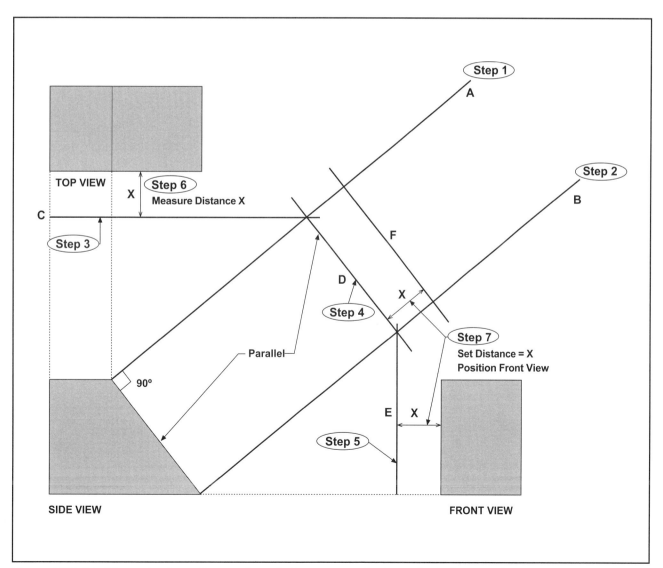

Figure 4.7.5. Start by projecting reference lines that are perpendicular to the inclined surface.

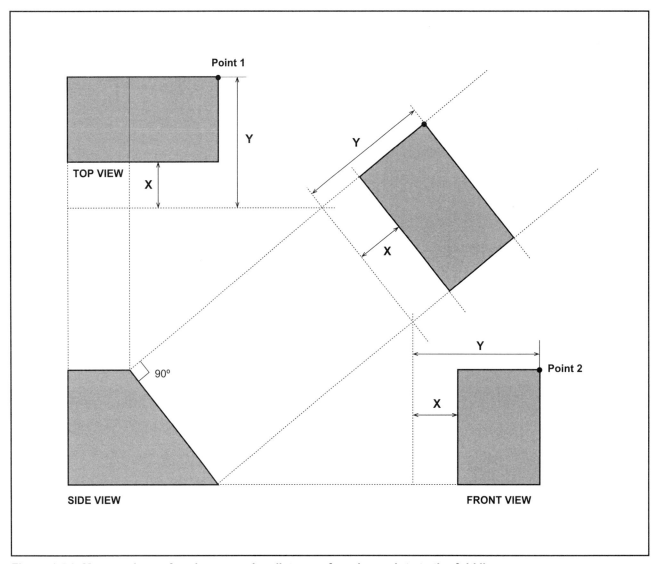

Figure 4.7.6. Map out the surface by measuring distances from key points to the *fold line*.

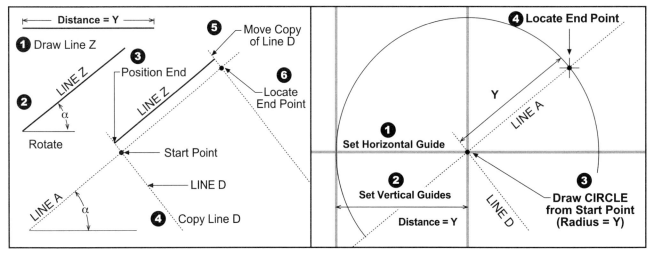

Figure 4.7.7. Use graphical methods to transfer points and distances from one view to another.

critical step in the entire process. Because of this, don't forget these construction lines must be *perfectly perpendicular* to the inclined face of the block in the side view.

There are several ways to draw construction lines without having to measure the exact angle of the sloping face. The simplest way is to copy the line representing the *edge* of this face in the side view, then rotate the copy exactly 90 degrees. This then becomes **Line "A."** Using this method, the copied line will always be perfectly perpendicular to the original. Now, duplicate **Line "A"** to get **Line "B."**

Once these two construction lines are in place, the next step is to begin drawing a <u>fold line</u> (**Line "C"**). The sole purpose of this line is to provide a reference point or *datum* from which you can measure key points. These points will then be transferred to the auxiliary view.

Keep in mind, the exact position of **Line "C"** relative to the top and side views is not really important here. What *is* important is the top view and the front view are positioned so they are the *exact same distance* ("**X**") from the fold line as shown in **Figure 4.7.5**.

With the first part of the fold line now in place, proceed by drawing lines "**D**" and "**E**" as shown. To position these lines correctly, make sure **Line "D"** is *perfectly parallel* to the inclined face of the block and **Line "E"** is positioned distance "**X**" from the front view. To ensure **Line "D"** is parallel, use either of the following techniques:

- Copy the line representing the *edge* of the inclined surface and reposition the copy; or
- Copy either **Line "A"** or **Line "B"** and rotate the copy 90 degrees in any direction.

Once the fold line has been established, measure the distance from **Line "C"** to the edge of the block in the *top* view. This will be the first key point to be set up in the auxiliary view. Project this information as follows:

1. Make a copy of **Line "D"** – this ensures the copy will be perfectly parallel to the original.
2. Move the copy so it becomes **Line "F,"** then move it until it is **Distance "X"** away from **Line "D"** as shown.

Now that **Distance "X"** has been established, begin plotting the shape of the inclined surface in the auxiliary view as shown in **Figure 4.7.6**. First, pick a series of key points in the top and/or front views that define the corners of the inclined face. In this case, it is simply a rectangle. Therefore, all you need to know are the lengths of the long and short sides. The long side has

The exact method you choose for creating parallel lines is up to you – simply ensure **Line "D"** is *parallel* to the inclined surface of the block.

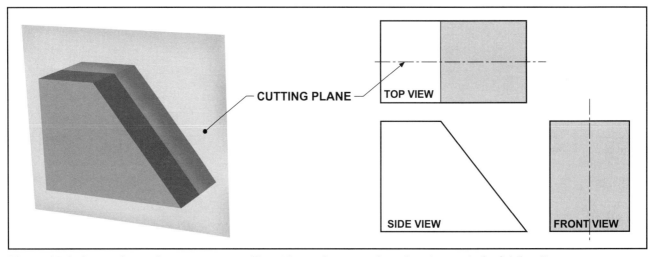

Figure 4.7.8. As an alternative, create an auxiliary view using a *cutting plane* instead of a folding line.

already been determined as **Line "F."** All that remains is to measure the length of the short side and transfer this information to the auxiliary view.

The length of the short side can be mapped out using either **Point "1"** in the top view or **Point "2"** in the front view. In this case, it does not matter which point you choose since both provide the same information. Therefore, measure the distance from either point back to the *fold line* and transfer this information to the auxiliary view.

At this point, you may be wondering exactly how you can transfer information between views. There are actually several ways to do this using quick and easy graphical techniques. Two of these methods are illustrated in **Figure 4.7.7**. Simply choose whatever technique is most efficient for you.

Method 1:

1. Draw a new reference line with a length equal to "**Y**." Call this **Line "Z**."

2. Measure the exact angle between **Line "A"** and the horizontal; Call this angle "**alpha**" and rotate the new reference line exactly *alpha* degrees.

3. Use the rotated line as a "measuring stick" to locate the end point along **Line "A"**; Move it into position so the bottom end is over the starting point.

4. Copy **Line "D**."

5. Move the copy of **Line "D"** into position at the upper end of **Line "Z**."

6. Locate the end point at the intersection of **Line "A"** and the copy of **Line "D**."

Method 2:

1. Plot the starting point which is the intersection of **Line "A"** and **Line "D"**; Move a *horizontal Guide* into position directly over this starting point.

2. Place a *vertical Guide* into position directly over this starting point; Place a *second vertical Guide* at a distance equal to **"Y"** to the left of the starting point. To do this:
   a. Draw a reference rectangle of any size; Use the numeric option to set the exact width of this rectangle equal to **"Y."**
   b. Reposition the *right* side of the reference rectangle so it snaps to the first vertical *Guide*.
   c. Move the second vertical *Guide* into position and align it with the *left* edge of the rectangle.
   d. Delete the rectangle.

3. With "Snap to Guides" active, draw a circle from the center outward; Snap the center of this circle to the starting point and snap the outer edge to the second vertical *Guide*; The radius of the completed circle should therefore be exactly equal to **"Y."**

4. Use the intersection of the circle and **Line "A"** to find the end point.

These methods are more difficult to describe in words than they are to apply. In time you will find yourself mastering these and other drawing techniques as you create your own blueprints and construction patterns. Keep in mind, while the example block has a simple structure that is easy to draw in an auxiliary view, the exact same method also works to map out more complex structures as well.

Creating a Primary Auxiliary View ("Cutting Plane" Approach)

The "folding line" approach to creating a primary auxiliary view might seem a bit tedious. Knowing how to properly map out the fold line can certainly be difficult in the beginning. Fortunately, there is another way to plot an auxiliary view that is a bit easier. As you will see, this method is also ideally suited for mapping out auxiliary views of symmetrical subjects.

The first step is to imagine a *cutting plane* that divides the subject in half as shown in **Figure 4.7.8**. By positioning this cutting plane over a centerline in the top, front, and auxiliary views, it can replace the folding line and provide a more convenient datum for measuring key points to be plotted in the auxiliary view. Measurements can then be taken in the front and top views relative to this centerline as shown in **Figure 4.7.9**.

Just as with the folding line approach, the first step is laying out construction lines **"A"** and **"B."** These will define the outline of the auxiliary view.

The techniques outlined in **Method 1** and **Method 2** can be used with just about any computer illustration program.

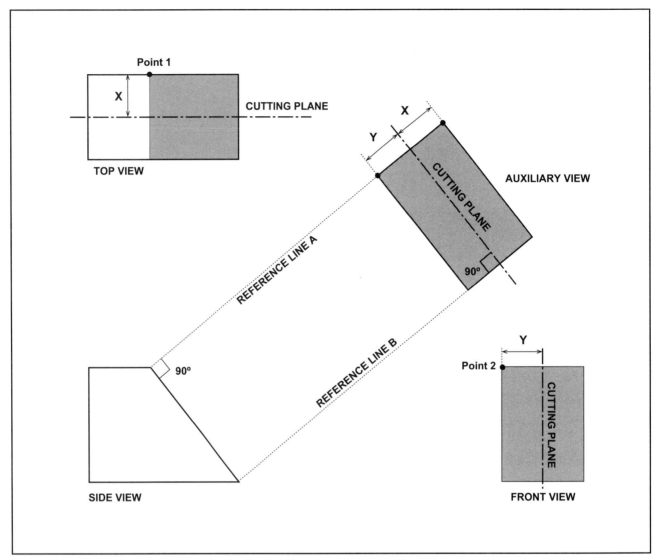

Figure 4.7.9. Measure key points and transfer the distances to the auxiliary view.

As before, the construction lines must be *perfectly perpendicular* to the inclined face of the block in the side view. In the auxiliary view, the centerline representing the cutting plane must be *perfectly parallel* to the inclined face.

The cutting plane approach is ideal when the object being drawn is perfectly symmetrical. In such cases it is not necessary to plot the entire auxiliary view – only one half of the view needs to be created. Since the subject is perfectly symmetrical, when you draw one half of the auxiliary view, you can simply "mirror" what you have drawn to create the other half.

Plotting Curves in an Auxiliary View

A cut cylinder is shown in **Figure 4.7.10**. This is an ideal subject to practice drawing auxiliary views. While the cross section of the cylinder is merely a circle, the cut face becomes an *ellipse* when the cylinder is "sliced" at an

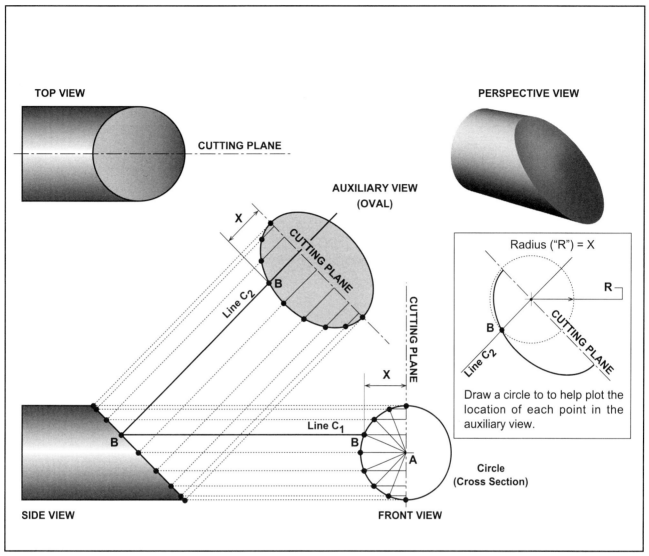

Figure 4.7.10. Map out an auxiliary view depicting the face of a cut cylinder by plotting key points.

angle as shown. To draw the outline of the cut face, plot a series of key points in a normal view. Then, transfer these points into an auxiliary view using projection. This process is similar to reflecting construction lines off a miter line. In this case, however, the reference line is not fixed at a 45-degree angle. Instead, it must be *parallel* with the inclined face of the subject.

Start by choosing key points in the front view. It's up to you to decide how many points you need in order to draw the shape. With a symmetrical subject such as this, you may only need information from the side view and front view to plot the auxiliary view. In addition, once you have drawn one half of the angled face, simply "mirror" it to form the complete outline.

In this example, the circle is first divided into *quadrants* and then two of the quadrants are divided into four parts each. This can be accomplished by drawing *radial lines* from the center outward as shown.

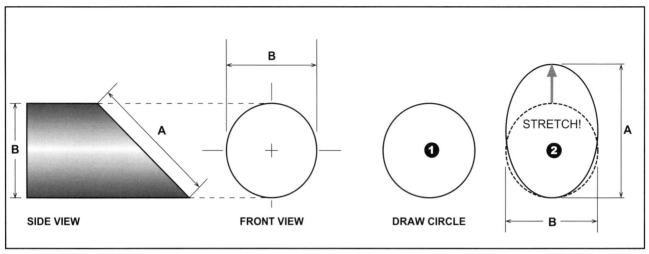

Figure 4.7.11. "Stretch" simple shapes to make a quick and easy auxiliary view.

Once the key points have been determined, project them into the side view. From there, the points are then *reflected* into the auxiliary view. To accomplish this, do the following:

1. Reflect a construction line from the side view into the auxiliary view for each point; Each construction line in the auxiliary view must be *perfectly perpendicular* to the inclined face of the cylinder as seen in the side view.
2. Measure the distance "**X**" from the point in the *front* view to the centerline (i.e. cutting plane).
3. Transfer this distance ("**X**") to the auxiliary view in order to plot the position of the same point relative to the centerline in that view.

As an example, look at **Point "B"** in **Figure 4.7.10**. Start in the front view and project back into the side view by drawing construction **Line "C_1"** to locate **Point "B"** on the edge of the inclined surface. Next, reflect this construction line into the auxiliary view (**Line "C_2"**). An easy way to do this is to copy the line representing the *edge* of the sloping face in the side view and then rotate it 90 degrees.

With **Line "C_2"** in place, measure the distance between **Point "B"** and the cutting plane in the *front* view ("**X**"). Transfer this measurement into the auxiliary view. One way to do this is to draw a circle with its center located where **Line "C_2"** intersects the cutting plane in the auxiliary view. The radius of this circle should be equal to "**X.**" The location of **Point "B"** in the auxiliary view will then be where the edge of the circle crosses **Line "C_2"** as shown.

As you can see, the process of plotting shapes in an auxiliary view can be a bit tedious, but it always works. You may be wondering at this point if there are any shortcuts. If you are using a computer illustration program, there is one great shortcut that you probably won't hear about in any drafting textbooks. When the subject is symmetrical and has a basic cross section, you can simply copy and "stretch" the cross section to get a reasonably accurate auxiliary view.

This technique is illustrated in **Figure 4.7.11**. Since the cross section of the example cylinder is known to be a circle, just copy and then stretch this circle into an oval to form the true shape of the inclined face. All you need to know is the correct length and width of the inclined face. That information, of course, can be found in the front and side views.

Start by measuring **Line "A"** which is the *length* of the inclined face in the side view. Next, measure **Line "B"** which is the *width* of the circular cross section in the front view. Copy the circle in the front view (or draw a new circle having the same diameter). Using the numeric option, change the *height* of the new circle to match the known length of **Line "A."** Voila! You just created the exact same auxiliary view that was plotted point-by-point in **Figure 4.7.10**.

4.8: Secondary Auxiliary Views

When you are dealing with an inclined plane, creating a *primary auxiliary view* is fairly straightforward. The methods illustrated here can be used to map out many different shapes for a variety of subjects. You may encounter situations, however, where the plane is *oblique* relative to the principal planes of projection. In such cases, you will be unable to plot the outline using a primary auxiliary view.

Finding the true shape of an oblique plane requires creating two different auxiliary views. First, draw a primary auxiliary view based on measurements taken from normal views. This then provides the basis for creating a secondary auxiliary view that will depict the true shape of the oblique plane.

To begin, pick an edge on the plane that is depicted *true length*. Next, establish a line of sight that is parallel to this edge. The logic of this concept may not seem readily apparent. Therefore, make sure you study the example block shown in **Figure 4.8.1** carefully. If you have difficulty following along, don't worry. Once the traditional technique for mapping out a secondary auxiliary view has been explained, other methods will also be demonstrated. These alternate techniques may be easier to apply.

In this example, select the *line* representing **Edge "A"** as a starting point because it is shown true length in the top view. To establish a line of sight, imagine this line is a piece of wire. If you were to hold the wire in your hand and look at it from one *end*, it would appear as a *point*. Now, if you can find a view of the block where **Edge "A"** appears as a point in this manner, the oblique plane will then appear as a *line*. This is known as an edge view of the plane as illustrated in **View "A"** of **Figure 4.8.1**.

Sidebar:

Obviously, the "copy and stretch" approach will only work in certain circumstances. Still, you can often use this trick to quickly map out simple shapes in an auxiliary view.

Before you can find the true shape of an oblique plane, you must first find an *edge view* of the plane.

When a line is perpendicular to a plane, it appears as a *point*. If you have difficulty visualizing this concept, refer back to **Figure 4.4.2**. You can also review the second paragraph on **Page 113** of **Section 4.4**.

Hopefully, one or more edges of an oblique plane will appear true length in a normal view. If all edges are oblique, start by using *revolution* to adjust the orientation of the plane so that at least one edge is parallel to a plan view.

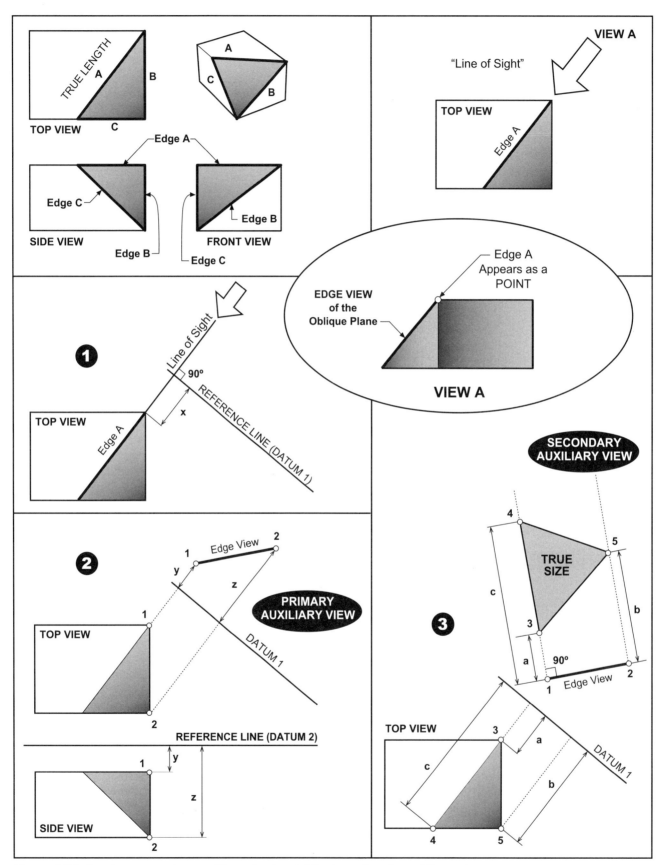

Figure 4.8.1. Create a *secondary auxiliary view* to plot the true size of an oblique plane.

View "A" is a primary auxiliary view. Drawing this view as shown, however, is not necessary. You simply need to find the *line* representing an edge view of the plane. When you can draw this line, you will be able to map out the true shape of the oblique plane in a secondary auxiliary view.

Start by creating a line in the top view that is *parallel* to the chosen line of sight. To do this, simply extend the line representing **Edge "A"** as seen in **Step 1** of **Figure 4.8.1**. Now, draw a second line that is *perpendicular* to the line of sight. This new line then becomes **Datum 1** as shown. (Keep in mind, the location of **Datum 1** is arbitrary. Thus, distance "**x**" is up to you.)

Next, draw yet another line parallel to the line of site and extend it out from point "**2**" as seen in **Step 2**. Then, draw a horizontal line in between the top and side views as shown. This will provide a second reference line (**Datum 2**) for making measurements in the side view.

Now, with everything in place, plot key points "**1**" and "**2**" as shown in **Step 2**. To do this, measure distances "**y**" and "**z**" in the *side view* and transfer these measurements into the auxiliary view. Then, connect points "**1**" and "**2**" to form a line. This line represents the true length of the edge of the oblique plane as it is seen when viewed along the line of sight.

It has taken a bit of work to get this far, but you are not quite done. Now that the edge view has been found in a primary auxiliary view, it is finally time to draw a secondary auxiliary view that depicts the true shape of the oblique plane. Fortunately, the methods for creating this view are very similar to those used to create a primary auxiliary view.

This time, however, new construction lines will be needed. These lines must be *perpendicular* to the line representing the edge view as shown in **Step 3** of **Figure 4.8.1**. Plot key points by measuring distances from **Datum 1** (drawn in **Step 1**) to the top view. These distances will be transferred to the secondary auxiliary view to locate points "**3**," "**4**," and "**5**" as shown. By connecting these points, the true shape of the oblique plane can at last be found.

As you can see, this process can be painstaking. Just remember, your goal is to find an *edge view* of the oblique plane. This requires making a primary auxiliary view. Then, once that's done, the true shape of the plane can be mapped out in a secondary auxiliary view.

You may be thinking this is a lot of work. The process may even seem somewhat puzzling. Fortunately, however, there can be easier ways to get the same results. In this particular case, for instance, the oblique plane is a *triangle*. According to basic geometry, it is very simple to map out a triangle when you know the lengths of all three sides. As luck would have it, every edge of this plane happens to be shown true length in the plan views.

The easiest way to make a perpendicular line is to copy the original line and then rotate it 90 degrees.

The location of each reference line (**Datum 1** and **Datum 2**) relative to the plan views is completely arbitrary. You may place them anywhere you wish.

When points are plotted in an auxiliary view, note that measurements must come from a view other than the one from which the auxiliary view is being projected.

To review the concepts of where and what to measure when plotting points in an auxiliary view, refer back to **Figure 4.7.6** and **Figure 4.7.9**.

Creating a secondary auxiliary view is about as hard as it gets. If you can master this process, you can handle just about anything!

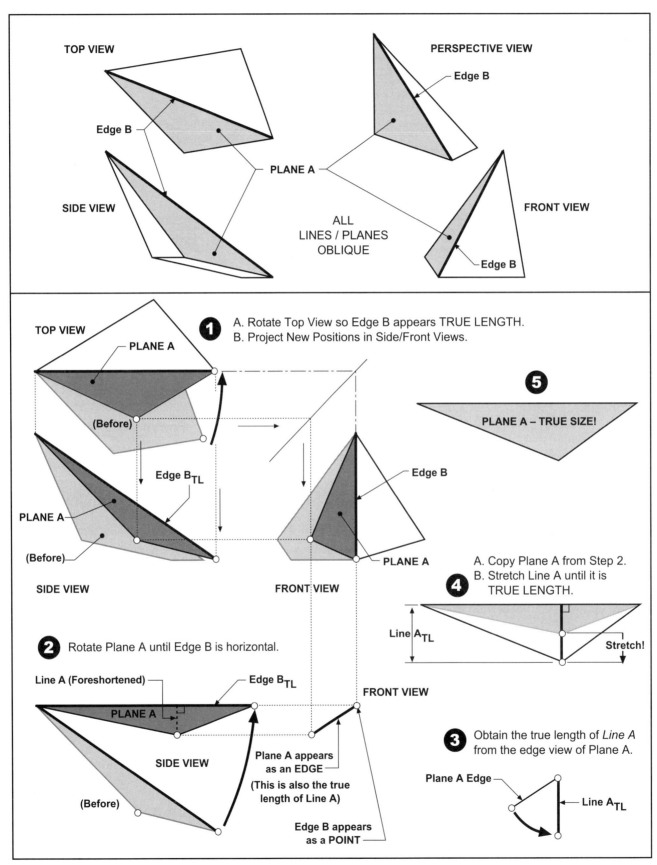

Figure 4.8.2. As an alternative, create a true-size view of an oblique plane using *revolution*.

Therefore, a quick and easy way to draw this shape would be as follows:

1. Start by plotting the length of **Edge "A"** in the top view; Label the end points of this line "**1**" and "**2**;" Locate point "**1**" at the intersection of **Edge "A"** with **Edge "B"** and locate point "**2**" at the intersection of **Edge "A"** with **Edge "C**."

2. Measure the length of **Edge "B"** in the front view and the length of **Edge "C"** in the side view.

3. Draw a circle with a radius equal to the length of **Edge "B"** and center it at point "**1**;" In a similar fashion, draw a circle with a radius equal to the length of **Edge "C"** and center it at point "**2**."

4. To find point "**3**," plot the location where the two circles intersect.

5. Connect "**1**," "**2**," and "**3**" to draw an outline of the oblique plane.

This "shortcut" may work only in certain cases. If you recall, however, you have already seen a practical technique for dealing with oblique lines – *revolution*. This method can be used to find the true length of oblique lines in nearly every case. Thus, revolution can also help you map out oblique planes. **Figure 4.8.2** shows how you might use this technique to find the true shape of an oblique plane without the need for making auxiliary views.

After reviewing the methods of creating auxiliary views presented in this and the previous section, you might be wondering if there are any special "tricks" that can help you solve problems like this. The answer is "Yes!" When building a model, there are two additional approaches for finding the true size of both inclined and oblique planes. Depending on the situation, these alternate methods can sometimes be easier to implement.

Approach 1

Rather than painstakingly mapping out the shape of oblique planes in your drawings, you could opt to skip this process altogether. To do this, consider building only those parts that can be measured directly from the plan views. From there, start assembling these components on your model. Then, as they are coming together, make construction patterns for the missing surfaces directly on the model. Here's how:

For an illustrated example of *Approach 1*, refer to **Section 7.4**.

1. Start building the model using shapes that can be obtained directly from the plan views; When you have assembled these pieces, you'll have defined the *edges* of any missing inclined or oblique surfaces.

2. Place a piece of paper or cardboard on the model and trace the edges of the missing surfaces onto the paper; The tracing thus becomes a *template* for the missing part.

3. Cut out the tracing and test for fit; Tweak the outline as needed and then repeat this process until you achieve an acceptable fit.

This approach works great when the edges that make up inclined or oblique surfaces can be defined by other parts of the model. If you want to use this method, you may find it helpful to build a *mockup* of your structure before starting final construction. This mockup can be used to work out key details such as the true shape of inclined or oblique surfaces. Once you have a complete set of accurate patterns from this process, you can build your final model. In cases where the structure is too complex to solve in this manner, however, you may want to try another approach.

Approach 2

To "solve" inclined or oblique surfaces without drawing any auxiliary views, try one of the following:

- Build your model in 3D; Create auxiliary views using the special features available in your 3D program; The software will do most of the work for you and provide the finished views you need; This method is fairly easy and very precise.
- Build your model in 3D using a program that has special features for creating *developments* of surfaces; These will be discussed in more detail in **Chapter 6**; Such 3D "power tools" can be used to "unfold" your model and give you the correct patterns needed to build the various parts; Doing this could eliminate the need for auxiliary views altogether.

4.9: Summary

If you want to make construction patterns and templates from your drawings, you will need to distinguish between those lines that can be measured and those that cannot. In fact, this is one of the most important model design concepts you can master.

When a surface, line, or feature is perfectly *parallel* to a plan view, it will appear actual size or *true length* in that view. Anything that appears true length can be measured directly from the drawings. On the other hand, any line, surface, or feature that does not appear true length in a particular view should *not* be measured in that view. Such features are said to be *foreshortened*.

Three "primary" views showing a subject's height, width, and depth form the basis of multi-view drawing. These primary views are obtained by projecting from one of the three *principal planes of projection*. A *normal line* is parallel to at least two of these principal planes of projection. Because of this, it will appear true length in up to four different plan views. A *non-normal line* is one that is either *inclined* or *oblique* relative to the principal planes of projection. *Inclined lines* will appear true length in as many as two plan views while *oblique lines* will not appear true length in *any* plan view.

For more information on how to make patterns for building 3D computer models, read **Volume 2** of this series. This approach offers many advantages over tried and true 2D methods.

Using 3D techniques can help you figure out the geometry of your model and solve difficult problems with less effort. As a result, 3D computer modeling techniques could be the ultimate "power tools" for modelers who want to design and build their own structures from scratch.

A *normal plane* is parallel to two different principal planes of projection, but is perpendicular to the third. Such planes will appear true size in up to four different plan views. An *inclined plane* is not parallel to any principal planes of projection, but is perpendicular to one. As a result, the *edge* of an inclined plane appears as a *line* that is true length in two different plan views. On the other hand, an *oblique plane* appears foreshortened in *every* plan view. Because of this, it is never true size in any view.

The technique of *revolution* is extremely useful for determining the true length of oblique lines and the true size of oblique planes. Simply *revolve* a line or feature about the correct center point until it is parallel to a principal plan view. Once it is parallel, it will appear true length or true size.

The most common approach for finding the true size of inclined and oblique planes involves creating an *auxiliary view*. Because they are parallel to the principal planes of projection, the six principal plan views are considered *normal views*. On the other hand, auxiliary views are not parallel with *any* principal plane of projection. Instead, these views are parallel with the face of the inclined or oblique plane. This causes the plane to appear true size in the auxiliary view.

A *primary auxiliary view* is one that is derived from information contained in the principal plan views, i.e. the *normal views*. This works well for inclined planes, but not for oblique planes. When a plane is oblique, start by drawing a primary auxiliary view that depicts an *edge view* of the plane. Then, use this information to create a *secondary auxiliary view* in which the oblique plane appears true size.

Congratulations! You have successfully worked through some of the most difficult material contained in this book. Just remember, the concepts presented in this chapter provide a firm foundation for many of the techniques you will be using to make construction patterns and templates from your drawings.

What's Next?

Now that you've learned how to get accurate measurements from your drawings, the next topic to be discussed is working with cross sections. This will be covered in **Chapter 5**. Once you have that under your belt, you will be ready to make the most of the advanced pattern-making methods presented in **Chapter 6** and **Chapter 7**. It won't be long before you'll be using these powerful techniques in your next project.

Topics in This Chapter:

Chapter

Cross Sections

5.1: Overview

Whenever you are making patterns for a physical model (or a 3D computer model), there will often be times when you need to know the *cross section* of one or more parts. Fortunately, the basic techniques needed to solve many of these problems can be fairly straightforward. A step-by-step example of how to draw the cross section shape of an airplane fuselage has already been presented in **Section 3.6**. Here in this chapter you will learn more about working with cross sections.

Cross section information can be extremely useful for the model builder. It may even be indispensable when building the structure of your model. Yet, cross sections can sometimes be very difficult to visualize. This may be the case when internal structural details of the subject are obscured or hidden.

If your subject has a complex internal structure, you might have a large number of hidden lines in your plan views. This is not desirable because it can cause confusion. Since working drawings must always be as clear as possible, a better approach is needed. The solution is to create one or more *section views*.

The concept of a *section view* was first introduced in **Section 2.9**. These views provide critical information about the internal structure of your model when such information is not clearly evident in the plan views. The draftsman uses the term "section" while the modeler may be more comfortable saying "cross section." In reality, both terms represent the same basic thing.

No matter what you are building, you can streamline the process of making useful templates and construction patterns for your models when you are able to lay out or "plot" cross sections. Even more, this ability is almost essential when creating 3D computer models. In fact, many of the techniques used to construct 3D objects require that you start by drawing the cross section.

5.2: Strategies for Determining Cross Sections

Cross sections can be illustrated by creating formal section views at various points as shown in **Figure 5.2.1**. This is most convenient for complicated

NOTE: Underlined terms appear in the Glossary.

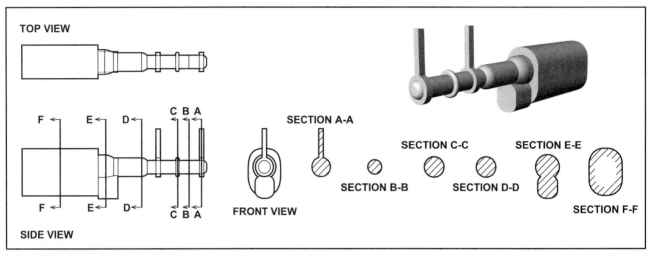

Figure 5.2.1. Create multiple section views to adequately describe the geometry of complex subjects.

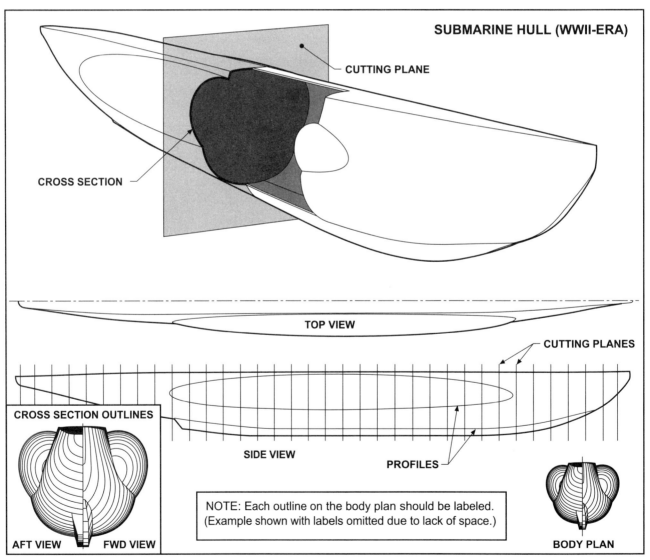

Figure 5.2.2. Consolidate multiple cross section outlines for complex shapes into a *body plan*.

structures or when your subject is made up of many different components that each have their own unique cross section. Some subjects, however, might require so many different section views to define their shape that space might not be available to show them all. Examples include naval ships and submarines that have complex hull shapes with smooth-flowing, "organic" lines and curves.

Naval architects have devised a solution to this problem by creating what is known as a <u>body plan</u>. When making plan view drawings for complex ship hulls, formal section views can be omitted. Instead, the cross section shape of the hull is plotted at specific locations and these outlines are combined in a single view. An example of this approach is illustrated in **Figure 5.2.2**. Here, each outline represents the intersection of a *cutting plane* with the hull of a vintage submarine similar to the type used in World War II. By consolidating all these outlines together into a single view, the result is a clean and compact representation that shows the shape of the entire hull.

Note how the body plan is split along the centerline of the vessel and divided into two halves. The left half depicts the cross section outlines from the rear of the boat looking forward while the right half shows the shape of the hull from the front looking aft. This can be a very effective way of documenting complex shapes. In fact, this approach works not only for drawing naval vessels, but also for depicting many other types of subjects as well.

Keep in mind, you will need to document the *exact location* of each cutting plane used to generate a cross-section outline. This can be done by drawing vertical lines in the side view and/or the top and bottom views as illustrated in **Figure 5.2.2**. To link each cutting plane with its corresponding cross section outline, assign it a unique name and/or number. Clear labeling is essential.

In addition, terminology may cause some confusion when discussing section views. This is why the text of this chapter refers to cross section shapes as "outlines" rather than "profiles." If you recall the discussion in **Chapter 4**, the *profile plane of projection* is used to create the left and right side view. This means the term "profile," by its traditional definition, refers to an outline drawn either in the left or in the right *side* view – not in the front or rear view.

Remember, in 3D modeling, profiles are 2D lines used to build 3D shapes. These lines can appear in *any* view. Therefore, they are not restricted to being in a side plan view.

All this gets a bit more complicated when you begin to plot patterns for making complex shapes like the hull of our example submarine. As you will see in **Section 5.6**, cutting planes can also be used to slice the hull *lengthwise* to plot the shape in the side view or even in the top and bottom views. To be technically correct, only those outlines created by a cutting plane that is parallel to the profile plane of projection would be referred to as "profiles." Still, the simplest way to look at all this is to think of a cross section as *any* outline created by the intersection of a cutting plane with your model.

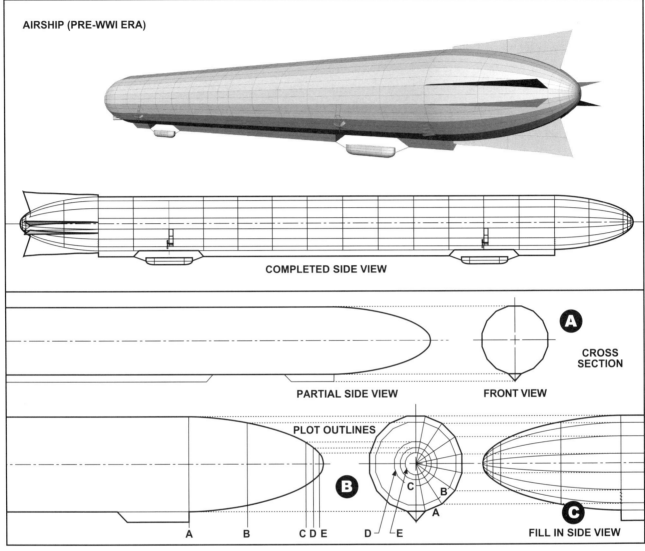

AIRSHIP (PRE-WWI ERA)

COMPLETED SIDE VIEW

PARTIAL SIDE VIEW   FRONT VIEW

CROSS
SECTION

PLOT OUTLINES

FILL IN SIDE VIEW

A   B   C D E   D   E

Figure 5.3.1. Cross section outlines are easiest to draw when subjects have a *uniform* cross section.

5.3: Shapes With a Uniform Cross Section

When drawing section views, the simplest subjects are those with a <u>constant cross section.</u> These are the easiest to draw since there is only one cross section outline for the entire structure. Examples of shapes that have a constant cross section include:

- A piece of pipe
- Tubing
- A 2 X 4 stick of lumber
- A length of extruded plastic or metal

Stepping up a notch on the scale of difficulty, you may encounter subjects that have a <u>uniform cross section</u>. This type of structure was first mentioned in **Section 3.6**. Here, the *shape* of the cross section does not vary, but the *size* does. Since the overall shape remains the same all along its length, this type of subject is only slightly more difficult to draw than one with a constant cross section. Examples of shapes that have a uniform cross section include:

- Cone
- Airship
- Wing of an airplane
- Hull of a modern nuclear submarine

Subjects with a uniform cross section are fairly easy to map out in blueprint form because the cross section shape is basically the same no matter where you place a cutting plane along the length of the subject. In fact, all you really need to do is *scale* the cross section outline at each location. This process is easiest when the shape is perfectly symmetrical. When this is the case, you may be able to plot the cross section outline in either the front or the rear plan view using information from just one other view as a guide. You could, for example, transfer *height* information for the cross section from the side view or obtain information about the *width* from either the top or the bottom view.

A practical example of such a structure is the "rigid dirigible" (i.e. airship) shown in **Figure 5.3.1**. This craft, a generic example of the type flown by the Germans prior to World War I, has a cigar-shaped hull. Note how the central portion of the hull has a constant cross section. The ends, however, are tapered. Even then, the cross section remains uniform from one end to the other. This cross section is a multi-sided <u>polygon</u> or "<u>multigon</u>." To create a section view for this airship, you need only know the diameter at any point along the hull, plus the exact number of sides that make up the cross section shape. In this case, the number of sides can be determined by counting the "facets" of the hull.

Based on available reference information, imagine this hull has 16 sides or "facets" around its circumference. This would result in a cross section that could be represented by a 16-sided multigon. Since the middle section is simply a tube-like structure with a constant cross section, you need only one cross section outline for the entire middle portion of the airship. On the other hand, several different cross section outlines must be plotted in order to adequately describe the shape of each tapered end.

To begin plotting the cross section of the cigar-shaped center portion of the hull, start by specifying the overall diameter. This can easily be determined from any plan view. If you were drawing this airship from scratch, however, you would not have any views from which to start. In that case, you would need to do some research and find out the overall length and diameter of the hull to use as a starting point. Armed with this information, the general process

A *polygon* is a 2D geometric shape with a specific number of sides. It is also a fundamental building block for 3D mesh models. Since the term "polygon" has a special meaning to 3D modelers, the term "multigon" will be used in this book to describe a regular 2D geometric shape.

of plotting or "resolving" orthographic plan views for an airship such as the one in this example can begin. This process is illustrated in **Figure 5.3.1**:

1. Draw a 16-sided multigon in the front view and plot the exact center of the shape as shown in **Part A**.
2. Project this information into the side view to determine the correct height of the airship.
3. After blocking out the overall height and length, draw the correct *profile* of the hull in the side view.
4. Transfer height information from the profile of the tapered bow as seen in the side view in order to plot the various cross sections for this part of the airship in the front view; This is shown in **Part B**.
5. Use projection from the *front view* to mark the locations of lines that denote "facets" of the hull in the side view as shown in **Part C**; Fill in the remaining details in the side view.
6. *Mirror* the front view to create a rear view.
7. Fill in remaining details in the rear view by projecting information from the side view.

To draw a 16-sided multigon using a computer illustration program, start by setting *Guides* in place to mark the top and bottom of the hull along with the horizontal and vertical centerlines in the front view. Next, select the *Multigon Tool* and tell the program you want to draw a figure with 16 sides. Using a modifier key, place the *center point* of the multigon where the horizontal and vertical centerlines meet in the front view. Draw the multigon from the *center outward* until you reach the *Guides* denoting the location of the top and/or bottom of the hull. (You may need to hold down the "Shift" key while doing this to control the orientation of the multigon.)

To draw the cross sections of the tapered ends of the hull, simply copy and scale the 16-sided multigon as needed. The results of this process are illustrated in **Part B of Figure 5.3.1**. You can accomplish this by projecting information from the *side* view to use as a guide. With the main cross section as a starting point, draw vertical lines representing *cutting planes* over the tapered bow in the *side* view. Find the point where each cutting plane intersects the top edge of the hull profile in the side view. Project these points into the front view by drawing construction lines as shown. Each line forms a "guide" denoting the upper edge of a multigon in the front view. Draw the multigon from the center outward until the top edge reaches the appropriate construction line. Repeat for the remaining cross sections as shown.

As an alternative, simply copy the main cross section outline in the front view and scale it as needed. Use the "Clone" command to create a copy that exists on top of the original. Then, use the "Scale" command to resize the copy until the edge of the multigon intersects with the construction line

A computer illustration program can be used not only for drawing blueprints and construction patterns, but also for creating custom decals, photo-etching, and even patterns for laser-cutting and CNC machining. To get up and running quickly, read *How To Draw Anything With a Computer: A Quick-Start Guide for the Craftsman, Hobbyist, and Do-It-Yourselfer*, part of the *Modeler's Notebook Reference Series* available from:

www.ModelersNotebook.com

A *modifier key* can alter the default behavior of a drawing tool. Try holding down the "Alt" or "Option" key to draw a multigon from the center outward. At the same time, use the "Shift" key to *constrain* the tool for better control over the alignment of the multigon.

projected from the side view. The advantage of using the "Scale" command is that the copy will remain *centered* over the original.

When all the outlines are in place, be sure they are properly centered on each other. You can do this by using the "Align" command. Select all the outlines and then tell the program to center them both vertically and horizontally. The main cross section outline will be the "anchor" when performing this step. As a result, you might want to *lock* this outline to prevent it from shifting out of position. (Just don't forget to unlock it when you are done.)

Once the front plan view for the example airship has been established, use the information in this view to fill in details in the side plan view as shown in **Part C** of **Figure 5.3.1**. Begin by drawing *radial lines* in the front view that originate in the center and radiate outward to each corner of the multigon. Then, project from these points back into the side view.

With some drawing programs, you may be able to use the "Clone" command in conjunction with the "Scale" command to streamline the process of making scaled cross section outlines. On the other hand, if you resize a copy by stretching it manually, you will have to reposition it when you are done. This is more work.

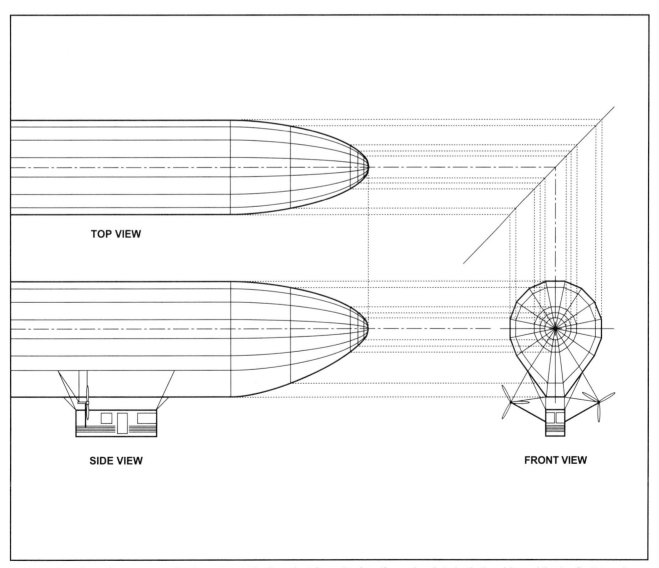

TOP VIEW

SIDE VIEW

FRONT VIEW

Figure 5.3.2. When the cross section is asymmetrical, project from the front/rear view into both the side *and* the top/bottom views.

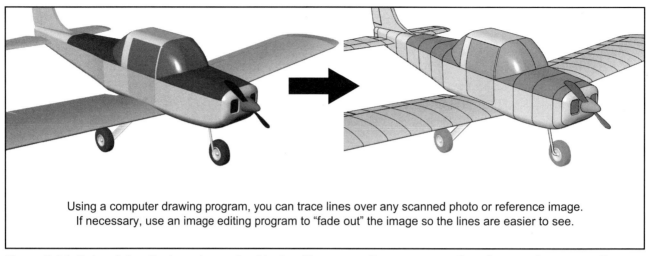

Using a computer drawing program, you can trace lines over any scanned photo or reference image. If necessary, use an image editing program to "fade out" the image so the lines are easier to see.

Figure 5.4.1. Determining the true shape of subjects with a non-uniform cross section often requires more effort.

To use the "Scale" command effectively, try a value such as 90% to "shrink" the copy by 10% each time. Continue until it is approximately the right diameter. Then, change the percentage value to 99% in order to resize the outline more precisely. If you make a mistake during this process, simply activate "Undo" and try again with another value.

Note how the location of "facets" in the hull seen in the side view can only be determined by projecting information from the front view. The front and rear views, however, can only be determined by plotting the cross section of the airship. As you can see, this makes knowing the overall cross section the starting point for drawing the entire airship.

This is an excellent example of how determining cross sections can be critical to the success of a model project. In fact, to draw a subject like this airship, all you really need is one cross section outline plus a side-view profile. The remaining details can then be derived from these two pieces of information. This is true because the hull is perfectly symmetrical. Thus, only a few other details need to be worked out in order to finish drawing the entire airship.

Unfortunately, the shape of the subject may not always be perfectly symmetrical. In such cases, in order to plot the cross section, information is needed from not one but *two* different plan views. For our example airship in **Figure 5.3.1**, the diameter of the multigon was projected only into the side view. Since the hull is symmetrical, this shape will be exactly the same in the top/bottom views. If the airship were not symmetrical, however, you would need to project from the front view into the side view and also from the front view into the top and/or bottom view as well.

This concept is illustrated in **Figure 5.3.2**. Here, a slightly different airship hull is shown. This version – a generic example similar to the type built by the British during World War I – is not completely symmetrical. Note how the outline of the hull is formed by projecting between three different plan views. You may recognize this as the same procedure used to map out the cross section of the example airplane in **Chapter 3**.

5.4: Non-Uniform Cross Sections

Many modeling subjects are likely to have a non-uniform cross section. In these cases, you will need to draw as many cross section outlines as necessary in order to adequately describe the subject. Remember the submarine example in **Figure 5.2.2**? The hull of this vessel, based on a type that was commonly used in World War II, is an "organic" shape with smooth, flowing lines. This is just one of many possible modeling subjects that offers the challenge of figuring out complex, non-uniform cross sections.

The procedure for mapping out shapes like this is similar to the process used for subjects with a uniform cross section. The primary difference will be the number of section views or outlines that must be drawn. A further complication is that information needed to map out these shapes may not be readily available in the plan views. When drawing a ship's hull, for example, the side and top/bottom views may reveal very little about the true cross section other than the overall height and width.

Without specific reference that shows the true shape of the hull (such as a section view or a series of measurements), you may be forced to recreate the shape working mainly from photos. When this happens, you'll need to be able to visualize the cross section when looking at perspective views. If you remember the example airplane fuselage in **Chapter 3**, the shape was mapped out by taking a perspective image and tracing lines over it. Drawing an "overlay" in this manner can help you visualize the "flow" of a complex form, making the true shape easier to see. In fact, this process, illustrated in **Figure 5.4.1**, can be extremely helpful when mapping out shapes that have a complex cross section.

If you are faced with this challenge, try to take things one step at a time. Mapping out the form in 2D may be quite challenging. This is an excellent example of a situation where advanced 3D modeling tools can be a big help. With a computer modeling program, you can build a rough approximation or "mockup" of the shape without having to cut out or assemble anything on your workbench. Once completed, you can then "pose" the finished model to see how well it compares with available reference photos. You'll quickly be able to tell whether or not your model is shaped correctly.

By using this process, you may sometimes discover your assumptions about a shape are incorrect. It is far better to find this out during the prototype or "mockup" stage rather than after you have built the final model. Using 3D tools in this manner can help you work through any difficulties, as well as verify the accuracy of shapes – and the proper alignment and fit of parts – all prior to finalizing your drawings and construction patterns.

Another big advantage to using 3D tools is the ability to "slice" through a model at any point to reveal the true cross section. Once you build an object

Creating cross sections for 3D models can sometimes result in a "chicken and the egg" scenario. You may need to know certain cross section information *before* you can build any parts in 3D. But, once the model is built, 3D tools allow you to "slice" or section the model any way you wish.

In fact, 3D tools can make it relatively simple to visualize complex cross sections that would be very difficult to analyze with any other approach. For more information, check out **Volume 2** of this series.

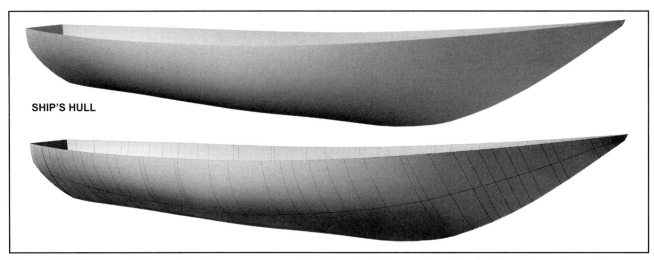

SHIP'S HULL

Figure 5.5.1. Draw multiple contour lines on perspective views to help you visualize the true shape of a subject.

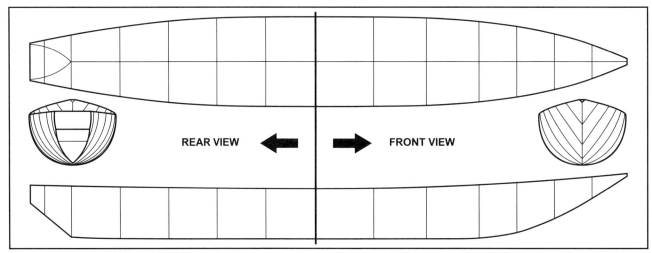

REAR VIEW ← → FRONT VIEW

Figure 5.5.2. Create a *dividing line* to determine which cross section outlines appear in the front and rear views.

in the computer, you can easily create cross section outlines wherever you wish. For example, this makes it relatively easy to generate a body plan from a finished 3D model of a shape like a ship's hull.

5.5: Working With "Blended" Shapes

When you are faced with designing the structure of a complex form, start by assembling all your available reference and studying the subject carefully. Attempt to *visualize* the true shape in order to understand how it looks from every angle. To do this, ask yourself some key questions:

- Can the overall shape be broken down into sub-assemblies?
- Is there more than one shape that makes up the cross section?
- Can any information about the shape be derived from available perspective photos or images?

Knowing your subject thoroughly is the real key here. You will need to become intimately familiar with the shape in order to successfully recreate it. This can sometimes be quite challenging for subjects that are a combination or "blend" of more than one cross section shape. For example, a boat or ship's hull might be based on a combination of "V-" and "U-shaped" cross sections. To see an illustration of such a ship, look at **Figure 5.5.1**. Here, the cross section of the hull varies in both size and shape from one end to the other. To illustrate the true shape more clearly, perspective images are shown both with and without contour lines sketched on the hull.

The "V" shape in the bow of this ship forms a streamlined wedge that cuts through the water. The cross section then gets "fat" in the middle (amidships), turning into a "U" shape. This helps the vessel displace water in order to carry a heavy load. The form then tapers again toward the stern. As a result, this hull is a combination of more than one cross section shape.

Mapping out this ship's hull requires being able to visualize exactly how the cross section transitions from one shape to another. The best way to do this is by drawing all the cross section outlines together in a *body plan*. The following example will walk you through this process from start to finish.

Begin by determining the cross section where the hull is *widest*. This is the most important outline to determine in advance. Look at the finished plan view drawings of this hull in **Figure 5.5.2**. Note how it is widest in the center (amidships). This will be the <u>dividing line</u> between the front and rear plan views. As a result, the cross section outline at this widest point will appear in *both* the front and rear views. All cross section outlines *forward* of this point will be drawn in the front plan view. This means all cross section outlines *aft* of this point will be drawn in the rear plan view.

Before proceeding, pause for just a moment and take a look at the following exercise. **Figure 5.5.3** shows a cross section shape that transitions from a "V" to a "U" similar to the ship's hull in our example. This shape, however, is constant in height so it is much easier to draw. Notice there are two key cross section outlines for this shape. These are shown in **Section A-A** and **Section D-D**. To map out this subject, start by blocking out the front plan view and positioning the vertical centerline plus the two primary cross section outlines as shown in **Step 1**.

Now that the two primary cross section outlines are in place, you can begin blending or "morphing" the two shapes together. Since the transition in this simple example occurs at a constant rate, divide the top and side views into equal *regions* as shown in **Step 2** of **Figure 5.5.3**. Project construction lines back to the front view to indicate the edge of each cross section outline at the transition point between each region.

Without access to 3D "power tools," you will have to "resolve" shapes manually using 2D methods. This is not necessarily as hard as it might sound. In fact, this process is an excellent exercise for learning model design skills. These skills can help you make construction patterns that can be used to build a model of just about anything you wish.

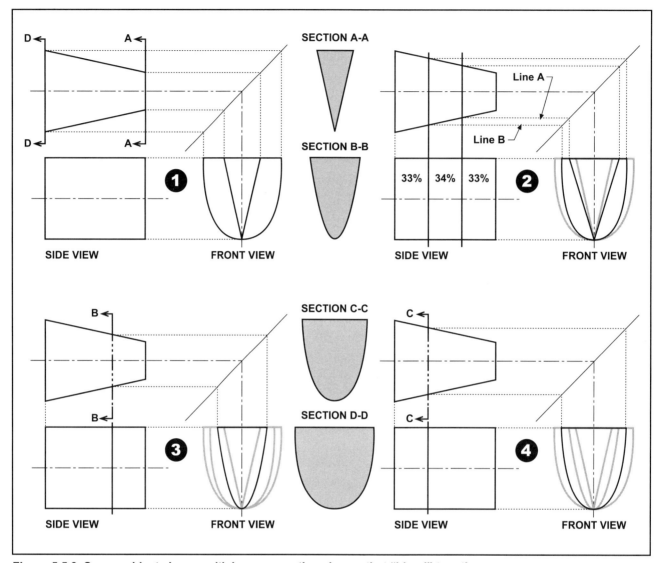

Figure 5.5.3. Some subjects have multiple cross section shapes that "blend" together.

The curve drawing tools of a computer illustration program make it very easy to copy an existing curve and then modify its shape. You can do this by selecting and then dragging the points that make up the curve. The shape of the curve through each point can also be adjusted quite easily.

With these construction lines in place, *Clone* the "V" outline and scale the copy until it aligns with **Line A** as shown. Now *Clone* the "U" outline and scale the copy until it aligns with **Line B** as shown. Once in place, modify these outlines. Why? The cross section is no longer a "V" shape at **Section B-B** as shown in **Step 3**. In the same way, it is no longer a "U" shape at **Section C-C**. Instead, the cross section is *in transition* at both these locations.

To create a transitional outline, modify the copied cross section outline so the shape is somewhere between a "U" and a "V." Now, when you look at all the outlines at the same time in the front or rear view, you can see how they "blend" from one shape to another. This is how a body plan is prepared.

By breaking up your subject using more regions, more cross section outlines will appear in the front view. In most cases, the goal should be to make the transition appear smooth and even with no sudden changes.

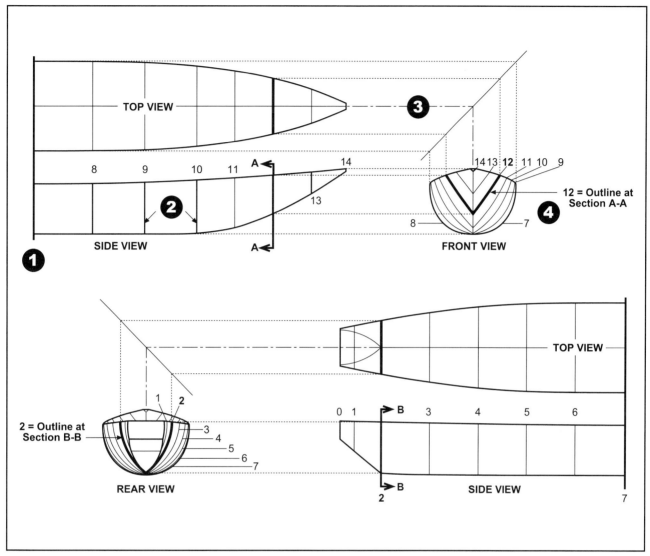

Figure 5.5.4. Position the cross section outlines of a ship's hull according to numbered "stations."

The process of mapping out the cross section outlines for the ship's hull in **Figure 5.5.2** is virtually identical to the exercise you just completed. The main difference is each cross section outline may vary in *height* as well as in width along the length of the ship. This requires projecting construction lines from both the top view and the side view to determine the correct location of each cross section outline in the front view. You can see an example of this process in **Figure 5.5.4**.

Do you remember when the concept of *frame stations* (or "stations") was introduced in **Section 3.6**? Frame stations are used in both aircraft and ship construction to denote where cutting planes slice through the structure. Each cutting plane reveals a cross section outline in that particular location. Since many different locations are needed to map out a complex shape, each must be carefully labeled for proper identification.

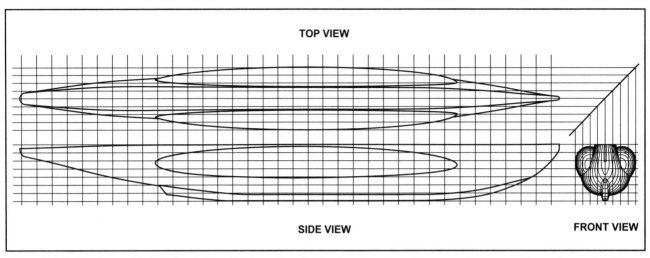

Figure 5.6.1. Create a *grid* of horizontal, vertical, and longitudinal section lines to map out cross sections of complex forms.

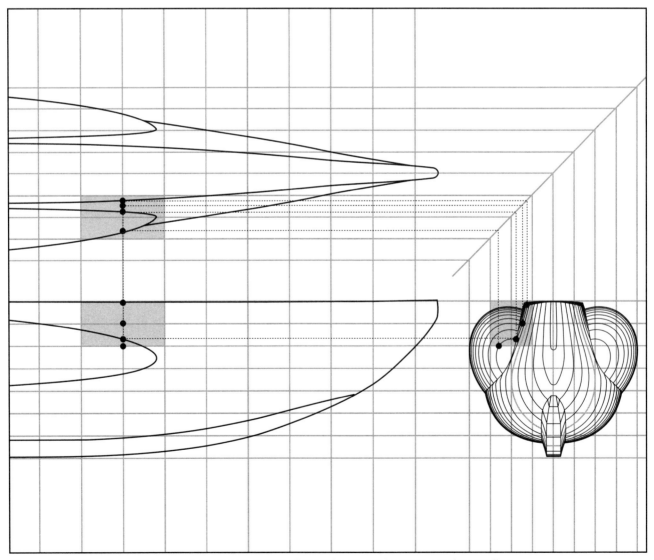

Figure 5.6.2. Use the grid to precisely locate points that make up each cross section outline.

The cutting planes, however, do more than just show the cross section outline at various points. They also denote where either a *bulkhead* or a *transverse frame* is positioned along the hull. A bulkhead marks the dividing line between watertight compartments on a ship. All other stations in between these bulkheads represent the position of transverse frames that help form the shape of the hull. These frames and bulkheads are then "skinned" with either wood planking or sheet metal in order to fill in the rest of the shape.

The outline of a frame or bulkhead is determined by the cross section of the hull at the corresponding station. In addition, marking each station with a unique number (or letter) simplifies the process of identifying all the outlines shown in a body plan. To keep everything on track, every cross section outline *must* correspond with a cutting plane. These cutting planes are depicted by straight lines drawn in the side, top, and bottom views.

Figure 5.5.4 shows the basic process of mapping out the cross section outlines for our example ship's hull:

1. Divide the top view into two halves based on a *dividing line* positioned at the widest point; Outlines from the dividing line forward will be projected into the front view while outlines from the dividing line aft will be projected into the rear view.

2. Position *cutting planes* at each frame station and assign each cutting plane a unique letter or number.

3. Use projection to transfer the *height and width* of the cross section at each station into the front or rear view.

4. Draw the cross section outlines so they create a smoothly flowing transition between each station; Assign each outline a letter or number that corresponds with its associated station.

5.6: More Complex Cross Sections

When you are dealing with a complex shape, projecting height and width information at each frame station may not be sufficient to map out the cross section outlines. In these cases, a more detailed and precise method may be needed. For complex forms like the submarine hull shown in **Figure 5.6.1**, add *horizontal section lines* in the side plan view to help map out the shapes. These lines represent horizontal cutting planes that slice through the object to create outlines in the top and/or bottom views. In a similar fashion, you can also add *longitudinal section lines* (i.e. fore-aft) in the top view. These lines represent *vertical* cutting planes that slice through the object to create profiles in the left or right side views.

All these lines come together to form a sort of "grid" over the plan views of the model. You can use this grid to "zero in" on a specific area in order to

The arrows on cutting planes should point in the direction you would be viewing the subject in order to see the resulting section view. This is why cutting planes in the side view that represent section outlines appearing in the rear view point *forward* while cutting planes representing section outlines appearing in the front view point *aft*.

Station numbering conventions may vary. The example shown here may not conform to the established standards used by Naval architects. Rather, it is merely intended to be intuitive and easy for modelers to use.

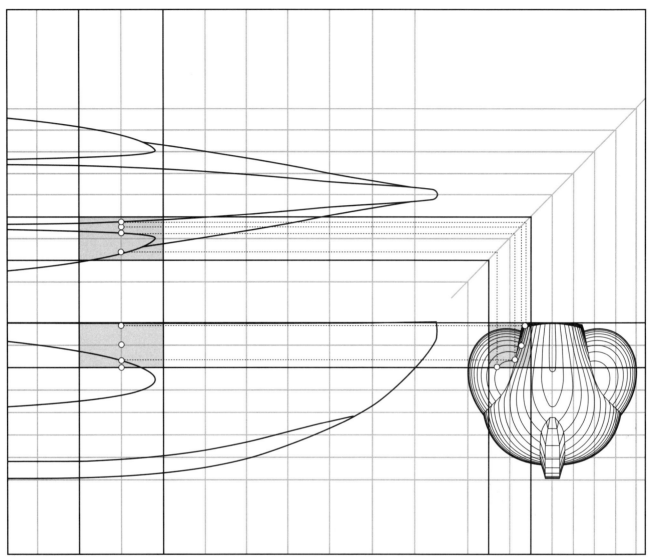

Figure 5.6.3. Change the color of grid lines to "zero in" and work on a particular area.

plot key points in the cross section outline. The challenge, of course, is mapping it all out. Just take things one step at a time.

Still, doing everything in 2D using projection can be a lot of work. In some cases, you may be able to take a few shortcuts. For example, when you add horizontal and longitudinal section lines to the plan views, the logical result would be outlines in the side and top views. These outlines result from the intersection of the horizontal and longitudinal *cutting planes* with the hull. Plotting them, however, might require a great deal of painstaking effort. The question to ask yourself is: "Do I really need these outlines?"

In many cases, the horizontal and longitudinal section lines are needed only because they help form a grid that allows you to focus on a specific portion of the cross section. As a result, you may not need to plot all the outlines resulting from these cutting planes intersecting the hull in the side and/or top views. Instead, try using the grid created by these cutting planes to plot the cross section outlines in the front/rear views point by point. This way, you can save time and effort by drawing only what is absolutely necessary in order to map out the shape of the hull. An example of this method is shown in **Figure 5.6.2**.

As you might imagine, adding all these lines can make your drawing very busy and complex. In addition, convention dictates everything must be properly labeled to avoid confusion. This adds even more complexity. Fortunately, there are some helpful tricks you can use to make this process a bit easier.

First, create your grid of section lines on a separate layer so you can make them appear and disappear as needed. Make sure all lines are perfectly synchronized between views. This means a horizontal section line in the front plan view must be in exactly the same position as the corresponding line in the side view. The easiest way to do this is to draw a single line across both views at the same time as shown in **Figure 5.6.2**. In the same way, extend your vertical section lines from the side view into the top and/or bottom views as needed.

While you're at it, it may be extremely helpful to make the grid very light in color. This will help minimize confusion when your drawing becomes clogged with lines. For example, try using a *stroke color* of "10% black," "10% cyan" or "10% magenta."

When using a computer illustration program, the *stroke* setting determines the color, thickness, and style of a line.

Speaking of colored lines, here is a very useful trick: As you plot key points in a cross section outline, select the grid lines that surround the area in question and change the line color. For example, suppose your grid lines are light grey as shown in **Figure 5.6.3**. To zero in on one section of the grid in each plan view, select the lines that border the area and change the color to something bright and readily visible. You might choose red, green, bright blue, or even black to make the lines stand out clearly from everything else in the drawing. When you are done working in that specific grid section, change the lines back to the original color.

If all this sounds rather tedious, it certainly can be. Fortunately, plotting multiple cross section outlines becomes much easier when using 3D "power tools." Once your model is built in the computer, you can "slice it" as needed to get all the outlines and profiles you could possibly want. Without access to these kinds of 3D tools, however, you will have to find a way to accomplish the same task working strictly in 2D.

5.7: Summary

Section views provide vital information about the structure of any subject. You can draw individual section views or combine multiple cross section outlines in a single view. Combining multiple cross section outlines into a single view creates what is called a *body plan*.

The simplest subjects are those with a *constant cross section* such as a pipe or a piece of tubing. Subjects with a *uniform cross section* are also easy to map out because the cross section shape is the same no matter where you place a cutting plane along the entire length of the subject. In these cases, you need only know the shape of the cross section plus its height or width at any point.

Some subjects have a combination or "blend" of more than one cross section shape. In such cases, plot as many cross section outlines as necessary. Knowing your subject well is the key to this process. You must be able to visualize how the cross section *transitions* from one point to the next.

The most logical locations for cutting planes are points along the hull of a vessel known as *stations*. Mark each station with a unique letter or number that corresponds with a specific cross section outline. When height and width information is not sufficient to plot the cross section, add *horizontal section lines* and *longitudinal section lines* to form a "grid" on top of the subject.

At this point, you have covered how to draw blueprints and how to create the various views you will need to build your projects. You should be able to measure objects in your drawings and use this information to make basic patterns such as cross sections. Now, all that remains to be discussed are some advanced pattern-making techniques.

What's Next?

In the next two chapters, you will learn about some of the basic shapes that form the "building blocks" of many different model projects. More importantly, you will see how to develop construction patterns and templates needed to build these shapes. Finally, you will be introduced to powerful techniques for plotting transitions and intersections between different shapes.

With all this under your belt, you should be able to tackle making blueprints for just about any subject. Are you ready to start designing your next project? Read on!

NOTES

Topics in This Chapter:

Chapter

6

Developments

6.1: Overview

A lot of material has been covered up to this point, including:

- Techniques of orthographic projection used to create multi-view drawings.
- Common drafting standards and conventional practices.
- Distinguishing between lines that are true length and those that are foreshortened.
- Creating auxiliary views and sections.

All these topics play a vital role in the process of making construction patterns and templates for your projects. At this point, you might be asking yourself: "Is there anything more?"

The answer is: "Yes!" Some of the most useful and powerful 2D methods of all will be covered in these last two chapters of the book. Both are chock full of good information. In fact, the topics still to be presented could prove very valuable once you begin to design and build your own projects.

As you will see, many shapes and objects can be created by cutting parts out of sheets of material or "sheet stock" and then assembling them. The challenge then becomes finding a way to make patterns for these parts.

Take, for example, a simple cylinder. If it is small enough, you might be able to use an existing off-the-shelf component such as a pipe or a piece of tubing. But, what if you need a very large cylinder or one that has an odd diameter? In that event, you may need to make it yourself from scratch.

Using the advanced techniques for making construction patterns demonstrated in this chapter, you can <u>develop</u> the surface of a cylinder to create a flat "template" for building it from scratch. The patterns needed to do this are known as <u>developments</u>. You might think of this process as *unfolding* an object as illustrated in **Figure 6.1.1**.

Just as a box can be unfolded in this manner, other objects like a cylinder can be *unrolled* in a similar fashion. In fact, a surprising number of seemingly

NOTE: Underlined terms appear in the Glossary.

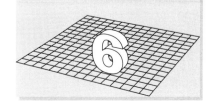

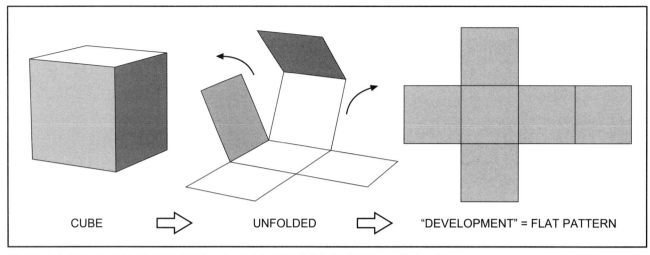

CUBE ⟹ UNFOLDED ⟹ "DEVELOPMENT" = FLAT PATTERN

Figure 6.1.1. Some objects can be *developed* (i.e. "unfolded") to create flat patterns.

complex shapes can be created this way. The individual pieces that make up these shapes become the "building blocks" needed to make a model of the subject. As a result, knowing how to "develop" or break down a shape into flat patterns is a very valuable skill for any modeler to learn.

Unfortunately, the art of developing surfaces can seem challenging at times. Even figuring out patterns for what appear to be simple geometric shapes can sometimes be a daunting task. Thus, you may find yourself using many or all the techniques covered so far in this book as you <u>unfold</u> or <u>unroll</u> structures to create flat patterns and templates for your projects.

6.2: Geometric Solids

Models are often built from three-dimensional variants of basic two-dimensional shapes such as squares, rectangles, circles, and multigons. When a geometric figure takes on a three-dimensional form, the resulting shape is known as a <u>geometric solid</u>. Many such solids are illustrated in **Figure 6.2.1**. Since you might need to use many of these shapes when creating patterns for your projects, it's a good idea to become familiar with them.

Geometric solids fall into several broad categories:

- Cones
- Cubes
- Cylinders
- Polyhedrons
- Prisms
- Pyramids
- Spheres

Cubes

Everyone is familiar with the cube. This shape is built from a series of squares. In some cases, however, the squares are not arranged at right angles to one another. This causes the object to "lean" in one direction. When this occurs, the resulting shape is known as an oblique parallelepiped. Cubes and boxes are discussed in **Section 6.4**.

Cylinders

A cylinder is formed by "extruding" a circle. Cylinders are quite useful in modeling. A right cylinder stands upright and is easy to develop. On the other hand, an oblique cylinder "leans" at an angle in one direction. This makes the oblique cylinder more challenging to develop.

Some cylinders may be cut or *truncated*. This complicates the development process even more. Cylinders are covered in detail starting in **Section 6.5**.

Prisms

Closely related to the cube is the prism. You may think of a prism as being triangular in cross section, but a prism can actually be constructed from just about any regular geometric shape. A right prism stands upright with edges that form 90-degree angles to one another. On the other hand, an oblique prism "leans" at an angle in one direction. A prism "sliced" or cut on one end is said to be truncated. Prisms are discussed in **Section 6.7**.

Cones

Cones are very useful shapes in modeling. Developing cones can be rather tricky, but the techniques come in quite handy in a variety of circumstances. As a result, all modelers should become familiar with and know how to develop patterns for cones.

A cone that stands upright is known as a right cone. A cone that "leans" in any direction is an oblique cone. If a cone does not extend all the way to a point, it is a truncated cone. Cones are covered in detail starting in **Section 6.8**.

Pyramids

A pyramid has a base with four or more sides and then rises to a point. Thanks to the famous landmarks on the Giza Plateau in Egypt, these are very familiar shapes. But, did you know a pyramid does not always have a square base? As it turns out, they can also be formed from a pentagon, a hexagon, and other multi-sided geometric shapes. In addition, pyramids can also be *truncated*. When this occurs, the development process becomes more complicated. Pyramids are discussed in **Section 6.9**.

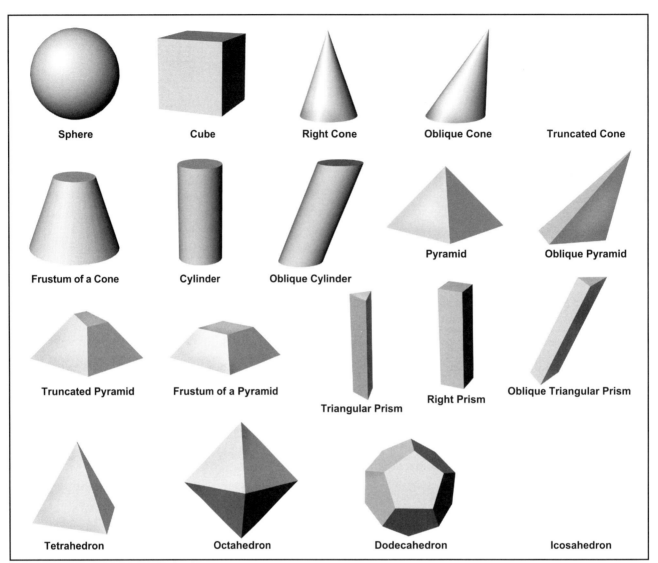

Figure 6.2.1. Many different structures can be made from three-dimensional shapes known as *geometric solids*.

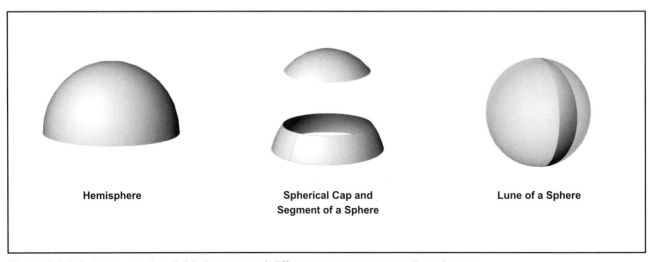

Figure 6.2.2. Spheres can be divided up several different ways to create other shapes.

Spheres

A sphere is, of course, a three-dimensional form of a circle. Cutting a sphere in half yields a hemisphere. There are also other shapes formed from parts of a sphere. Some of them may not be familiar. These shapes, illustrated in **Figure 6.2.2**, include:

- Segment
- Spherical Cap
- Lune (also known as a gore)

While it is not possible to develop or "unfold" a sphere due to the compound curves involved, it is possible to *approximate* the surface of a sphere using flat panels. This involves creating shapes called *gores*. These parts, when assembled, form a close approximation to the surface of a sphere. This process is commonly used to create globes from flat pieces of paper. See **Section 6.10** for more information on developing a sphere.

Polyhedrons

A polyhedron is created by combining multiple instances of simple, two-dimensional geometric shapes to form a three-dimensional figure. Each 2D shape becomes a side or "facet" of the overall form. In fact, polyhedrons (or "polyhedra") with a large number of sides can resemble a faceted "ball."

Keep in mind, all the shapes that make up the sides of a polyhedron do not have to be identical. They can also be combined with other shapes. **Section 6.11** includes tips on developing patterns for this type of object.

6.3: Forming Three-Dimensional Shapes

The study of three-dimensional forms is the foundation of 3D modeling. Understanding how to make these shapes becomes much easier when you are familiar with some basic 3D modeling concepts. In addition, many of the steps needed for "unfolding" geometric solids become much simpler if you have access to 3D tools. Because of this, certain 3D modeling concepts will be introduced here in this chapter.

The most basic technique for creating a three-dimensional shape is known as extruding. With this process, a simple two-dimensional outline becomes a three-dimensional object by adding "height" to the shape. To keep things simple, think of extruding as an operation performed straight up or straight down at a 90-degree angle to the reference plane or horizon. The 2D shape lies parallel with this horizon.

As an example, look at a simple prism in **Figure 6.3.1**. To understand how this shape can be created by extrusion, begin by analyzing the cross section.

This discussion will also serve as a bridge to **Volume 2** of this series which covers how to make patterns for building 3D models.

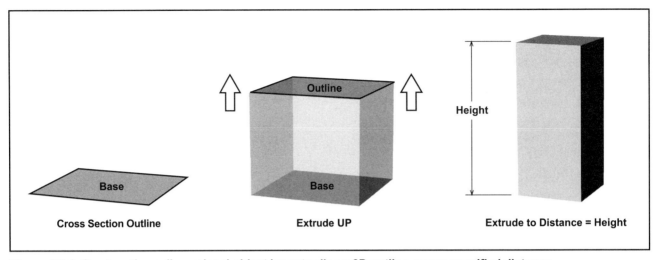

Figure 6.3.1. Create a three-dimensional object by *extruding* a 2D outline over a specified distance.

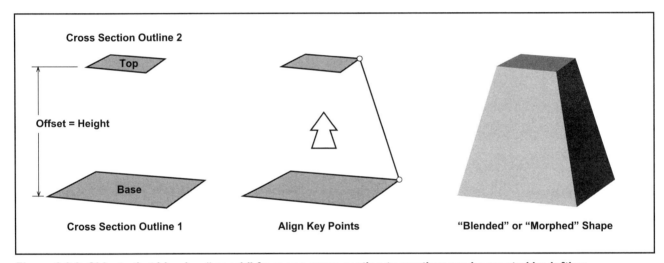

Figure 6.3.2. Objects that blend or "morph" from one cross section to another can be created by *lofting*.

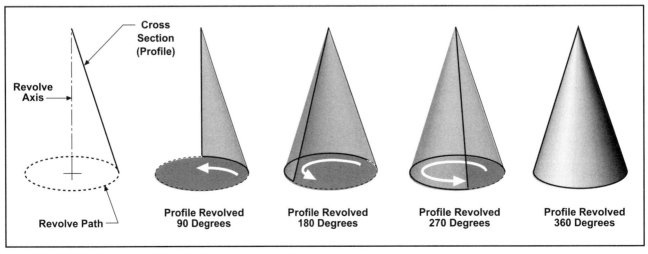

Figure 6.3.3. *Revolve* an outline or *profile* (in this case, an angled line) to create a 3D model of a cone.

In this case, the object is a *right prism* where the cross section is a *rectangle*. As a result, this shape can be formed by *extruding* the rectangle over a specific distance as shown. The distance is simply the desired height of the prism.

Prisms, cubes, and cylinders are all geometric solids that can be created by extrusion. To form these objects, all you need to know is the cross section shape plus the height. This concept comes in very handy when making patterns for objects that will be created using 3D modeling tools. Keep in mind, however, extrusion works only when the object has a *constant cross section*.

For objects that do not have a constant cross section, other construction methods are needed. One such technique is called <u>lofting</u>. This process, illustrated in **Figure 6.3.2**, is similar to extruding except that lofting creates a smooth transition (a "blend" or "morph") between different cross sections. If you specify cross section outlines at two or more points along the length of an object, the software will calculate or *interpolate* the resulting shape. To exert more control over the appearance of the finished product, you may be able to provide more cross section outlines, depending on the program.

Some shapes can be created by a process known as <u>revolving</u>. This means rotating a two-dimensional shape or <u>profile</u> around a specified <u>axis of rotation</u>. Revolving duplicates what occurs in the real world with a process known as <u>lathing</u>. A woodworker or machinist can place a piece of wood or metal on a machine called a *lathe*. The machine spins the material rapidly while the operator cuts into the spinning object using a tool to create perfectly symmetrical shapes. To revolve an object in 3D, all you need is an outline representing the desired profile and two points that specify the axis of rotation.

A cone is an excellent example of a shape that can be created by revolving. The 2D profile needed to create a cone is simply an angled line as shown in **Figure 6.3.3**. When the base of the cone is parallel with the top plan view, this line can easily be extracted from any side, front, or rear view. This concept is very intuitive and extremely useful for making construction patterns. If you know a shape can be formed by revolving, you are one step closer to drawing the profile needed to build it. In the case of the cone, understanding how this shape is revolved also makes it possible to "unroll" the shape to create a flat pattern. You will learn more about this in **Section 6.8**.

There are many other handy tools for creating three-dimensional shapes in the computer. Using 3D techniques can help you figure out the geometry of your model and solve difficult problems with less effort. In addition, some 3D modeling applications provide powerful features that make it much easier to create developments of complex shapes. As a result, 3D computer modeling techniques could be the ultimate set of "power tools" for modelers who want to design and build their own structures from scratch.

It may also be possible to extrude an object at an angle, but that process can be more difficult to visualize.

To see an example of lofting in action, refer to **Section 7.2**.

Revolving or *lathing* is a very powerful method for building objects because you can create incredibly complex shapes from very simple patterns.

Some programs may permit you to revolve a profile along a path that is not a true circle. You may be able to choose a path that is an oval or even a geometric shape. This could make it possible to create very complex shapes with relative ease.

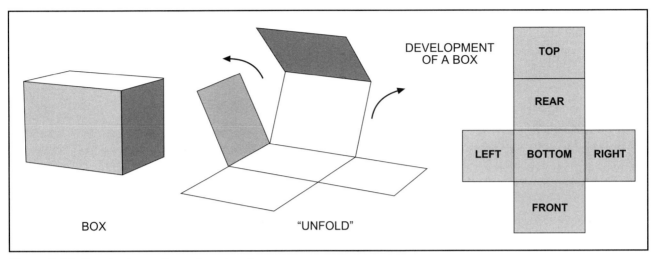

Figure 6.4.1. Developing patterns for a box is very easy.

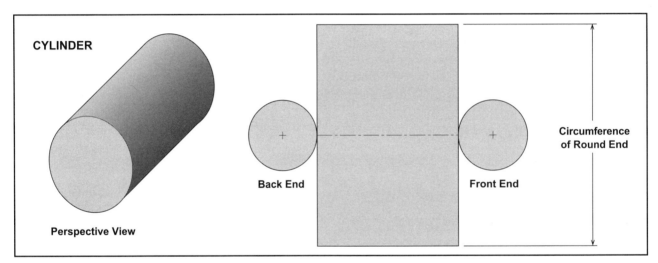

Figure 6.5.1. Rounded objects can be *unrolled*. As a result, cylinders are a little more tricky to develop.

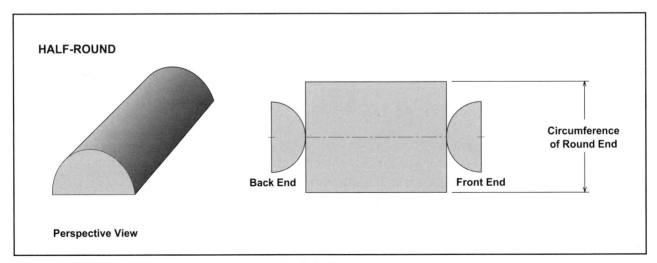

Figure 6.5.2. Make a *half-round* by cutting a cylinder in half.

6.4: Cubes and Boxes

The development of patterns for a cube (or a box) is probably the easiest pattern-making process of all. A box has six sides that are perpendicular to one another. The box can be unfolded as shown in **Figure 6.4.1**. Note how the steps needed to create the development of a box are exactly the same as those used to create multiple views of an object via orthographic projection.

The result will be a true-size construction pattern for each side of the box. In the case of a cube, each side will be an identical square. In the case of a box, each side may be either a square or a rectangle. As a result, all you need to know are the length and width of each side. As long as the sides of the subject are parallel to the principal planes of projection, this information can easily be extracted from the plan views. Either the top or bottom view will provide dimensions for both the top and bottom surfaces of the box while either side view will give you the dimensions for both side pieces. Dimensions of the front and rear pieces can then be extracted from either the front or rear view.

Once measured in the plan views, separate the sides of the box into individual panels if desired or leave them connected to one another. It all depends on how you plan to construct the object. A paper model, for example, would be *folded* into shape. Thus, the sides should remain linked together as shown in **Figure 6.4.1**. In this event, all you would need to do is cut, score, and fold the parts in order to assemble the box.

6.5: Cylinders

To develop patterns for a cylinder, determine the exact shape of each end and then "unroll" the middle until it is perfectly flat as shown in **Figure 6.5.1**. Unlike a box which can be folded into shape, a cylinder is round – hence the need to unroll it.

A *right cylinder* that sits perfectly upright is *circular* in cross section, making it very easy to develop. The middle of such a cylinder unrolls into a *rectangle* with a length equal to the length of the cylinder and a height equal to the *circumference* of the round end. The patterns for each end are simply circles with a diameter equal to the height of the cylinder as shown. Only basic geometry is needed to map out this type of structure.

A variation of this example is the <u>half-round</u> as shown in **Figure 6.5.2**. This is simply one half of a cylinder. Therefore, the width of the developed rectangle will be equal to the circumference of the semi-circular end. Since a semi-circle is one half of a circle, you can use the geometry of a circle to find the true length of this circumference.

With either an *oblique* or a *truncated* cylinder, the cross section is still a circle. In these cases, however, the ends of the cylinder are shaped like an *oval* or *ellipse*. This makes such a cylinder harder to develop.

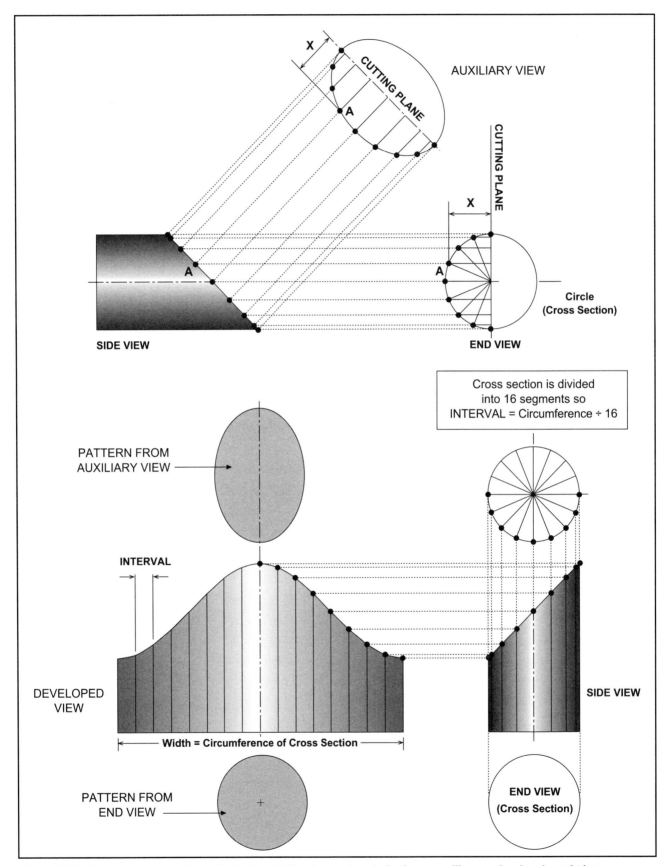

Figure 6.5.3. Develop a *truncated cylinder* by plotting key points in both an auxiliary and a developed view.

You have already seen the techniques needed to plot the shape of the angled end for a truncated cylinder. This was covered in **Section 4.7** where techniques were presented for making an auxiliary view using a cutting plane. What remains is to plot the correct shape of the middle part of the cylinder.

As with all such shapes, start by determining the cross section. Even though the end is truncated, the cross section of the cylinder is still a circle. Thus, the cylinder appears as a circle in the end view. The true shape of the cut end, however, can only be seen in an *auxiliary view*. To create this view, start with a side view of the cylinder where the angled face is seen as an *edge*.

Once the true shape of the angled end has been drawn, begin developing the central portion of the cylinder as shown in **Figure 6.5.3**. Since one end has been cut at an angle, this central portion is no longer a rectangle. To figure out the correct shape, divide the cylinder into *sections* using radial lines in the end view as shown. These radial lines divide the *circumference* of the cross section into equal parts. If you then "unroll" this circumference, the resulting shape will also be equally divided.

To find out what this shape looks like when it is unrolled, transfer the radial lines in the top view into the side plan view using projection. Then, start laying out the overall shape of the unrolled or *developed view* by plotting key points. The overall width of this shape will be equal to the *circumference* of the cylinder. The bottom is a horizontal line as shown.

The top outline of the unrolled shape can be determined by projecting lines from the side view. To do this, first divide the overall shape into 16 equal parts. These parts correspond with the radial lines already drawn in the top view. Finally, plot key points along the outline of the pattern as shown. Each point will be located where one of the division lines intersects with the corresponding construction line projected from the side view.

As you can see, the width of the unrolled shape will always be equal to the circumference of the cylinder. In this case, however, the height will vary due to the fact the end has been truncated. By dividing the unrolled shape into sections, you can plot the correct height at each division.

6.6: The Helix

You are probably familiar with the *spiral*. By definition, it is a geometric shape that exists only in two dimensions. As a result, a true spiral may not be of much use to modelers. On the other hand, a three-dimensional shape based on the spiral – called a <u>helix</u> – can be used in making model parts.

The form of the helix can be found in many common items such as coil springs or the threads on a fastener. There are two basic types of helix. The cylindrical or <u>regular helix</u> resembles a coil of wire that is wrapped around a

In the example shown, the cylinder is divided into 16 equal sections.

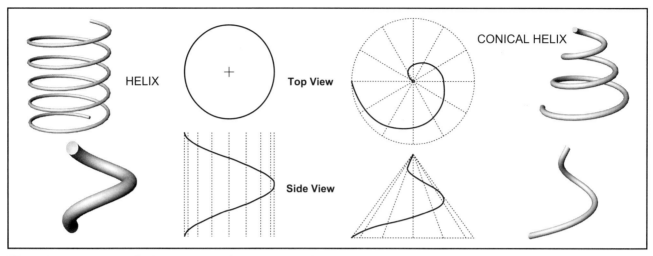

Figure 6.6.1. Wrap a coiled shape around either a cylinder or a cone to form a *helix*.

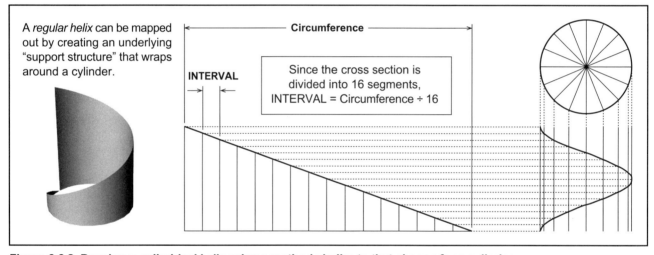

Figure 6.6.2. Develop a *cylindrical helix* using a method similar to that chosen for a cylinder.

cylinder. In a similar fashion, the <u>conical helix</u> looks like a coil of wire that gets wrapped around a *cone*. When drawing a regular helix, note that it appears as a *circle* when viewed from directly above. On the other hand, a conical helix looks like a *spiral* when viewed from above.

You are probably familiar with seeing a regular helix drawn in the side view using zig-zagging straight lines. While this may be the common way to represent such objects, it is not really a true representation of the shape of a helix. The correct shape is illustrated in **Figure 6.6.1**.

Developing a regular helix requires plotting the location of key points using a special view. This view is actually a development of the underlying cylinder. After "unrolling" this cylinder, the resulting shape will be similar to that depicted in **Figure 6.6.2**. (This illustration may remind you of the paper pattern used to make a can of frozen orange juice or a can of biscuits.)

Start with the top plan view or "end view" as shown. The cross section of the underlying cylinder is a perfect circle. Divide this cross section into equal parts using radial lines and then transfer these lines to the side plan view. (In this example, the circle is divided equally into 16 parts.) With both the end view and the side view equally divided, begin developing a flat pattern for the cylinder as shown.

In this case, the development of the cylinder is needed to locate points on the helix. When you "unroll" the cylinder, a rectangle results where the width is equal to the circumference of the cylinder's circular end. This rectangle can then be divided into 16 equal segments just as you divided the cross section of the cylinder in the end view. To obtain the correct width of each segment, divide the total width of the rectangle by 16.

If the helix rises at a constant rate as it goes around the cylinder, the developed shape will appear as a diagonal line running from the bottom to the top of the unrolled cylinder. To plot this line, connect the bottom right corner and top left corner of the unrolled surface as shown in **Figure 6.6.2**. This divides the rectangle into two *right triangles*. Now, discard the topmost triangle.

What remains is a "developed view" that you can use to construct an accurate side view of the helix. To do this, project lines from the developed view into the side plan view. Each projected line will start where a division on the unrolled surface intersects with the sloped line. Next, project from the top view down into the side view. These projected lines begin where each radial line in the top view intersects with the circumference of the circle.

To finish, plot points in the side view where the lines projected from the developed view intersect the lines projected from the top view. Once all these points have been plotted, connect them with a smooth line to draw the correct shape of the helix.

Another form of helix can be made by wrapping a spiral around a cone. By varying the height of the spiral to create a sloping line, the result is a *conical helix* as shown in **Figure 6.6.3**.

To correctly draw this shape, start by plotting the outline of the spiral inside a circle in the top plan view. The circle represents the *base* of the underlying cone. Next, begin drawing the shape of the helix in the side plan view. To do this, divide the base of the cone into sections using radial lines in the top view as shown. You must carefully label each radial line during this process.

Now, divide the side view of the cone into a number of sections using horizontal lines. Use the *same number of sections* that were chosen to divide the top view. Number each section starting at the bottom of the cone and working upward. With these section lines now drawn in the side view, begin plotting points on the helix. Transfer the horizontal location of each key point from the top view. Then, locate the vertical position of the same point

A flat pattern for a conical helix can be created by dividing the underlying cone into sections with radial lines and then "unrolling" it. The helix can then be plotted by marking key points along each radial line. To see how to develop a cone, refer to **Section 6.8**.

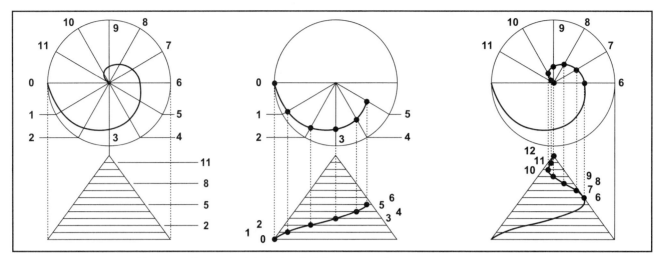

Figure 6.6.3. Plot the side view of a *conical helix* by dividing a cone into sections.

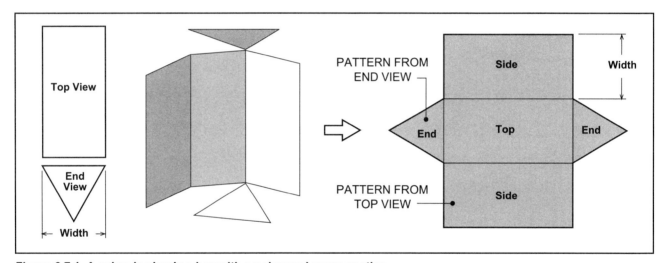

Figure 6.7.1. A *prism* is simply a box with a polygonal cross section.

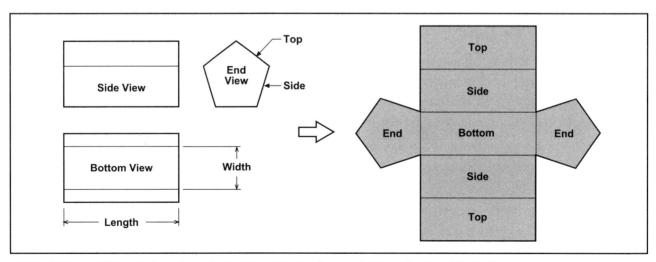

Figure 6.7.2. A prism can have just about any cross section or shape as long as it has three or more sides.

in the side view as shown. Once all these points are plotted, connect them with a smooth curve to draw the shape of the helix.

6.7: Prisms

You might think of a prism simply as a *box*. Unlike a box, however, the prism is not limited to being square in cross section. In fact, a prism can be made from just about any regular multigon – including a square, a rectangle, or a triangle. You can also make prisms from other regular geometric shapes such as a pentagon, hexagon, or octagon.

As mentioned in **Section 6.2**, a *right prism* stands upright while an *oblique prism* "leans" in a given direction. A *truncated prism* is cut at an angle.

To develop a prism, start with the cross section as depicted in the end view. A square or rectangular cross section is the easiest to develop. Simply imagine a six-sided box that is unfolded in the same manner as what you have already seen in **Section 6.4**. To create a development, you need to determine the length and width of each side of the box. This information can often be obtained from the plan views.

While a square or rectangular prism is the easiest type to develop, the process for non-truncated right prisms is also straightforward – no matter what the shape. Always start with the cross section and use this to determine the exact number of sides. Each side will be a rectangle with a length equal to the length of the prism and a width equal to the *length of one side* of the cross section shape as shown in **Figure 6.7.1** and **Figure 6.7.2**.

Truncated prisms are a bit more challenging to develop, but not much. As shown in **Figure 6.7.3**, when a prism is truncated, you can create an *auxiliary view* to find the true outline of the angled end. (If the other end is parallel to a plan view, its outline will be the cross section in that view.) As you can see, it is very important to have accurate plan views from which to start.

The side, front, and rear orthographic plan views often contain nearly all the information needed to develop a prism. Simply extract the needed outlines for each side or "facet" from the plan views and then "stitch" them together to form the complete development as shown. If any side is not parallel to one or more plan views, create an auxiliary view for that side. This will provide the true-size pattern for any non-parallel side.

Oblique prisms are more challenging because patterns for either end cannot be found in the plan views. In addition, due to the angled ends, the sides are not all identical like they are with a right prism. As a result, you may need to determine the pattern for each side individually.

If the prism has only four sides, each can be derived directly from the plan views as illustrated in **Figure 6.7.4**. On the other hand, if the prism has only three sides or more than four sides, some will not be parallel to the plan

To learn more about creating auxiliary views, refer back to **Section 4.7**.

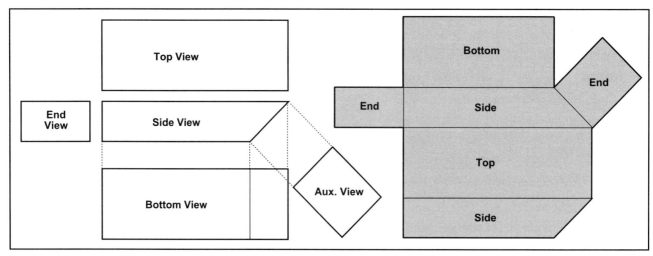

Figure 6.7.3. Even when a prism is *truncated*, most of the needed information is available in the plan views.

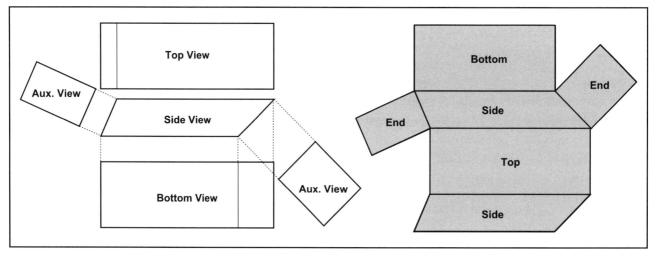

Figure 6.7.4. Developing an *oblique prism* requires a little more effort.

views. In such cases, create an auxiliary view for any side not parallel with a plan view. As an alternative, you can also use revolution to *revolve* the prism until each side is parallel to a principal plan view. As you can see, there is often more than one way to solve these kinds of problems.

Figure 6.7.5 shows an oblique hexagonal prism with six sides. Because each end of this prism is angled, all six sides are different. This means a separate pattern will be needed for each "facet" of the prism. As a result, auxiliary views are required as shown. Fortunately, this particular shape is symmetrical about its centerline. This means you need only to find patterns for the upper and lower face, plus the remaining faces on one side. You can then create a mirror image to draw the other half as shown.

While doing this kind of development may seem daunting, just remember to break it down into pieces and handle each part one step at a time. This will keep the process from becoming overwhelming. In many cases, all the information you need to create the patterns is already contained in the plan views. In other cases, you may need to create one or more auxiliary views. If it looks hard, don't worry. You've already practiced all of the techniques needed to successfully make these kinds of developments.

6.8: Cones

Cones might seem tricky to develop, but they are among the most useful shapes for modelers. The development of a cone looks like pie with one or more pieces missing. This is illustrated in **Figure 6.8.1**. There are two practical methods for developing this kind of shape. You can do it graphically or you can use mathematical formulas to make the job easier. In either case, the trick to mapping out a cone is knowing the true length of its *side*.

Right Cone – Graphical Method

As illustrated in **Figure 6.8.2**, a cone is shaped like a *triangle* in the side plan view. It is most important to know the true length of the *side* of the cone. This will be the length of the sloping line ("**S**") that makes up part of the triangle shown in the side plan view. To begin mapping out the development of the cone, start by measuring the true length of this line.

Next, plot the top plan view of the cone. In nearly every case, this will be a perfect circle as shown. Divide this circle into *sections* using radial lines. Label each line with a unique number where it intersects the circular base of the cone. These will be referred to as *section numbers*.

When dividing a cone into sections using radial lines in the top view, it is up to you to determine how many lines are needed to plot the the resulting development.

You can also project these radial lines into the side plan view and label them there as well. While this is not absolutely necessary, it will help you understand how the development of the cone is created. In addition, this technique comes in very handy when developing truncated or oblique cones or when you need to map out the location of features found on the surface of a cone.

Now, you can begin plotting your development by drawing a large circle. The radius of this circle must be equal to "**S**" as shown in **Figure 6.8.2**. Divide this circle into sections that correspond with the radial lines in the top view. To do this, measure the <u>chordal distance</u> "**C**" between section numbers in the top view and transfer this distance to the development of the cone. The procedure for doing this is very specific:

1. First, pick any point on the edge of the large circle; This will be the *starting point* and first section number.
2. Next, use a *construction circle* of radius equal to "**C**" to plot the *chordal distance* between the starting point and the next division.
3. Repeat this process to locate the remaining points where each section line intersects the edge of the circle; Continue until all sections have been correctly plotted on the development.

Using the graphical method, the *chordal distance* is only an approximation. To be more precise, use mathematical formulas for circles and arcs to determine the exact values.

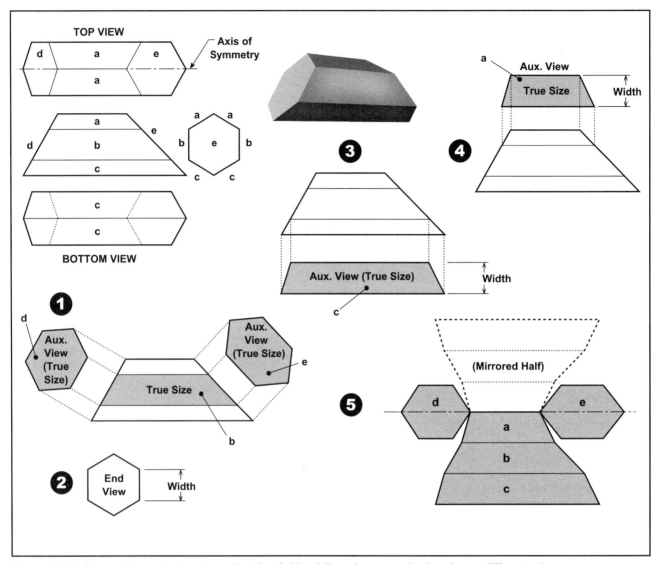

Figure 6.7.5. Due to the angled ends, each side of this oblique hexagonal prism has a different shape.

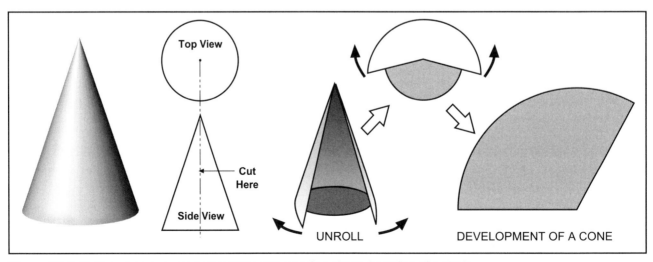

Figure 6.8.1. Split a cone open and *unroll* it to get a wedge-shaped portion of a circle.

4. To complete the pattern, draw a radial line from the *center point* of the circle to the *first* section number and from the center point to the *last* section number as shown; This marks the beginning and end of the wedge-shaped "pie piece" that forms a pattern for the cone.

Now you can see how the development of a cone is formed by cutting it open and "unrolling" it to form a flat shape. If you projected the radial lines from the top view into the side view, you can also draw radial lines from the center point of the development to all the other section numbers along the edge of the large circle as shown. Note how the radial lines on the development correspond with the same lines drawn in the top and side views. With a non-truncated right cone, this is not absolutely necessary. On the other hand, if your cone has any surface features that need to be located on the development, this will be very helpful.

Right Cone – Mathematical Method

Knowing basic geometry and a little algebra can be very helpful when developing cones. As you have already seen, it is possible to obtain the true length of the sloping side of the cone from the side plan view. Instead of measuring this length from the plans, you can also determine it mathematically by using formulas for solving a triangle.

Either way, once the true length of the side of the cone is known, this becomes the radius of a large circle used to develop the cone. Since the cone is only a *portion* of this circle, however, you need to know the <u>central angle</u> of this wedge-shaped portion. This angle, illustrated in **Figure 6.8.3**, can be found using the mathematical formula for the length of an arc:

$$\text{Arc Length } = \text{Radius} * \theta \quad \textit{Where } \theta \textit{ is measured in radians}$$

In this case, the arc length happens to be the circumference of the circle that makes up the base of the cone. You can calculate this by measuring the diameter of the circle in the top plan view and plugging this value into the basic formula for finding the circumference of a circle:

$$\text{Circumference} \quad = \quad \textbf{Pi} * \text{Diameter}$$

Pi is a special value used in circle and angle calculations. This is a *constant*, meaning its value never changes. For most modeling calculations, you can use the following value for **Pi**:

$$\textbf{Pi} \quad = \quad 3.14159$$

Once you have values for **Pi** and for the Arc Length, use the following variation of the formula to find the central angle:

$$\theta \quad = \quad \text{Arc Length / Radius}$$

To create a *construction circle*, you must control both the radius and center point of your circle. For more information on drawing with a computer illustration program, read *How To Draw Anything With a Computer: A Quick-Start Guide for the Craftsman, Hobbyist, and Do-It-Yourselfer*, part of the *Modeler's Notebook Reference Series* available from:

www.ModelersNotebook.com

For detailed information and step-by-step examples of how to work with formulas for many of the geometric shapes you may encounter in your model projects, read *Easy Project Math: A Problem-Solving Guide for the Craftsman, Hobbyist, and Do-It-Yourselfer*, part of the *Modeler's Notebook Reference Series* available from:

www.ModelersNotebook.com

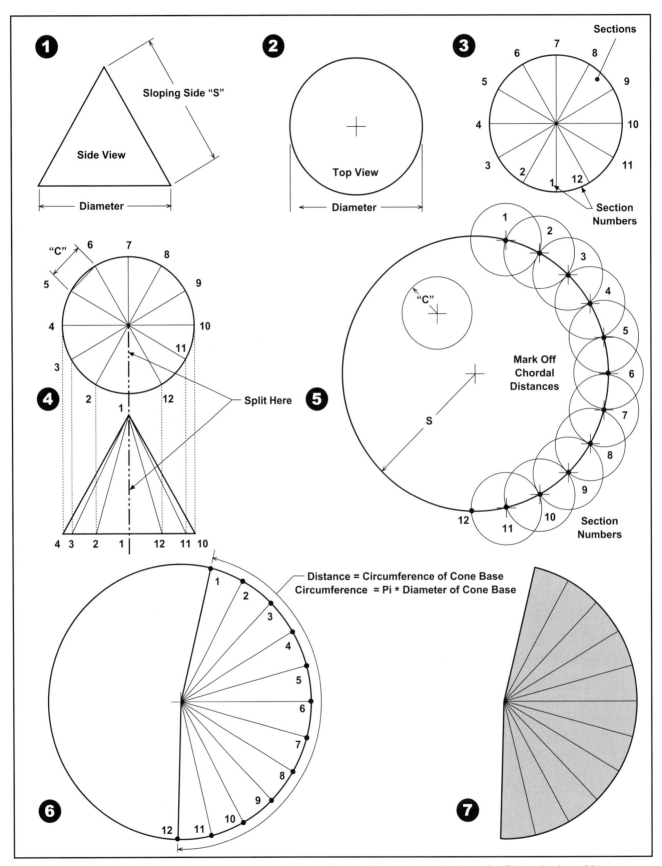

Figure 6.8.2. Develop patterns for a cone using a circle with a radius equal to the length of the sloping side.

Solving this formula will give you the central angle measured in *radians*. Unfortunately, this angle is not measured in degrees. As a result, you must use the following conversion formula to find the central angle in degrees:

$$\text{Degrees} \quad = \quad (\text{Value in radians} * 180) / \textbf{Pi}$$

This is the last bit of information needed to create the development of the cone. Now, draw a large circle with a radius equal to the length of the cone. Then, draw two radial lines from the center to the edge of this circle. Place these lines so the angle between them is equal to the central angle as shown in **Figure 6.8.3**. Voila! You just created a pattern for a cone. As you can see, by using a little math, the goal can often be accomplished with less work.

Truncated Cones

A cone that does not extend all the way to a point is said to be *truncated*. To be technically correct, however, a truncated cone is really one that is cut at an angle as illustrated in **Figure 6.8.4**. When the tip of the cone is cut parallel to the base, the result is a special shape called a <u>frustum of a cone</u>. This is also shown in **Figure 6.8.4**.

A frustum of a cone is just as easy to develop as a regular cone. Look closely, and you will see that a frustum is what is left when you subtract a smaller cone from the top of a larger one. In this case, the upper portion of the cone is trimmed away while the remainder becomes the frustum. So, to create a development of a frustum, simply create a development for a "whole" cone and then "subtract" an area equal to the development of the smaller cone at the tip. This process is illustrated in **Figure 6.8.5**.

In the side plan view, *extend* the side of the frustum to a point in order to determine the height of the "whole" cone. Next, measure the distance along the sloping side between the tip of the cone and the top of the frustum. Also measure the distance from the top of the frustum to the *bottom* of the cone. These measurements are values "S_1" and "S_2" in the illustration. Use this information to create a development just as you would with a regular cone.

The trick here is to start the development process by drawing a circle with a radius equal to "$S_1 + S_2$." Then, draw a smaller circle centered on the same point with a radius equal to "S_1." Draw radial lines on the larger circle to map out the wedge-shaped pattern. The smaller circle then represents the area to be *removed* from this shape in order to create a template for the frustum.

Developing a truncated cone is quite different. An example of such a cone is shown in **Figure 6.8.4**. This shape is easy to draw in the side plan view, but more difficult to draw in the top plan view. Even though it looks similar to a frustum of a cone, it takes quite a bit more work to develop this shape. You will need to plot not only the overall shape of the cone, but also key points

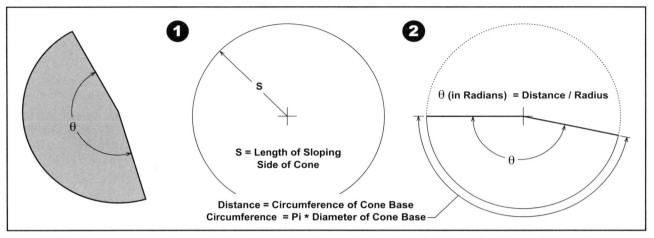

Figure 6.8.3. A cone can also be created by calculating the *central angle* that defines the shape of the wedge.

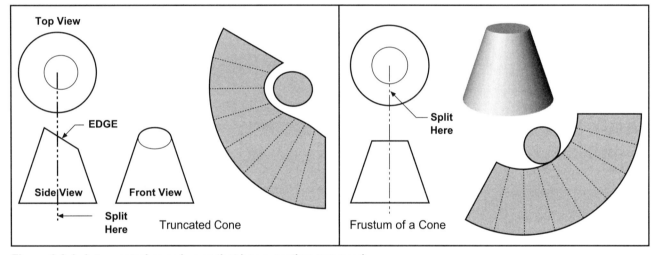

Figure 6.8.4. A *truncated cone* is one that has a portion removed.

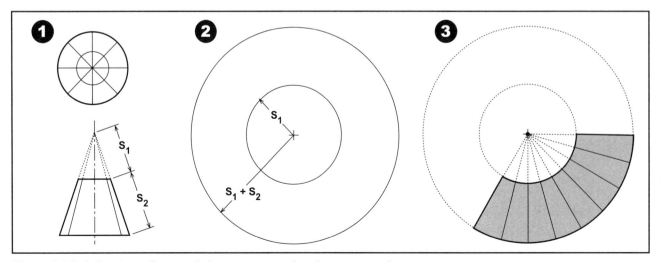

Figure 6.8.5. A *frustum of a cone* is just as easy to develop as a regular cone.

that define the outline of the truncated portion. In the end, the final shape of this development may not look like anything you might expect.

As you will see, while the top of a frustum is a circle, the top surface of a truncated cone is an *ellipse*. In order to determine the shape of the area that needs to be cut from this cone, you should start with a side view where the top surface is depicted as an *edge*. This is illustrated in **Step 1** of **Figure 6.8.6**.

Begin by mapping out a regular cone as if it were not truncated at all. The strategy will be to develop a "whole" cone and then plot the shape of the area that will be "removed" in order to create the truncated cone. This can be accomplished by dividing the top view into sections using radial lines just as you did with a regular cone. In this case, however, the radial lines *must* be projected into the side view. From there, you can map out key points by obtaining information about their position from the side view.

There is a trick to mapping out these key points. You need to know the vertical location of each point as measured *along the sloping side* of the cone. This is not the same as measuring the *vertical* distance between the point and the base or the point and the tip. Fortunately, this information can be found in the side view. But, there is a catch – some extra work will be required.

Looking at **Step 1** of **Figure 6.8.6**, notice the key points "**A**" and "**E**" along the centerline of the cone as seen in the top view. Imagine a *cutting plane* that extends all the way through this centerline. If you were to cut the cone in half along this centerline, you could then measure the distance along the edge of the cone from the tip to "**A**" and from the tip to "**E**." This corresponds with distances "S_A" and "S_E" as shown in **Step 2**. These distances are depicted *true length* in the side view.

On the other hand, the remaining key points all lie on radial lines representing vertical cutting planes that are *foreshortened* when seen in the side view. As a result, you cannot determine the distances from the tip of the cone to any of these points without performing an extra step. In this case, *revolution* is the key to finding these distances.

In order to get the correct values, *revolve* the cone until each point lies in a plane that is parallel to the side view. An example of this trick is illustrated in **Step 3** of **Figure 6.8.6**. With the cone revolved 45 degrees in a counterclockwise direction, you can now measure the distance from the tip of the cone to **Point** "**B**" and from the tip to **Point** "**D**" in the side view.

As you can imagine, this process can be time consuming. Fortunately, there is an easy shortcut for accomplishing the same result. Simply *project* all the points in the side view by moving them *horizontally* until they intersect with the sloping side as illustrated in **Step 4** of **Figure 6.8.6**. Then, in turn, measure the distance "**S**" from the tip of the cone to each projected point.

If you recall the discussion in **Section 4.6**, the technique of revolution can be used to find the true length of lines that appear foreshortened in a plan view.

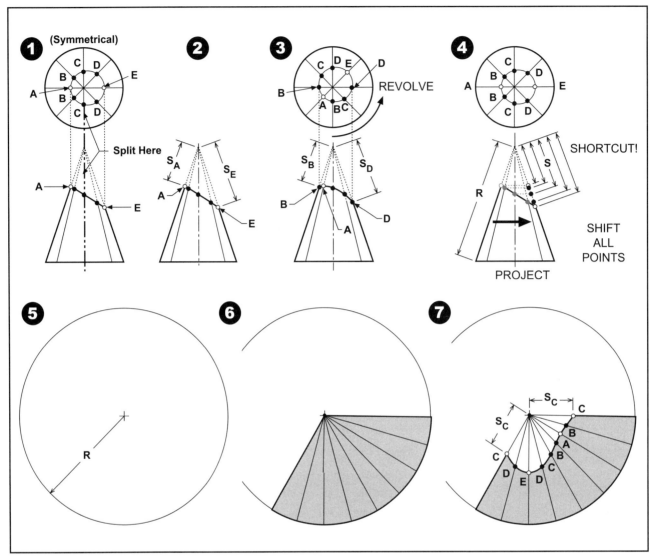

Figure 6.8.6. Develop a truncated cone by plotting key points along the outline of the area to be removed.

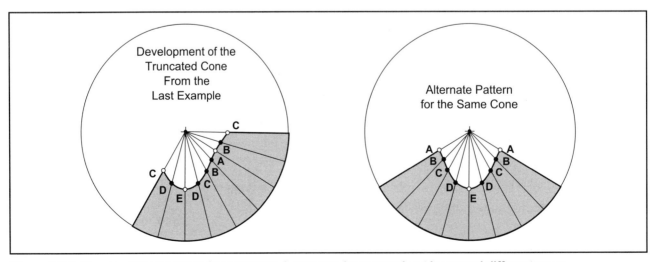

Figure 6.8.7. The developed pattern for a truncated cone can be mapped out in several different ways.

With all these measurements in hand, begin drawing the development. First, set up the pie-shaped wedge by making a circle with a radius equal to "**R**" as shown. To find the value for "**R**," *extend* the cone in the side view until it reaches a point and then measure the distance of the entire sloping side. This is illustrated in **Step 4** of **Figure 6.8.6**.

Once the circle has been drawn as shown in **Step 5**, plot the exact center point. Next, map out the correct shape of the wedge-shaped pattern just as you would any normal cone. (This is illustrated in **Step 6**.) This time, however, be sure to draw in *all* the radial lines on the pattern. You will use these lines to plot the key points needed to calculate the outline of the area to be removed.

Remember, this pattern is created by "splitting" the cone open and "unrolling" it. To do that, you must select the location where the cone is to be split. (The exact location, however, is arbitrary.) In this example, the vertical line running through **Point "C"** in the top view was chosen. This is the vertical centerline in the side view. As a result, **Point "C"** will lie along the first radial line. This corresponds with the *outside edge* of the pie-shaped wedge.

Keep in mind, since this pattern wraps around the cone until both sides meet, **Point** "C" also lies along the opposite edge at the same time. All the remaining points then fall in between as shown. Each point lies along one of the radial lines that divide up the pattern.

One at a time, select each radial line and plot the location of each key point ("**A**" through "**E**"). To do this, mark off the appropriate distance "**S**" from the exact center of your circle as measured along the radial line. This will show the location of the key point in the developed pattern. Note how the points repeat because the cone is symmetrical. **Point "A"** represents the location where the cone is tallest while **Point "E"** represents where it has been trimmed the most. Points "**B**," "**C**," and "**D**" fall on either side of the axis of symmetry. Thus, each is repeated twice. Once all key points have been plotted, connect them by drawing a smooth curve as shown in **Step 7**.

When it comes to the shape of the truncated portion, notice how the horizontal line in the top view connecting **Point "A"** and **Point "E"** lies along the axis of symmetry. You could just as easily have chosen to split the cone along this line. Simply choose whatever location makes it easier for you to visualize and then map out the truncated shape.

If you look at **Figure 6.8.7**, you can see an alternate pattern for this same cone. In this case, it was split along the line connecting **Point** "A" and **Point** "E" in the top view. The two patterns look completely different. Yet, when assembled into a cone, both yield the exact same result.

Another example of a such a cone is shown in **Figure 6.8.8**. Just remember, you always need to find a side view where the truncated surface appears as an *edge*. This makes it relatively easy to plot the correct outline of the area to

Cones can be truncated in any number of different ways. No matter what the outcome, the process of creating the development for a truncated cone is always the same.

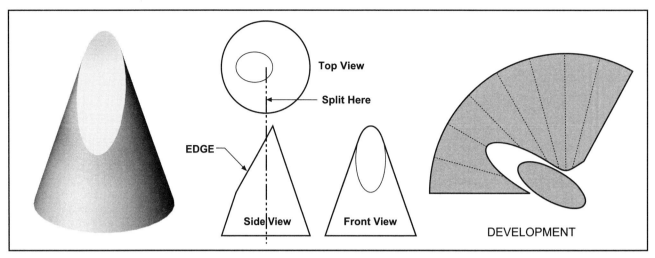

Figure 6.8.8. When developing a pattern for a truncated cone, you never know what you might get.

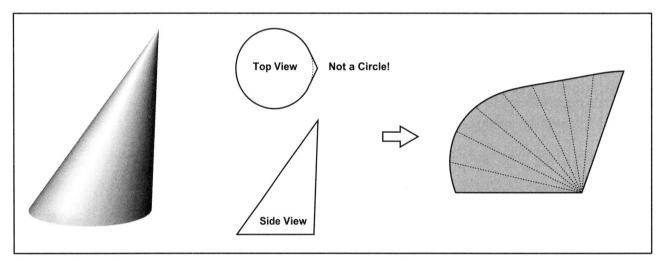

Figure 6.8.9. An *oblique cone* is really a regular cone where a portion of the *bottom* has been truncated.

be removed from the cone. Note how strange the final developed shape appears. You never know what you're going to get when you start developing truncated geometric shapes like this.

Oblique Cones

An oblique cone does not point straight upward, but can be said to "lean" to one side instead. To understand how you might create a development for such a cone, imagine tilting it until the tip is pointing straight up. When oriented in this manner, you can see that it is really a regular cone with part of the *bottom* cut off at an angle. As a result, you might think of such a cone as a regular cone that is truncated at the bottom instead of at the top.

Oblique cones may look simple at first glance, but they can be complex to develop. As an example, look at the oblique cone shown in **Figure 6.8.9**.

Notice how different the top view of such a cone appears. In this case, the top plan view is not simply a circle as with other cones. This means you will need to create an *auxiliary view* to see what the cone really looks like when viewed in cross section. This will then form the basis of a development for the cone. Be prepared to use lots of radial lines in order to plot the location of a sufficient number of key points for this type of cone.

Overall, the method for developing an oblique cone is very similar to the process used in creating patterns for a truncated cone. In this case, however, the cone must first be re-oriented so that it stands upright. To do this, extend the *bottom* of the cone and then revolve the entire figure until it becomes a *truncated right cone* as illustrated in **Figure 6.8.10**.

Once the cone has been made "whole" in this manner, remove part of the bottom to get the desired shape. As before, the radius of the circle used to develop the cone will be equal to the length of the sloping side of the "whole" cone. This time, however, key points are measured along the radial lines in the side view starting at the *bottom*. Use as many points as necessary to plot a smooth curve in the development. In this example, the cone is unrolled by splitting it at **Point "D."** This represents the centerline in the side view.

Looking at **Point "A,"** you can see how it is located where the cone is still "whole." On the other hand, **Point "G"** is located where the cone has been trimmed the most. Since the trimmed portion is symmetrical, you need only plot **Point "A"** through **Point "G."** Then, the remaining points around the cone will be a mirror image of **Point "B," Point "C,"** and **Point "D."**

As before, *project* these key points in the side view by moving them horizontally until they intersect with the sloping side of the cone. Next, measure the distance from the *bottom* of the cone to each point. Then, transfer this distance to the radial lines on the development. Once all points have been plotted, connect them with a smooth curve to finish the pattern.

Plotting Surface Features

Cone shapes on your models may have surface details and cutouts. If you want to include these details in your patterns, you will need a way to plot the location and outline of each feature during the development process. Fortunately, you have already seen how to do this with truncated and oblique cones by adding radial lines in the side view.

The key to plotting surface features on a cone is adding radial lines to the side view and then transferring them into the developed view.

Plotting surface features, however, requires more than just a handful of reference lines. You can create a *grid* of sorts by adding concentric circles in addition to the radial lines. This will further divide the cone into "bands." An easy way to do this is to draw a series of *horizontal lines* that split the cone into sections in the side view. These lines will then translate into a series of concentric "rings" on the developed pattern as shown in **Figure 6.8.11**.

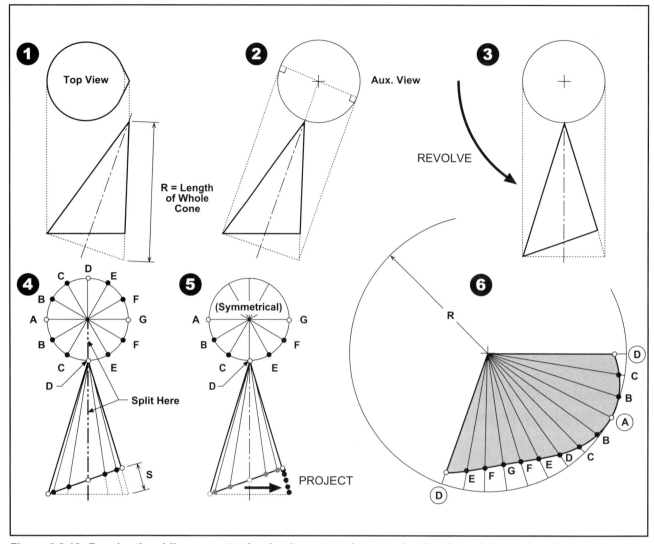

Figure 6.8.10. *Revolve* the oblique cone to develop it as a regular cone that has been truncated on the bottom.

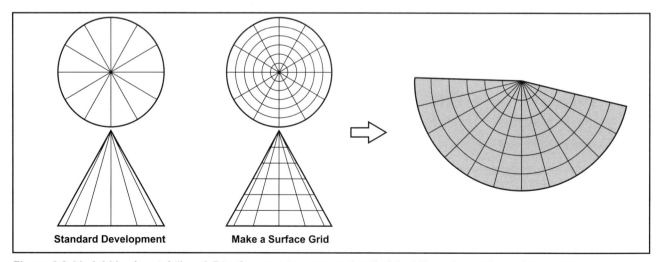

Figure 6.8.11. Add horizontal "bands" to the cone to create a detailed "grid" on the surface of the pattern.

To see a practical application of this technique, look at the space capsule illustrated in **Figure 6.8.12**. Notice how this capsule is shaped like a frustum of a cone. You can see, too, the prominent details and markings on the outer surface of this craft. To end up with useful patterns for this subject, the shape and location of each detail should be included as part of the development.

For example, developed patterns for the markings might be used to make a set of *decals* for this model. Or, if you wished to build this capsule as a 3D model, these patterns could be used to create a *texture map*. In either case, the exterior details can be mapped out by creating a grid on the surface of the cone. Even though this process might get a little complicated, the procedure is still very straightforward. Simply take things one step at a time.

Conical Helix

The conical helix was first discussed in **Section 6.6**. As you have seen, patterns for a *regular helix* are based on a cylinder while the *conical helix* is based on a cone. One way to plot the shape of a conical helix is to create a development of a cone and then map the helix onto it. Assembling this flat pattern will give you the underlying cone shape that defines the form of the conical helix.

The process for mapping out a conical helix is similar to what you have already seen with truncated and oblique cones. The first step is to develop the underlying cone as shown in **Figure 6.8.13**. Next, plot the location of key points along the helix using the side, front, and rear views. Then, transfer these points to the development one at a time. Finally, connect all the points with a smooth curve. Although you may need to plot many different points to map out this shape, the procedure for locating each one is no different than what has already been demonstrated.

Fun With Cones

As mentioned at the beginning of this section, cones are among the most useful shapes for modelers since they are commonly found in all sorts of structures. While it might seem tricky at first to develop patterns for these types of shapes, just remember to take things one step at a time. The job might get easier if you break down the parts as much as possible into the simplest set of basic "building blocks" or components.

Figure 6.8.14 shows a practical example of an object made up almost entirely of cones – the Gemini Space Capsule. While the details in the illustration are somewhat simplified for clarity, you can see how this structure is built from relatively simple components. In fact, most of the shapes involved are frustums of a cone. There is also a short cylinder as well.

Using the techniques outlined in this section, you can make all the patterns you need to build a subject like this from scratch.

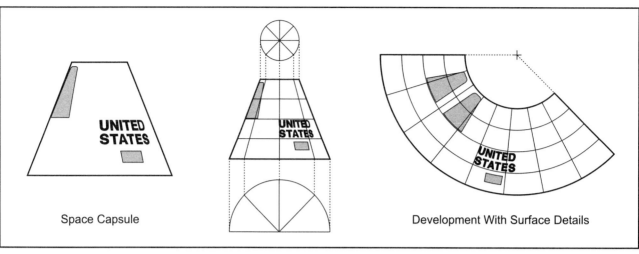

Space Capsule

Development With Surface Details

Figure 6.8.12. Map out the shape and location of surface features by creating a "grid" of radial and horizontal lines.

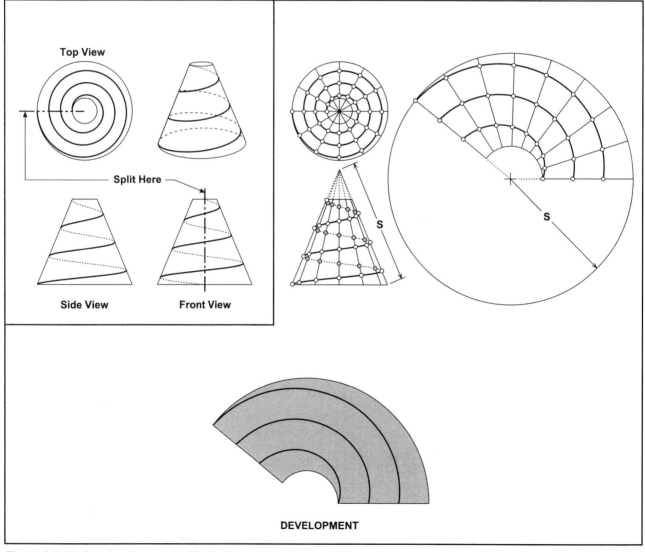

Top View

Split Here

Side View

Front View

S

S

DEVELOPMENT

Figure 6.8.13. Develop the *conical helix* by creating a pattern for a cone and mapping out key points on the surface.

6.9: Pyramids

While pyramids don't have a round base, it's easy to see how similar they are to a cone when seen in the side view. In fact, the process of developing a pyramid is actually quite similar to the process of developing a cone. Fortunately, working with pyramids is even easier. In fact, if you can handle creating patterns for a cone, tackling a pyramid should be a very simple task.

Regular Pyramids

A typical pyramid with a square base is shown in **Figure 6.9.1**. This type of shape is known as a <u>regular pyramid</u>. To create a development for such a pyramid, find the true length of the line representing one of the sloping *corners*. This measurement is labeled "**SL**" (for "slope") in the illustration.

Unfortunately, the corner of a pyramid is represented by an *oblique line*. As a result, this line is nearly always *foreshortened* in every plan view. Therefore, use *revolution* to find the true length of this line as shown. Once you have the correct measurement, you can begin laying out patterns for the pyramid.

Start by labeling each corner of the base of the pyramid in your top plan view as illustrated in **Step 1** of **Figure 6.9.2**. Then, also in the top view, measure the distance along one side of the pyramid from the first corner to the second corner. Label this distance "**S**" (for "side") as shown.

Next, begin creating the development by drawing a large circle just as you did for a cone. In this case, however, the radius of the circle will be equal to "**SL**" as shown in **Step 2** of **Figure 6.9.2**. Now, pick a point on the edge of this circle to act as a starting point. Label this **Point** "**A**" as shown. The exact location does not really matter. Simply pick a point and then label it to correspond with the first corner on the base of your pyramid.

To continue, create a *construction circle* centered on **Point** "**A**." This circle should have a radius equal to "**S**." Use this circle to find the location of the *second* corner of the pyramid (**Point** "**B**") as illustrated in **Step 3** of **Figure 6.9.2**. Repeat this process to plot the remaining corners of the pyramid along the edge of the circle.

Once all the corner points have been plotted, connect them with straight lines as shown in **Step 4** of **Figure 6.9.3**. Finish by drawing *radial lines* from each point back to the center of the circle as shown in **Step 5**. The result will be a complete and accurate pattern for your pyramid.

This method also works when the base of the pyramid is not square. For example, in **Figure 6.9.4** you can see a pyramid with a *rectangular* base. The development is created the same way you would make patterns for a pyramid with a square base. Then, **Figure 6.9.5** shows a *pentagonal* pyramid. The technique for creating these patterns is the same as well.

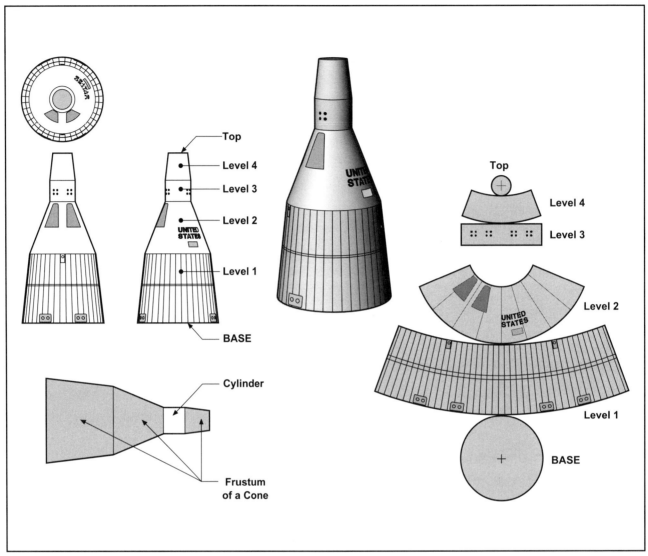

Figure 6.8.14. This space capsule is an example of a model made up of several cone shapes.

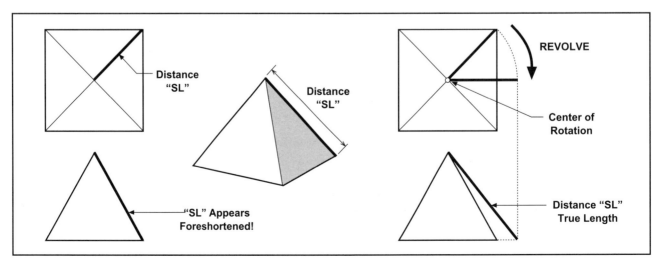

Figure 6.9.1. Developing a pyramid is somewhat similar to developing a cone.

Truncated Pyramids

Just as with a trimmed cone, a pyramid that does not extend all the way to a point is said to be *truncated*. To be technically correct, however, a truncated pyramid is cut at an angle as shown in **Figure 6.9.6**. When the top is parallel to the base, the result is a special shape called a frustum of a pyramid.

If you can develop a regular pyramid, creating patterns for a frustum of a pyramid should be very easy. Just as with a cone, the frustum is simply what is left when you subtract a smaller pyramid from the top of a larger one. The upper pyramid is trimmed away from the "whole" to form the frustum. As a result, in order to create a development for this type of shape, you must develop the "whole" pyramid first.

This process is illustrated in **Figure 6.9.7**. Start by extending the sides of the frustum to a point in the side plan view. Next, use revolution to find the true length of one corner of the whole pyramid. (This distance is labeled "SL_1" in the illustration.) Begin drawing your development by making a circle with a radius equal to "SL_1" and pick a starting point on the edge of this circle. Plot the locations of each bottom corner of the pyramid on this circle just as you would with any regular pyramid. Once these points have been plotted, connect them with the center of the circle by drawing radial lines as shown.

Now, go back to the side plan view. Using revolution, determine the distance from the top of the *frustum* to the tip of the *whole pyramid* as measured along one corner. This distance, labeled "SL_2" in the illustration, will be the same at every corner of the frustum.

With this value in hand, return to the development. Draw a second, smaller circle with a radius equal to "SL_2" and center this smaller circle on the larger one. Next, mark the points where the inner circle intersects with each radial line. By connecting these points, you will know the outline of the area to be removed from the development to create the frustum.

As you can see, dealing with a frustum of a pyramid is very straightforward. Developing patterns for a truncated pyramid is quite similar to this process, but more work is required. Because the top of a truncated pyramid is sloping or *inclined* rather than flat, each corner of the pyramid will be a different length. Therefore, you will have to measure the length of each corner and use this information to plot the location of key points. These points form an outline of the area to be trimmed away from the development of the pyramid.

As before, the development begins with a circle. In this case, however, the distance from the center of the circle to each key point along a radial line will be *different*. Thus, you cannot use a smaller circle to quickly plot the locations of these points. Instead, you must use *revolution* to determine the correct distance between the center of the circle and each key point. This process is illustrated in **Figure 6.9.8**.

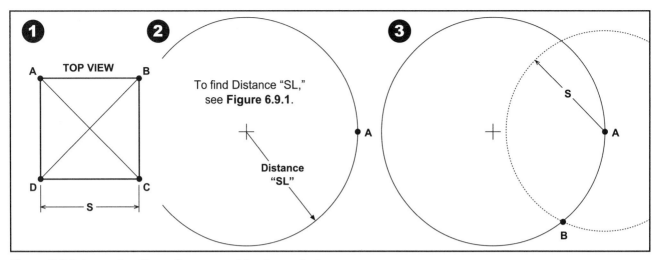

Figure 6.9.2. Lay out patterns for a pyramid using a circle.

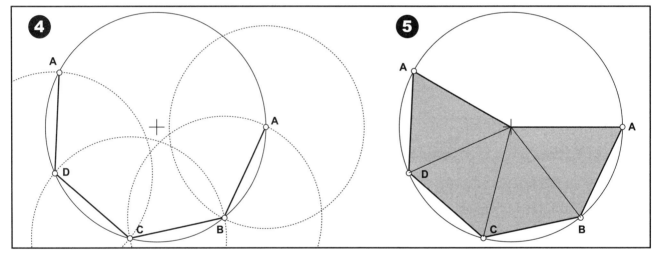

Figure 6.9.3. Connect the plotted points and add radial lines going through the center of the circle.

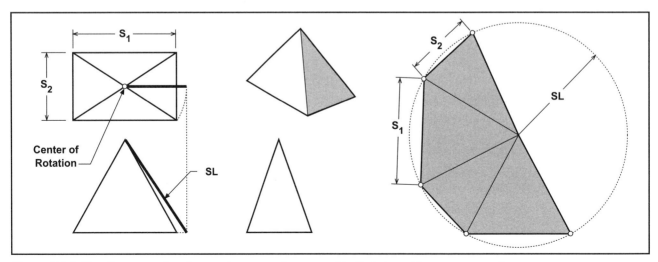

Figure 6.9.4. Use the same development process for pyramids that do not have a square base.

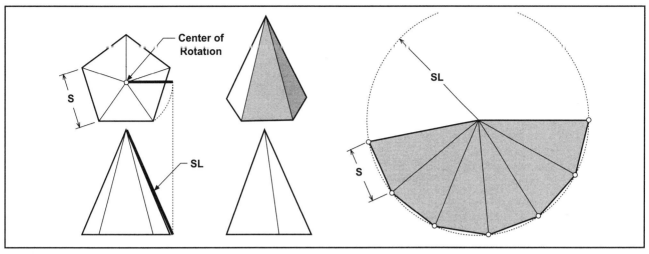

Figure 6.9.5. The same technique works for pyramids with polygonal cross sections such as this pentagonal pyramid.

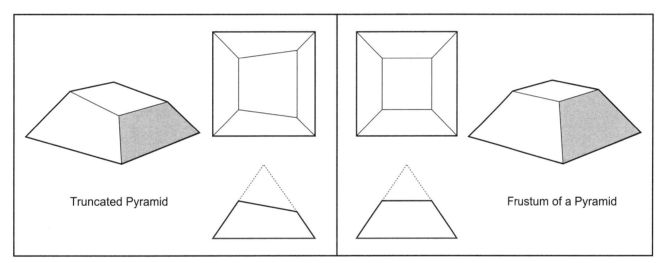

Figure 6.9.6. A *truncated pyramid* has a portion of the top removed.

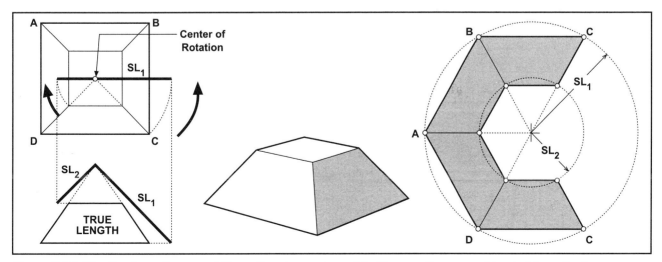

Figure 6.9.7. The *frustum of a pyramid* is really a larger pyramid with a smaller one subtracted from the top.

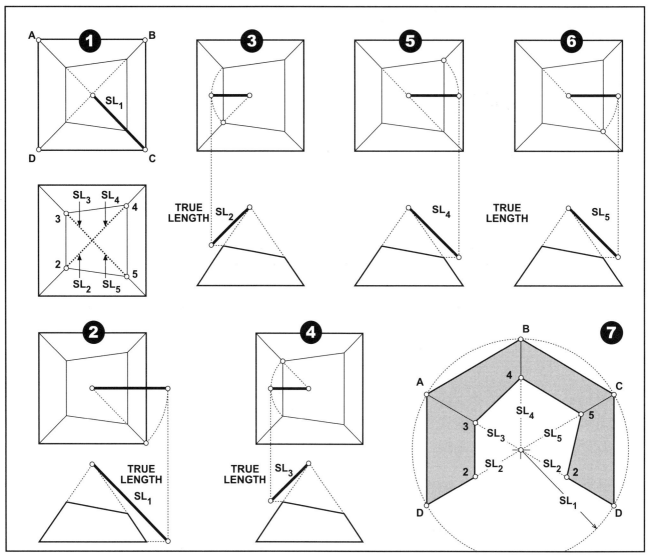

Figure 6.9.8. Developing a *truncated pyramid* involves a little more work.

To begin, carefully label all the parts of the pyramid as shown in **Step 1**. The four corners of the base can be labeled "**A**," "**B**," "**C**," and "**D**."

Next, extend the pyramid to a point just as you did with the frustum of a pyramid. The length of the sloping corner from the tip to the base will be labeled distance "SL_1" just as before. This time, however, also measure the distance from the tip to each corner of the truncated portion on top. These distances will be labeled "SL_2," "SL_3," "SL_4," and "SL_5." Label each corner of the top portion of the pyramid to correspond with these lengths. This means these corners will be labeled "**2**," "**3**," "**4**," and "**5**" respectively.

Now, use revolution to find the true length of "SL_1" as shown in **Step 2** of **Figure 6.9.8**. This process must then be repeated for "SL_2," "SL_3," "SL_4," and "SL_5" as illustrated in **Step 3** through **Step 6**.

Once all these values have been determined, begin creating the development by drawing a large circle. The radius of this circle will be equal to "SL_1" as shown in **Step** 7. Next, pick a starting point along the edge of the circle and mark this **Point** "A." Then, measure the distance along one side of the base of the pyramid. Use this figure to mark off points "**B**," "**C**," and "**D**" just as you would with any regular pyramid.

Connect these points with a series of straight lines. To complete the shape, draw radial lines from the start and end points back to the center of the circle as shown. Finally, plot the locations of points "**2**," "**3**," "**4**," and "**5**" by measuring out from the center point along each radial line. Use distances "SL_2," "SL_3," "SL_4," and "SL_5" to find the correct location of each point. Connect these points together using straight lines. This marks the outline of an area to be *removed* from the overall pattern in order to finish the development as shown.

6.10. Spheres

As previously mentioned in **Section 6.2**, a sphere is made up of compound curves. Thus, it cannot be developed. It is possible, however, to *approximate* the surface of a sphere. The easiest way to do this is by creating a series of *gores* that wrap around the surface. This method is illustrated in **Figure 6.10.1**.

Begin by measuring the *circumference* of the sphere as shown in **Step 1**. Since it appears as a circle in all plan views, measure the diameter of this circle and use it to calculate the circumference. To do this, multiply the diameter times a special *constant* called **Pi**. (For the purposes of this example, you can use the value "**3.14159**" for **Pi**.) Now, take the result and divide it in half. This will be the total length of each gore.

A shortcut is to plot the outline of just one half of a gore and then mirror it. Taking the total length of the gore and dividing it in half, you will get value "D_1" as shown in **Step 1**. Another way to calculate this number is to take one half the *radius* of the sphere and multiply it by **Pi**.

Now, divide the top plan view into *12 equal sections* using radial lines. You can choose to create more or less sections, but this is an excellent place to start. If you want to use a different number, be sure none of the divisions fall at 0 degrees, 90 degrees, 180 degrees, or 270 degrees. You will see why this is necessary in just a moment.

Next, take one quarter of the sphere in the side plan view and divide it into four equal sections using radial lines. This process, shown in **Step 2**, divides a portion of the circumference into equal segments ("D_2"). Now, plot the location where each radial line meets the edge of the sphere. Then, draw horizontal lines from each intersection back across the side view as shown. You have now divided the sphere into a series of "bands" in the side view.

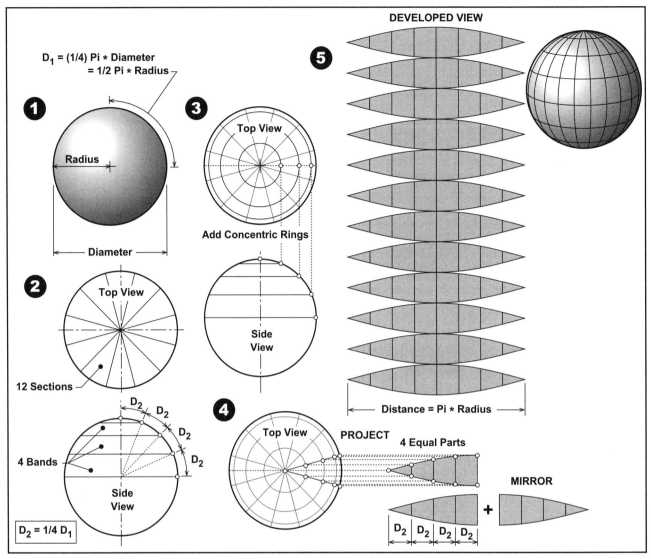

Figure 6.10.1. Developed patterns for a sphere – called "gores" – closely approximate the curved surface.

To divide the gores into sections, you can also measure or calculate the circumference of the sphere and divide this value by 16.

The next step is to plot a series of *concentric circles* in the top view. To do this, take the points in the side view where the horizontal bands meet the edge of the sphere and project them into the top view. This is illustrated in **Step 3**. With the points plotted in the top view, draw concentric circles through them as shown.

You can now begin laying out a pattern for one of the gores as shown in **Step 4**. As you can see, it is most convenient if the centerline of the gore falls on the horizontal centerline of the sphere as seen in the top view. Note how the location of the radial lines drawn in **Step 2** can affect the location of the centerline of the gore.

The developed pattern for the gore will be divided into four equal parts where the length of each part is "D_2" as shown in **Step 4**. To find the *width* of the gore at any point, locate the intersections of the radial lines and the concentric circles in the *top view* and project this information into the developed view as shown. Finish drawing the shape of the gore by creating a smooth curve through all the points. Finally, create a mirror image to form a complete outline of one gore. To complete the sphere, create twelve identical copies of the gore and connect them as shown.

6.11: Polyhedrons

As mentioned in **Section 6.2**, a *polyhedron* is created by assembling simple geometric shapes to form a complex three-dimensional form. If the sides or "facets" of the resulting shape are all identical, it is known as a <u>regular polyhedron</u>. But, all the facets do not have to be identical. Some polyhedrons (or "polyhedra") are made from a variety of different 2D geometric shapes. This makes the resulting objects more challenging to develop.

Of all the possible regular polyhedrons that can exist, there are five special types known as the <u>Platonic solids</u>. These shapes are defined by the fact that the same number of sides or facets always come together at each point or *vertex*. The five Platonic solids are as follows:

- The *Tetrahedron* is a 4-sided figure based on the triangle with 3 triangles at each vertex.
- A *Cube* is a 6-sided figure based on the square with 3 squares at each vertex.
- An *Octahedron* is an 8-sided figure based on the triangle with 4 triangles at each vertex.
- The *Dodecahedron* is a 12-sided figure based on the pentagon where 3 pentagons come together at each vertex.
- An *Icosahedron* is a 20-sided figure based on the triangle with 5 triangles at each vertex.

Polyhedrons can be quite complex. As a result, you might want to evaluate each one on a case-by-case basis. In any event, you will need to figure out the underlying *geometry* of the shape. Unfortunately, this geometry is three-dimensional. This makes it far more difficult to map out a polyhedron than to plot a regular 2D shape. For this reason, you should study the form carefully to help you visualize and "decode" how it goes together.

As you can imagine, this can be quite challenging when you are working strictly in 2D. Since polyhedrons are three-dimensional objects, it may be more helpful to "attack" them using 3D tools. Unfortunately, unless your program has special built-in functions for making these kinds of shapes, building polyhedrons in a 3D modeling application can also be quite tricky. While having 3D tools is nearly always better than working only in 2D, this is one case where having such tools may not provide a quick and easy solution.

In this particular example, twelve gores are needed to complete the entire sphere. Why 12? This was the number of sections chosen to divide the sphere in the top view back in Step 2.

Refer to Figure 6.2.1 for illustrations of the cube, tetrahedron, octahedron, dodecahedron, and icosahedron.

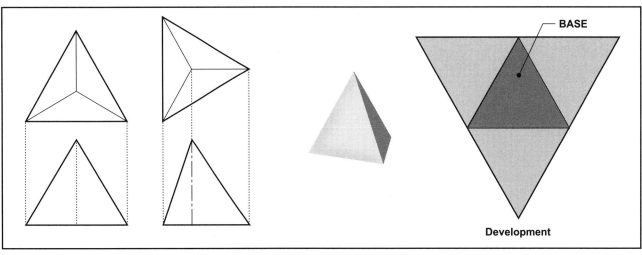

Figure 6.11.1. Create a *tetrahedron* by joining four equilateral triangles.

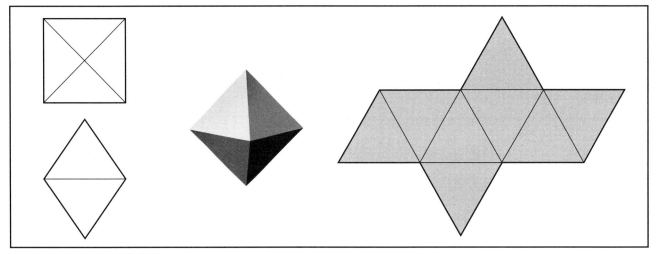

Figure 6.11.2. Assemble an *octahedron* by joining two square-base pyramids.

The two pyramids that make up the octahedron must have a square base.

Tetrahedron

The <u>tetrahedron</u> is one of the simplest polyhedrons. It is made by combining four *equilateral triangles* as shown in **Figure 6.11.1**. This shape is a regular polyhedron because all sides or "facets" are identical. Three of the sides come together to form a point while the fourth makes up the bottom of the shape. The good news is developing patterns for this object is very easy. All you need to know are the dimensions of one of the four equilateral triangles. Then, combine them as shown to make a complete pattern for the tetrahedron.

Octahedron

The <u>octahedron</u> is really just two regular *pyramids* put together as illustrated in **Figure 6.11.2**. This shape is also a regular polyhedron. If you can make patterns for a pyramid, you already know how to handle an octahedron.

Keep in mind, the development of any polyhedron is a flat pattern that can be "folded" into shape. One difference you will notice in creating such patterns for polyhedrons is that they are not arranged in a circular fashion as they are for other shapes such as the basic pyramid. You can still use a circle to plot the sides of the pyramid as already discussed back in **Section 6.9**. In this case, however, the development should be separated into individual panels. These panels can then be arranged to form the octahedron as shown.

Dodecahedron

The dodecahedron is made up of a series of pentagons as illustrated in **Figure 6.11.3**. Three such pentagons come together at each vertex. Keep in mind, this shape is very tricky to build in 3D. Fortunately, you need only figure out the shape of one face of the dodecahedron to make a pattern for it.

Figure 6.11.4 shows a development for a dodecahedron. You might think of this shape as being made up of two "flowers." The "petals" of each flower are made up of pentagons. Notice how the parts are arranged so they can be "folded" to form the dodecahedron.

Icosahedron

The icosahedron is made up of a series of triangles as illustrated in **Figure 6.11.5**. Five triangles come together at each point or vertex. These triangles form what appears to be a three-dimensional pentagon with a pointed "roof." This shape is even more difficult to build than the dodecahedron. The good news is you don't need to figure out complex geometry to make patterns for this particular object. Simply find the dimensions of any triangular face. Once you know the shape of one face, lay out the development as shown in **Figure 6.11.6**.

Other Shapes

The Platonic solids are well documented in geometry texts and courses. You should be able to find plenty of reference information if you wish to study these forms further. That said, what about other shapes? There could be times when you might need a custom object that does not readily match any standard shape. Or, you might want to use a common shape for your project but in a size that is not readily available. In such cases, you may be forced to figure out the geometry yourself in order to build the object.

Take, for example, the rather fancy-looking faceted "globe" illustrated in **Figure 6.11.7**. This complex shape is actually a vintage-style "drawer pull" used in making antique cabinetry. The geometry of this form appears quite complex and difficult to "decode." If you wanted to recreate such a shape from scratch, how could you do it?

There is often more than one arrangement of panels that can be used to make a particular polyhedron. Some shapes can actually be formed in a variety of ways. Try using different combinations and see what happens.

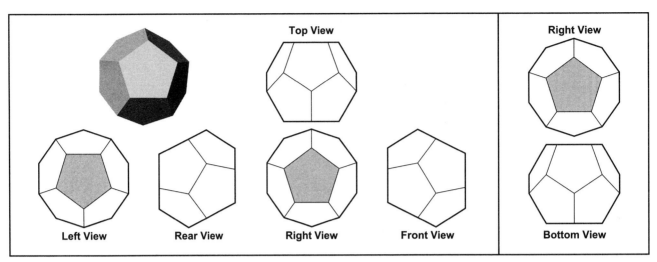

Figure 6.11.3. A *dodecahedron* is created by joining 12 pentagons together.

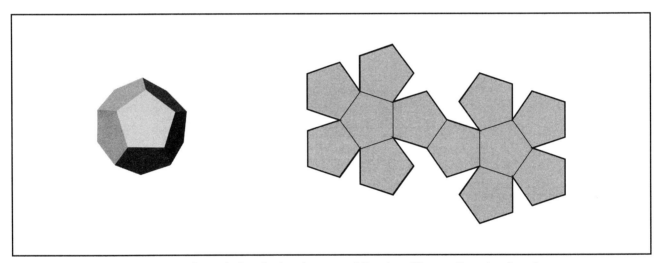

Figure 6.11.4. Create the pattern for a *dodecahedron* by assembling two "flowers" made of pentagons.

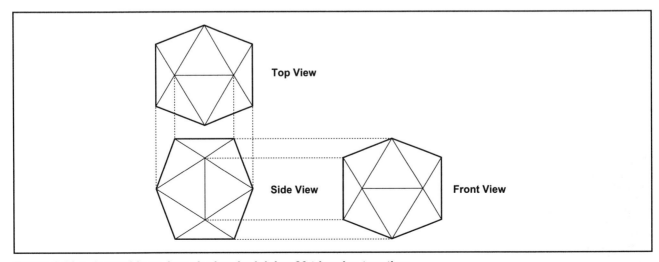

Figure 6.11.5. Assemble an *icosahedron* by joining 20 triangles together.

Begin by carefully analyzing the shape. Try to figure out how it goes together. Faceted shapes like these are often cut from solid material. Depending on your skills and equipment, this may or may not be a practical operation. (Of course, if you wanted to build this shape using a 3D computer program, traditional milling would not even be an option.) Even if you do decide to cut such a shape, you will still need to know every one of the angles involved.

How can these angles be determined? Imagine this shape is contained inside a *sphere* that is divided into "zones" as shown in **Figure 6.11.8**. You can accomplish this by drawing horizontal lines in the side view. Think of each line as a *cutting plane* that "slices" through the object. If you then look at the top plan view with this idea in mind, you can begin to visualize the *cross section* of the shape at each level.

This cross section information provides a practical way to map out the shape of this complex polyhedron and then create patterns for it. As it turns out, each cross section is a "multigon" that is arranged in a specific orientation relative to all the others. Imagine drawing these multigons and then moving them up or down in 3D space so they are arranged in the correct vertical position relative to one another. By doing this, you will have marked the locations of all the vertices of this polyhedron.

As you can see, the information needed to build this object includes the distances between the cutting planes that divide the shape into different zones in the side view, as well as the corresponding cross section at each "level." If you can draw all these outlines plus create a side view showing the correct vertical location of each cross section, you will be able to build this object in a 3D modeling program. From there, you can produce patterns for each facet or "face" of the object. These facets can then be cut and folded into shape.

Because the word "polygon" has a special meaning in 3D modeling, the term "multigon" is used in this book to describe certain two-dimensional geometric shapes.

Solving these types of problems requires working with three-dimensional geometry. This can be quite a bit more complicated than solving 2D geometry problems. As you can imagine, having access to 3D tools can be very helpful in these situations.

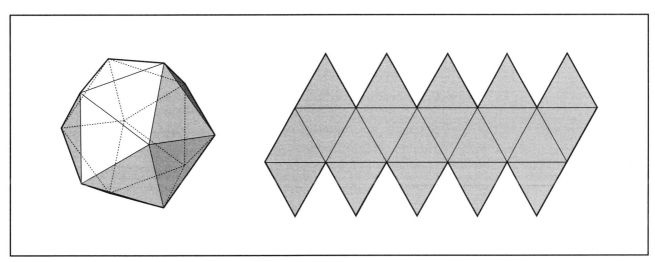

Figure 6.11.6. Create a pattern for the *icosahedron* by laying out the triangles in a grid.

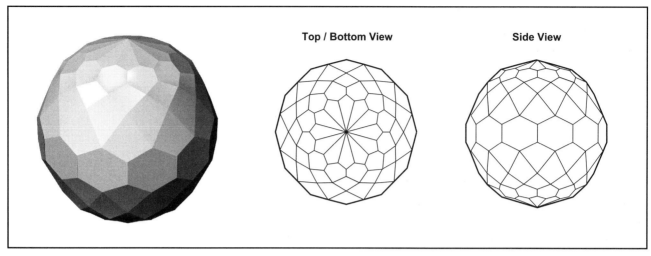

Figure 6.11.7. A "custom" polyhedron can involve complex, three-dimensional geometry or "architecture."

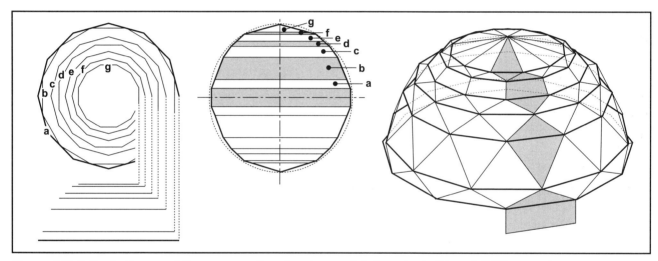

Figure 6.11.8. Try to figure out the *cross section* at various points in order to "decode" 3D geometry.

Science fiction modelers may recognize the object in **Figure 6.11.7** as part of a famous, fictional spaceship design.

To do this, draw the cross section outlines for this object in 2D. Then, import these outlines along with the side view template into a 3D modeling program. Use the side view template to arrange the cross section outlines relative to each other in the vertical axis. Finally, all that remains is to play "connect the dots" in order to create each facet that makes up the object.

If you are unable to work in 3D, it is still possible to map out complex shapes such as this one. The process, however, becomes more tedious. One approach is to employ *revolution* to figure out the dimensions of each facet – one surface at a time. To do this, *revolve* the entire object until a facet is parallel with one of the plan views. Or, you can create an *auxiliary view* to find the true shape of any facet. Fortunately, the surfaces that make up this object are symmetrical and they repeat over and over again. You therefore need only figure out a portion of the object in order to map out the entire shape.

As you can imagine, this process can be time consuming. With the basic techniques presented in this book, however, you will have all the tools you need to break down a complex object like this and figure out the individual parts. Once again, take things one step at a time.

6.12: Summary

Models are often constructed using basic, three-dimensional shapes. In many cases, these shapes can be "unfolded" or "unrolled" to make flat patterns or parts from sheet stock. Such patterns, called *developments*, can then be assembled to build the desired shape. While it is not possible to create a development for any object that has compound curves, it is sometimes possible to *approximate* such a surface using flat patterns.

Understanding how to make construction patterns for geometric shapes becomes much easier when you are familiar with basic 3D modeling concepts. The most basic method for creating a three-dimensional shape is known as *extruding*. This technique applies only to objects that have a constant cross section. Some objects with a non-constant cross section can be created by a similar process called *lofting*. Other shapes can be formed by *revolving*, a process that duplicates the real world technique of shaping objects on a lathe.

A *box* has six sides that can be unfolded to create a development much like the process used to create multiple views via orthographic projection.

To develop a *cylinder*, first determine the exact shape of each end and then "unroll" the middle portion.

A *helix* is a spiral-like shape that exists in three dimensions. This type of shape can be formed either by wrapping a sloping line around a cylinder or by projecting a spiral onto a cone.

A *prism* is just a box, but its cross section does not have to be square.

The development of a *cone* looks like a pie with one or more pieces missing. Cones can be developed graphically or by using mathematical formulas to find some of the key dimensions needed.

Developing a *pyramid* is very similar to the process of developing a cone.

A *sphere* cannot be developed because it has compound curves. A flat pattern can be made, however, that *approximates* the surface of a sphere. In this process, a series of panels called *gores* are mapped out.

Polyhedrons are complex geometric shapes formed by joining numerous two-dimensional panels or "facets" to create a complete object. Five basic types of polyhedrons are known as the *Platonic solids*. The development of these solids results in a pattern of individual panels that, when joined together, can be "folded" into the correct shape.

Custom objects can also be created by "decoding" their three-dimensional geometry. This process can be much easier if 3D tools are available to assist you in your efforts.

What's Next?

As you have seen, the process of creating developments is a very valuable skill for all modelers to master. This process can come in very handy in many different ways.

The next and last chapter covers some of the more challenging situations you may encounter when attempting to create construction patterns for your projects. For example, simple objects can be *combined* in many different ways. Where two objects meet, an *intersection* results. Sometimes a *transition* must be created between two different shapes. Both situations can complicate the development process quite a bit. Therefore, techniques for dealing with these scenarios will be presented in detail.

NOTES

Topics in This Chapter:

Chapter 7

Transitions and Intersections

7.1: Overview

As you have seen, creating developments can be tricky, but the process is fairly straightforward. If all possible subjects were built using only the basic shapes already discussed, modeling them would be fairly easy. But, as you know, many subjects are not quite so simple.

Now that you have seen how to make developments, all that remains is learning some "tricks" that can help you deal with more challenging situations. Some of these scenarios will be covered here in the last chapter of this volume.

For example, shapes can be *combined* in a variety of ways. When this occurs, you may need to create a transition that connects one part or structure with another different shape. An example of this scenario is illustrated in **Figure 7.1.1**. In other cases, two parts come together to form an intersection as shown in **Figure 7.1.2**.

Both these scenarios can make the pattern-making process more difficult. In this chapter, you will see different techniques for dealing with these situations. By the time you master the advanced topics outlined here, you should have all the skills you need to make basic patterns for just about any project.

7.2: Transitions

A *transition* is a form or shape that starts out having one cross section and then transitions to another. This type of assembly is used in modeling to connect parts that have different shapes. A round tube, for example, might be "plugged into" a square base or vice versa as shown in **Figure 7.2.1**. As you can see from the illustration, this requires a special transition assembly that can join both parts together.

If you recall, examples of transitional shapes were shown in **Chapter 5** where the design of a boat hull was demonstrated. Such transitions may not lend themselves well to the process of development, meaning these shapes cannot always be "unfolded" or "flattened." This is nearly always the case for structures that have compound curves. Sometimes, however, a transition *can*

NOTE: Underlined terms appear in the Glossary.

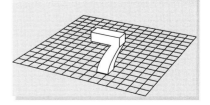

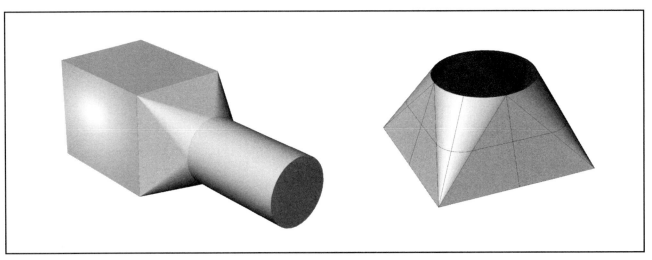

Figure 7.1.1. Create a *transition* assembly to join two parts that have different cross sections.

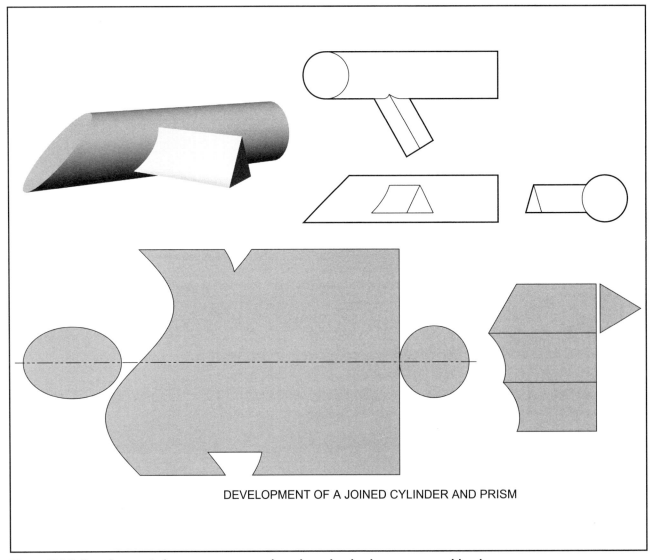

DEVELOPMENT OF A JOINED CYLINDER AND PRISM

Figure 7.1.2. Developments become more complex when simple shapes are combined.

be developed. When this happens, a modeler will need to know how to make patterns for the resulting parts.

As you can imagine, transitions can be tricky to develop. The easiest way to handle these types of shapes is to use a 3D modeling program. If your software can create developments, you can easily build a complex part in the computer and let the program do all the hard work of determining the correct patterns.

One way to build a transition is by *lofting*. This allows you to specify a cross section at two or more points. Unlike *extruding*, where the finished shape has a constant cross section, a lofted object can have many different cross sections along its length. This concept is illustrated in **Figure 7.2.1**.

To create this type of shape as a computer model, start by drawing the first cross section. Then, draw the second cross section. Center both outlines on

Not all 3D modeling programs can create developments.

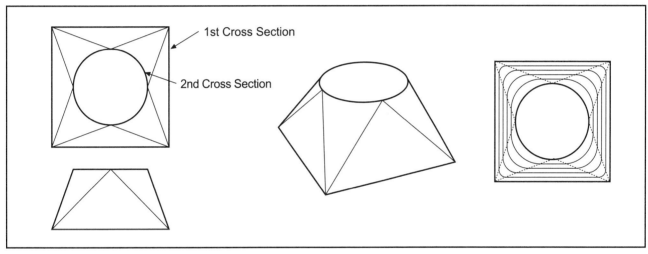

Figure 7.2.1. This example block allows for a transition from one cross section to another within the same assembly.

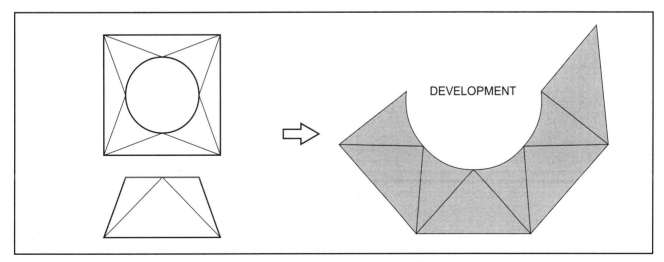

Figure 7.2.2. The simplest way to create transition shapes is by using a 3D modeling program.

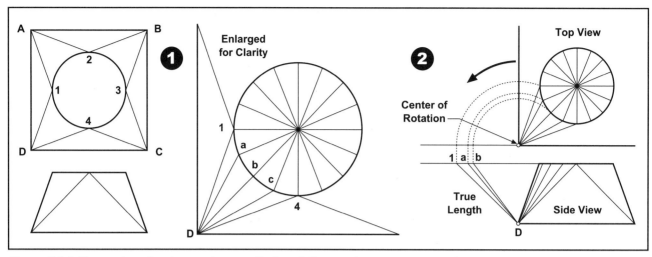

Figure 7.2.3. To create a development manually, break the part into segments and use revolution.

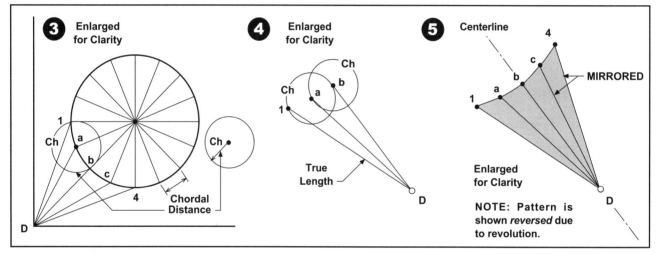

Figure 7.2.4. After finding the true length of each segment, use the *chordal distance* to determine proper spacing.

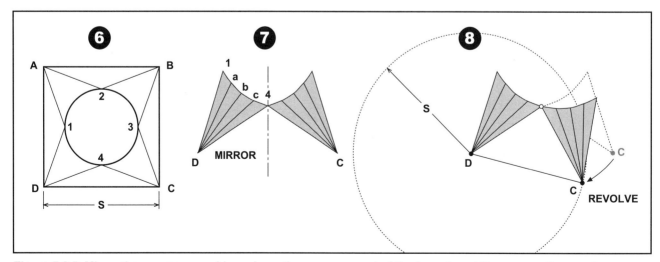

Figure 7.2.5. Mirror the corner assembly and use the measurement of the base to set the proper alignment.

each other and space them an appropriate distance apart. Next, activate the "Loft" command or function and select both cross section outlines. If you specify you want the resulting surface to be "developable," your program may be able to create the construction patterns for you. If this function is available, you will be able to *unfold* or *unroll* the resulting surface to get your development. As an example, finished patterns for a simple transition block are shown in **Figure 7.2.2**. Now, wasn't that easy?

If you don't have access to these kinds of 3D tools, you will need to find a way to make patterns for such transitions manually. One method is to divide the shape into many different sections or *segments*. These can then be combined to approximate the correct shape. Keep in mind, since the transition must be made from flat parts, the resulting shapes cannot have perfectly smooth, compound curves. You could, however, build a *segmented* shape and then smooth it out by sanding and puttying over the finished form.

As an example, a transition from a round hole to a square base is fairly straightforward. To do this, break the patterns into segments at each corner where the transition will occur as shown in **Figure 7.2.3**. The corners of the square base should be numbered. Each segment can then be labeled where its border intersects with the edge of the circular cross section.

Look at the segmented shape in the side plan view. Note how the portions in each corner resemble parts of a developed *cone*. It's not hard to see how the transition at each corner is somewhat similar to an *oblique cone*. You can use this fact to create suitable patterns for this type of part.

Start by determining the true length of the lines between the segments using *revolution*. This requires revolving the lines in the *top view* and projecting them into the *side view* as shown in **Figure 7.2.3**. Each line is labeled according to its end points. These lines go from **Point "D"** to "1," "a," "b," "c," "d," or "4." Thus, these distances can be labeled "D_1," "D_a," "D_b," "D_c," and "D_4." If you look closely, you will see that **Line "D_1"** is the same length as **Line "D_4"** and **Line "D_c"** is the same length as **Line "D_a."** Therefore, you can skip the process of revolving **Line "D_c"** and **Line "D_4."**

Now, measure the *chordal distance* on the circle between each line in the top view as illustrated in **Step 3** of **Figure 7.2.4**. You can use a construction circle to do this. (This circle is labeled "**Ch**" for "chordal distance" in the example.) Begin your development by positioning all the segment lines that were found true length. Each line will start at the same point ("D") and radiate outward. The points on the opposite end of each line will be spaced apart by the chordal distance you just measured. The process of laying out the segment lines in this manner is illustrated in **Step 4**.

Since **Line "D_1"** is the same length as **Line "D_4"** and **Line "D_c"** is the same length as **Line "D_a,"** lay out Lines "D_1," "D_a," and "D_b," and then create a

A program of choice for this type of operation is called *Rhinoceros*, also known as *Rhino 3D*.

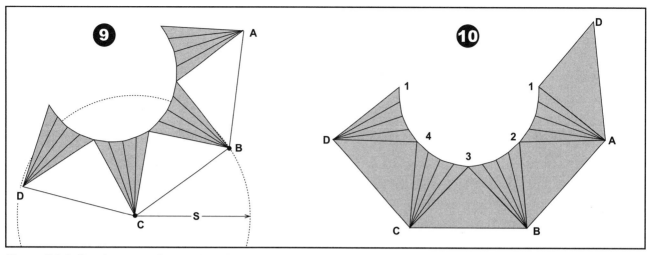

Figure 7.2.6. Continue creating copies of each part and align them to form a complete assembly.

mirror image of "D_1" and "D_a" to create Segments "D_4" and "D_c." This is shown in **Step 5**. Finally, connect the ends of the segment lines to form a complete outline.

Once you have completed these steps, you will have a pattern for *one corner* of the transition shape. Fortunately, since this block is symmetrical, you need only develop one corner plus one side. You can then duplicate these sections to form complete patterns for the entire assembly.

The next step is to begin laying out a *triangle* shape that lies in between each corner. This process is illustrated in **Figure 7.2.5**. Measure **Distance "S"** along one side of the square cross section of the block as shown in **Step 6**. This will be the distance between Points "D" and "C" on the transition block. Use this distance to lay out one half of the entire block.

Now, create a mirror image of the corner assembly and connect these two sections together at the top as shown in **Step 7**. Keep in mind, however, this will *not* be the correct orientation of the two sections in relation to one another. To orient them correctly, draw a construction circle with a radius equal to "S." Use this circle to find the correct spacing between Points "C" and "D" as shown in **Step 8**.

You have now mapped out two complete corner assemblies along with the triangle-shaped panel that connects them. Duplicate these parts as necessary and align each copy using the same construction circle just as you did before. By aligning the parts as shown in **Figure 7.2.6**, you will end up with a pattern for the entire transition part.

The same basic method can be used to develop transitions for a variety of other shapes as well. Just be sure to divide the part into *segments*, working out the true length for each in turn. Remember, take it one step at a time.

7.3: Intersections

You have now seen how a transition can be fabricated to join two parts with different cross sections. Sometimes, however, your structure will incorporate two or more shapes that come together without such a transition.

The joining of two similar or dissimilar shapes results in an *intersection*. Some of the biggest pattern-making challenges can occur when two or more shapes interact with each other in such a manner. An illustration of this problem was shown in **Figure 7.1.2**. For example, you might find it relatively easy to develop construction patterns for a simple cylinder. On the other hand, when that cylinder is combined with a *prism* as shown, the process of developing patterns for it becomes much more difficult.

In fact, creating developments for shapes that intersect can be one of the most difficult and challenging tasks you might encounter when making patterns for your projects. Unfortunately, even simple shapes can become complicated when they start interacting with other shapes.

You may find it helpful to try and visualize each situation. Imagine the intersection as a *three-dimensional line* created where two surfaces meet. Just like an object, this line exists in three-dimensional space. As a result, it can be *projected* to any plan view. When the line appears in a plan view, it becomes a two-dimensional representation of a three-dimensional *curve*.

The line of intersection defines the outline of an area that must be *removed* from one part in order for it to fit against another part. When making construction patterns, you will need to know exactly how much to remove from each part in order to achieve a proper fit.

In this section, a number of different example intersections will be shown. This will give you a general feel for what these intersections might look like. In most cases, the needed patterns can be determined using many of the techniques already presented in this book. These include *projection*, *revolution*, and the creation of *auxiliary views*. The exact technique(s) needed, however, will vary from one situation to another.

Plotting intersections is a great example of a task that becomes much easier when using a 3D modeling program. Computer software can easily determine exactly what your parts will look like when joined together. As a result, using 3D tools can save you a lot of time and effort. After all, why not let the computer do the "heavy lifting" for you? With a 3D model acting as a *template*, making plan view drawings of intersections becomes quite easy. In fact, some programs will even make the plan view drawings for you.

If you recall the discussion in **Chapter 6**, 3D objects can be formed by *extruding*, *lofting*, or *revolving*. Once these shapes are built in a 3D modeling application, you can move them into position relative to one another, and the

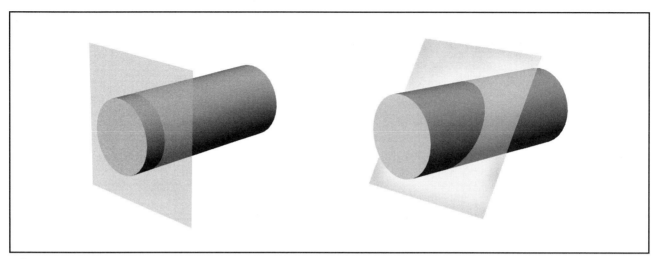

Figure 7.3.1. The intersection between a plane and a cylinder will either be a *circle* or an *ellipse*.

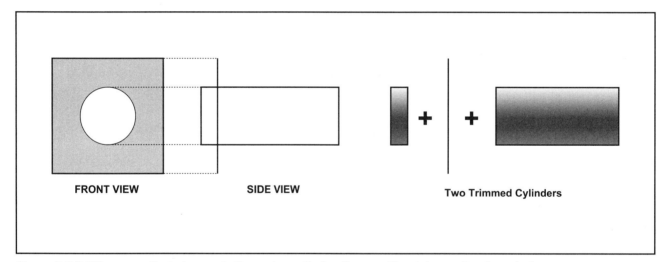

Figure 7.3.2. When a vertical plane cuts through a cylinder, the resulting intersection is a *circle*.

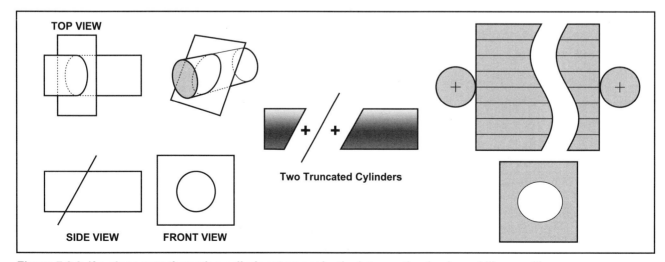

Figure 7.3.3. If a plane cuts through a cylinder at an angle, the intersection is shaped like an *ellipse*.

program will show you exactly how they look when combined. You may even be able to use 3D tools to extract perfect developments from the combined objects. The concepts, tools, and techniques for doing this will be discussed in detail in **Volume 2** of this series.

Plane and Cylinder

A plane can pass through a cylinder to "slice" it. This may create a *truncated cylinder* as illustrated in **Figure 7.3.1**. Depending on the angle of the plane as it slices through the cylinder, the resulting intersection will be either a *circle* or an *ellipse*. When the plane is perpendicular to the cylinder, it simply divides the shape into two smaller cylinders as illustrated in **Figure 7.3.2**. In this case, the intersection is merely a circle where the diameter is equal to the height of the cylinder.

In **Figure 7.3.3**, you can see how an angled cutting plane slices through a cylinder to create two smaller, truncated cylinders. You have already seen examples of developments for this type of shape. Plot the outline of the trimmed end by creating an auxiliary view. Then unroll the object.

Plane and Cone

A plane can pass through or "slice" a cone in two different ways. When the plane is parallel with the base of the cone, it divides the cone into two parts. One part is a smaller cone while the other part is a *frustum of a cone*. The intersection is simply a circle as illustrated in **Figure 7.3.4**.

All the information you need to create patterns for this situation is available in the plan views. In fact, the pattern for both the plane and the intersection can be found directly in the top plan view. Use the techniques outlined in **Chapter 6** to make the construction patterns for the resulting shapes.

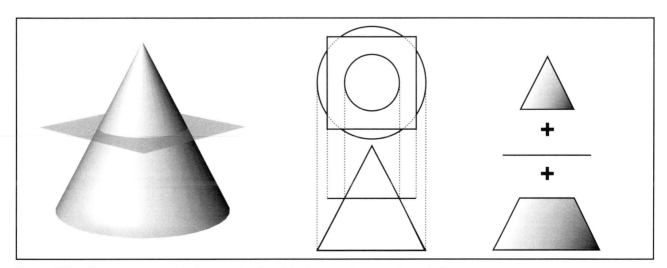

Figure 7.3.4. The intersection between a horizontal plane and a cone is a *circle*.

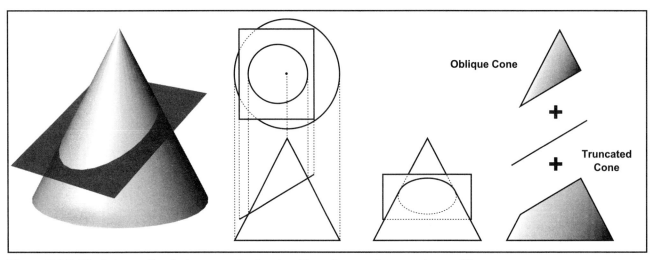

Figure 7.3.5. The intersection between an inclined cutting plane and a cone is an *ellipse*.

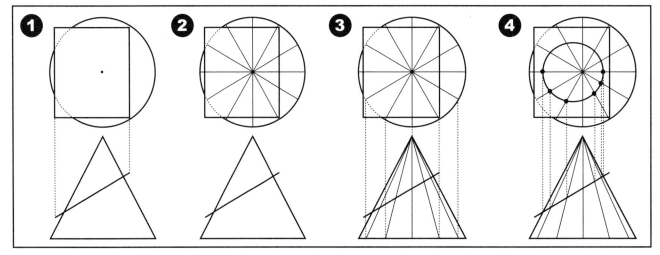

Figure 7.3.6. Add radial lines to the cone. Then, use projection to find the outline of the ellipse in the top view.

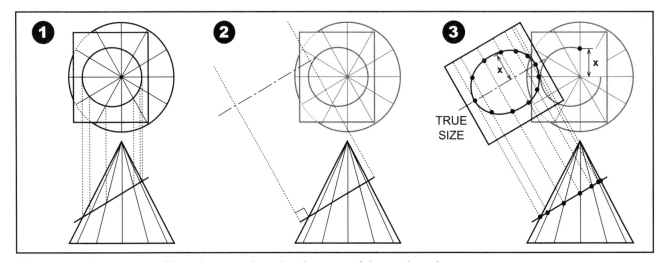

Figure 7.3.7. Create an auxiliary view to make a development of the cutting plane.

If a plane slices all the way through the cone at an angle, the intersection is an *ellipse* as shown in **Figure 7.3.5**. The plane divides the cone to create an *oblique cone* on top and a *truncated cone* below. You have already seen how to develop the patterns for both shapes in **Chapter 6**.

Finding the outline of the intersection in this situation involves creating an auxiliary view. To do this, start by drawing the outline of the ellipse in the top plan view. If the *edge* of the plane can be seen in the side view, plotting the shape of the ellipse in the top view is very straightforward.

Draw both the cone and the plane in plan view form as illustrated in **Step 1** of **Figure 7.3.6**. Divide the top plan view of the cone into *sections* using a series of *radial lines* as shown in **Step 2**. (This is very similar to what you would do when creating a development of a cone. It's up to you to decide how many lines you need.)

Next, project the radial lines into the side view as illustrated in **Step 3** of **Figure 7.3.6**. Find the intersection of each radial line in the side view with the *edge of the plane*. Then, project this information back into the top view as shown in **Step 4**. You can now plot the outline of the ellipse as it appears in the top view.

Keep in mind, since both the plane and the intersection (i.e. the ellipse) appear *foreshortened* in the top view, the outline you just plotted is *not* a true size pattern for the intersection. To find the true shape, create an auxiliary view. This process is illustrated in **Figure 7.3.7**.

As you can imagine, when the plane is either parallel or perpendicular to one or more plan views, the process of plotting the intersection is fairly straightforward. On the other hand, if the plane is *oblique* to the plan views, the task of plotting the intersection becomes much more challenging.

One method for dealing with this situation is to create both a horizontal and vertical *cutting plane* and pass them through *both* the cone and the oblique plane at the same time. By repositioning these cutting planes, you can plot points along the intersection of both surfaces. This technique is illustrated in **Figure 7.3.8**.

To begin, draw a line representing the vertical cutting plane in the top view as shown in **Step 1** of **Figure 7.3.8**. Make sure this line extends all the way through the cone and intersects with the oblique plane in two different locations as shown.

Next, draw the horizontal cutting plane (also shown in **Step 1** of **Figure 7.3.8**). This appears as a horizontal line in the side view. Position this line so it overlaps the oblique plane. By positioning both the horizontal and vertical cutting planes in the area where the cone and oblique plane intersect, you can plot points along the intersection between the two objects.

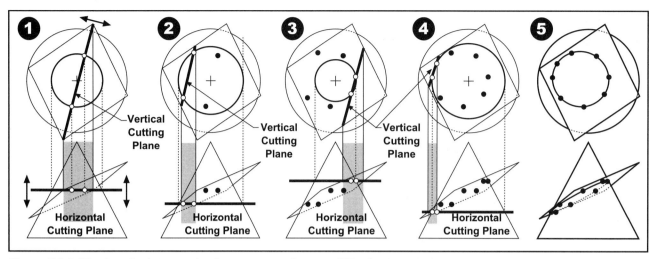

Figure 7.3.8. Plotting the intersection becomes much more difficult when the plane is oblique to the plan views.

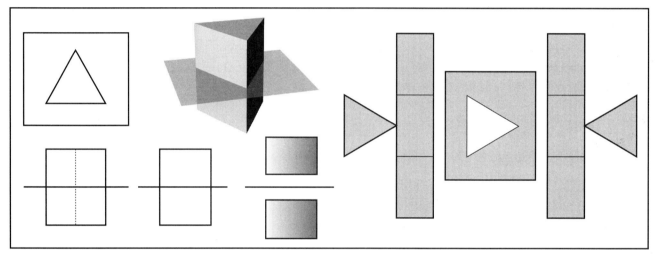

Figure 7.3.9. Calculate patterns for the intersection of a horizontal plane and a triangular prism from the plan views.

As you have already seen, the intersection between a horizontal cutting plane and a cone is a *circle* in the top plan view. Project the intersection of the horizontal cutting plane and the cone into the top plan view and draw this circle as shown.

Now, find two points where the line representing the vertical cutting plane intersects with the *circle* you just created in the top view. Project these points down into the side view. These will be two points along the intersection between the cone and the oblique plane.

Congratulations! You have just found two points along the desired intersection. Still, there is a bit more work to do for this is not quite enough to draw the entire shape. To find more points, *re-position* both the horizontal and vertical cutting planes and repeat the process. Place the cutting planes anywhere you want as long as you keep both planes within the area where the cone and oblique plane overlap. This process is illustrated in **Step 2** through **Step 4** of **Figure 7.3.8**.

By now, you will have found eight different points along the desired intersection. This should be enough to draw the correct shape in both the side and top plan views. Create a smooth curve connecting all points as shown in **Step 5** of **Figure 7.3.8**. This will be the intersection between the objects.

Unfortunately, this outline is foreshortened in both views. The true size pattern must therefore be found by creating an auxiliary view just as before. This is very difficult, however, because the oblique plane is not seen as an edge in any view. As a result, you will have to use *revolution* to revolve both objects until the oblique plane can be seen as an edge.

Once that is done, the procedure becomes the same as that already shown in **Figure 7.3.7**. Of course, had you done this to begin with, you could have found the intersection much faster. As it is, however, you have now seen how to plot the intersections in both situations.

Plane and Box or Plane and Prism

The intersection between a plane and a prism is illustrated in **Figure 7.3.9**. This situation is quite similar to the intersection between a plane and a cylinder. In this case, however, the prism does not have a circular cross section. Still, most of the information you need will be found in one or more plan views. To plot the intersection, project key points from one view to another as you fill in the details.

This is very easy when the cutting plane is horizontal. In this event, it divides the prism into two smaller prisms. Since the cutting plane is at a right angle to each prism, these are regular prisms, and they can be developed accordingly.

On the other hand, things get a little more difficult when the plane is at an angle relative to the prism as illustrated in **Figure 7.3.10**. When this happens, the plane creates two *truncated* prisms as shown. To find the patterns for all parts in this situation, use the techniques for developing an oblique and/or truncated prism.

As you have already seen, things are easiest when the plane can be seen at its *edge* in one of the plan views. If this is not the case in your particular situation, try using revolution to re-align the assemblies. When that is not feasible, you can still plot the intersection, but more work will be required.

If the intersecting plane is *oblique* to the plan views, you will need to create a *cutting plane* as shown in **Figure 7.3.11**. This process is similar to what you saw with an oblique plane and a cone. The difference in this case, however, is that only one cutting plane is used. This cutting plane is *vertical* and is arranged *parallel* to each face of the prism in the top view as shown.

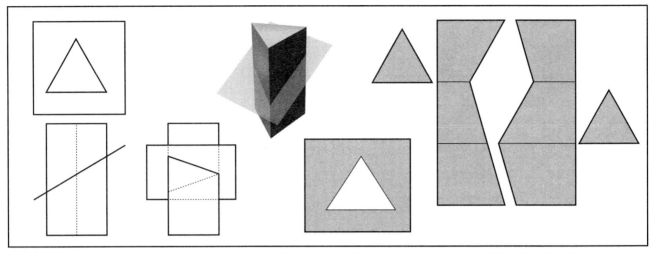

Figure 7.3.10. If the cutting plane intersects the prism at an angle, patterns are a more difficult to develop.

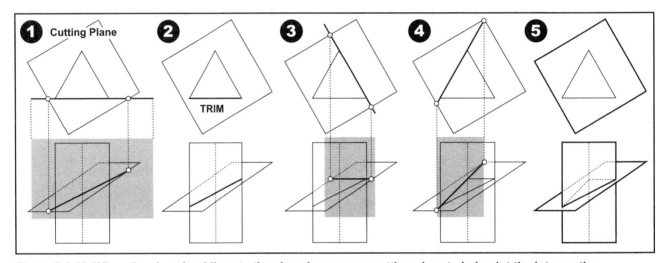

Figure 7.3.11. When the plane is *oblique* to the plan views, use a *cutting plane* to help plot the intersection.

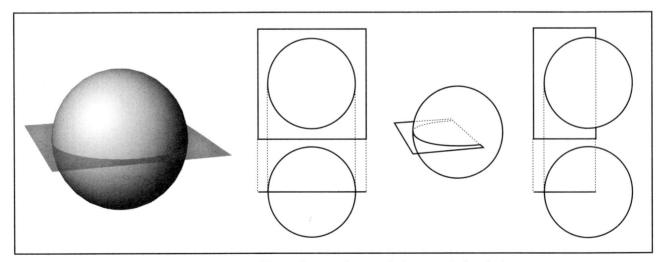

Figure 7.3.12. A horizontal plane intersects with a sphere to form a circle or part of a circle.

To begin, draw the plane and prism in plan view form. Even though you do not know the location of the intersection yet, you can still plot the outlines of both shapes. Next, create the cutting plane by drawing a line in the top view. Make this line parallel with one face of the prism and align it so the line overlaps one side as shown in **Step 1** of **Figure 7.3.11**.

Now, find two points where this cutting plane intersects the oblique plane in the *top view* and project these points into the side view. This is also illustrated in **Step 1**. Draw a line connecting these points. Then, trim it so any portions falling outside the outline of the prism are eliminated as shown in **Step 2**.

Repeat this process as shown in **Step 3** and **Step 4**. In each case, align the cutting plane so it is parallel with and overlaps one side of the prism in the top view. By the time you have done this once for each side of the prism, the intersection will be plotted as shown in **Step 5**.

Plane and Sphere

As seen in **Figure 7.3.12**, the intersection between a horizontal plane and a sphere is a *circle*. If the plane appears as an *edge* in one or more plan views, the process of finding this intersection will be very easy.

When the plane is horizontal (or vertical), the intersection will be either a circle or part of a circle. The actual results will depend on the size of the plane. If it is larger than the sphere, the intersection will be a complete circle.

On the other hand, when a plane intersects a sphere at an *angle*, the resulting intersection will appear as an *ellipse* in the plan view (see **Figure 7.3.13**). If you look carefully, however, you may notice the ellipse does not appear to be symmetrical. Instead, the outline is more egg-shaped. In this case, it almost looks as if one end of the ellipse has been "squashed."

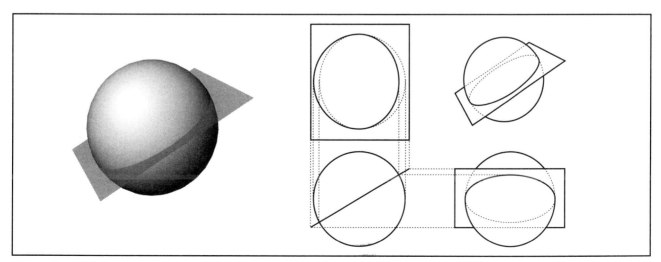

Figure 7.3.13. An angled plane intersects with a sphere to form a *distorted ellipse*.

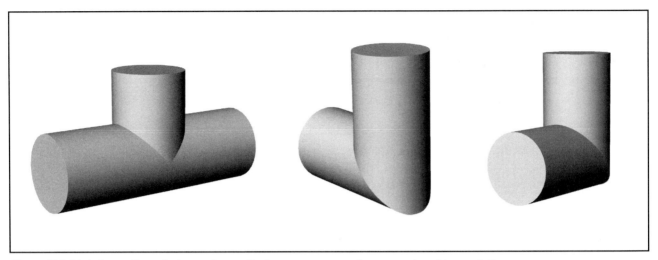

Figure 7.3.14. Intersections between two cylinders are commonly encountered in modeling.

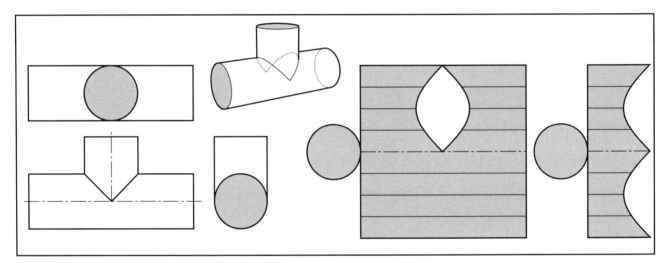

Figure 7.3.15. Create a "tee" intersection by *truncating* one cylinder while *notching* the other.

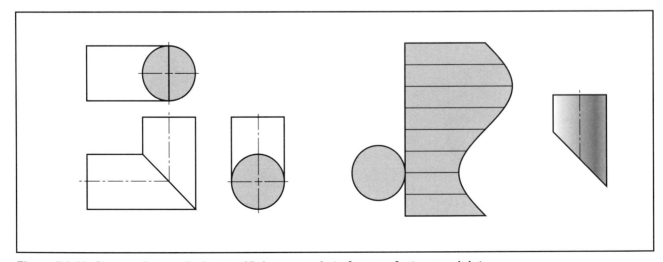

Figure 7.3.16. Cut or *miter* a cylinder at a 45-degree angle to form perfect corner joints.

Two Cylinders

Intersections between two cylinders are very common when making models. For example, this type of intersection might be found where two round *pipes* come together as shown in **Figure 7.3.14**. One cylinder can be truncated and the other notched to form a "tee" intersection as illustrated in **Figure 7.3.15**. Two cylinders can also be truncated or "mitered" at a 45-degree angle to form a corner connection as shown in **Figure 7.3.16**.

The first step in creating patterns for these situations is to determine the appropriate shape of the intersection. Since cylinders are circular in cross section, there are a limited number of possibilities. In most cases, you will be *truncating* the cylinders in one way or another. You have already seen how to make patterns for this type of object.

If you look closely, however, you may notice that joined cylinders often must be cut to form a "pointed" end. To handle these situations, simply *split* the cylinder into two *half-rounds* and truncate the end of each at a 45-degree angle. This process is illustrated in **Figure 7.3.17**. Once you have created developments for each truncated half round, join them together again. By breaking the parts into more basic components in this manner, the development process becomes much easier.

The mating half to a cylinder with a pointed end is another cylinder with a *notch* cut into it. Again, think in terms of breaking the parts down into smaller pieces that are easier to handle. As an example, the cylinder to be notched can be divided into two half-rounds as shown. The upper half-round is then further divided into two equal parts while the lower half-round remains intact. Truncate one end of each upper part to form one half of the notch. Finally, assemble the developments of all three sections to create a pattern for the complete notched cylinder.

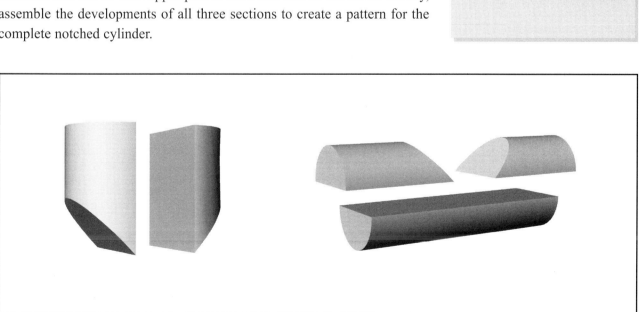

Figure 7.3.17. Split cylinders into half-rounds when needed to make the development process easier.

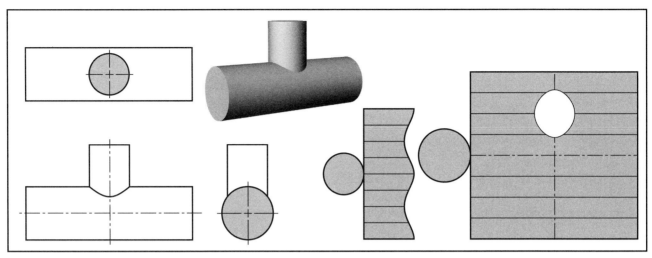

Figure 7.3.18. When both cylinders are not equal in diameter, the intersection can be harder to determine.

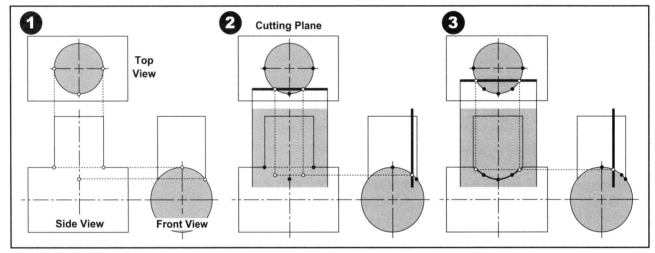

Figure 7.3.19. Use a series of vertical cutting planes to plot the outline of the intersection in the side plan view.

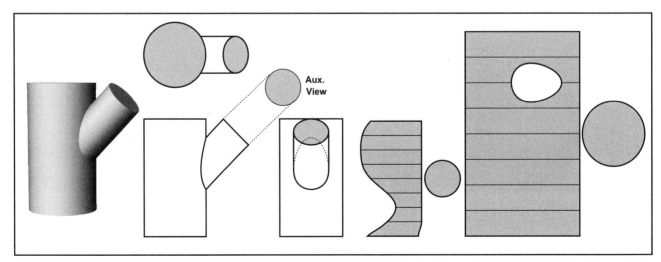

Figure 7.3.20. When two cylinders are not perpendicular, create an auxiliary view to find the intersection.

Intersections are easiest to figure out when the cylinders involved have the same diameter. With mitered corners, this is particularly easy since the intersection is simply a straight line in the side view. In all other views, the intersection is part of a circle.

On the other hand, what happens when you want to join two cylinders together that are *not* equal in diameter? In this case, you will need to know how to map out the correct outline of the intersection in the plan views.

As an example, **Figure 7.3.18** shows a "tee" intersection between two cylinders of unequal diameter. As long as these cylinders are perpendicular, the easiest way to plot the intersection is to use a series of *cutting planes*. This process, shown in **Figure 7.3.19**, allows you to use projection to derive what you don't know (i.e. the outline of the intersection) from what you *do* know (i.e. the layout in the plan views and the cross section of each cylinder).

To accomplish this, begin by using the information already in the plan views to plot as many points as you can. This is shown in **Step 1** of **Figure 7.3.19**. It's easy to see in this example how the plan views will allow you to locate three points right away. To find more points, create a vertical cutting plane and arrange it in the top view as shown in **Step 2**. This plane should be parallel to the centerline of the cylinder and positioned between the centerline and the outer edge as shown.

Find the points where this cutting plane intersects the circular *cross section* in the top view, as well as in the front or rear view. Then, project two lines from the points in the top view down to the side view. Also, project from the front view back to the side view as shown. The locations where these projected lines come together mark points along the intersection in the side view.

Since the cutting plane pierces the cross section *twice*, use this information to plot two points in the intersection. Repeat this process by shifting the cutting plane as shown in **Step 3** until you have plotted sufficient points to draw the outline of the intersection in the side view.

In contrast, when the two cylinders are not perpendicular to one another, the process is more complicated. This situation is illustrated in **Figure 7.3.20**. Arrange the combined objects so the cross section of one cylinder is parallel to the top plan view. Next, create an *auxiliary view* that shows the true cross section of the other cylinder. You can then pass a vertical cutting plane through *both* the top view and the auxiliary view to find key points in the intersection. This process is illustrated in **Figure 7.3.21**.

Two Prisms

When two prisms intersect, try to use the information already available in the plan views to find key points in the intersection. Knowing the actual

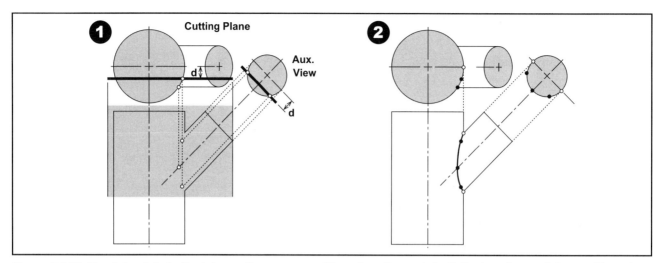

Figure 7.3.21. To plot points in the intersection, pass a cutting plane through *both* the top view and the auxiliary view.

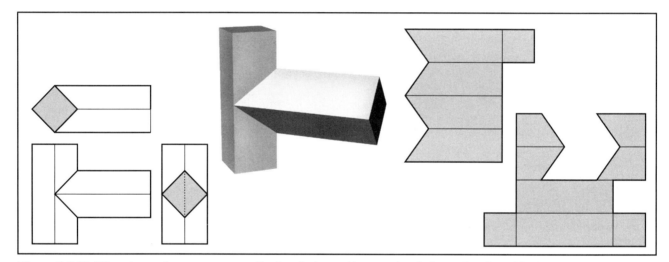

Figure 7.3.22. When two prisms are perpendicular, derive patterns using information found in the plan views.

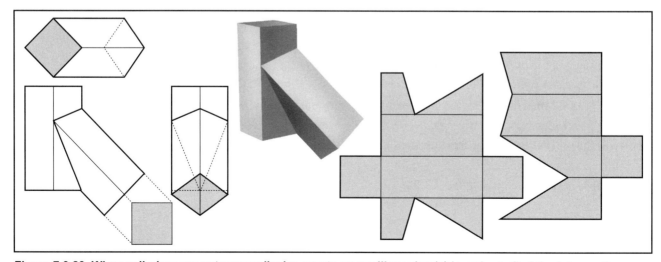

Figure 7.3.23. When cylinders are not perpendicular, create an auxiliary view(s) in order to find the intersection.

cross sections will be extremely helpful. If you can plot these cross sections, the process of finding the intersection should be very straightforward. This is quite easy when the prisms are perpendicular as shown in **Figure 7.3.22**.

To create your developments, use the technique of splitting parts into sub-sections that was first introduced in the discussion on joining cylinders. Start by finding the intersection in the plan views. Then, use this information to divide the prisms into smaller parts. You will end up with a half-prism along with one or more truncated half-prisms.

On the other hand, when prisms intersect at an angle as shown in **Figure 7.3.23**, an auxiliary view will be needed. This auxiliary view will help you determine the actual cross section of the angled prism. First, project from the auxiliary view back into the side view as illustrated in **Figure 7.3.24**. Then, from there, project from the top and/or bottom views and see where the lines intersect. This should help you quickly find the correct intersection as shown.

Cylinder and Prism

As shapes get more complex, plotting their intersections becomes more difficult. For example, when a cylinder and a prism are combined, the resulting intersections can be challenging even to visualize. Just remember, cutting planes are your friend. You can use as many cutting planes as needed to help you find key points along the intersection of the two objects.

Figure 7.3.25 shows example intersections between a cylinder and a square prism, as well as between a cylinder and a triangular prism. When the objects are perpendicular, the correct intersection can can often resolved using information found in the plan views. On the other hand, if the objects meet at an angle, more work will be required.

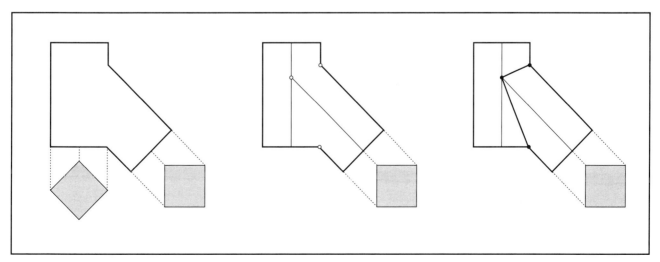

Figure 7.3.24. Project information from the auxiliary view and the adjacent plan views.

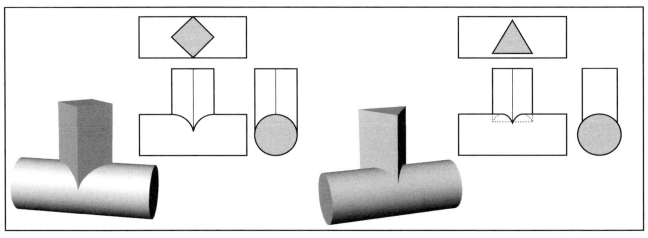

Figure 7.3.25. When a cylinder and a prism come together, the resulting intersections can be challenging to develop.

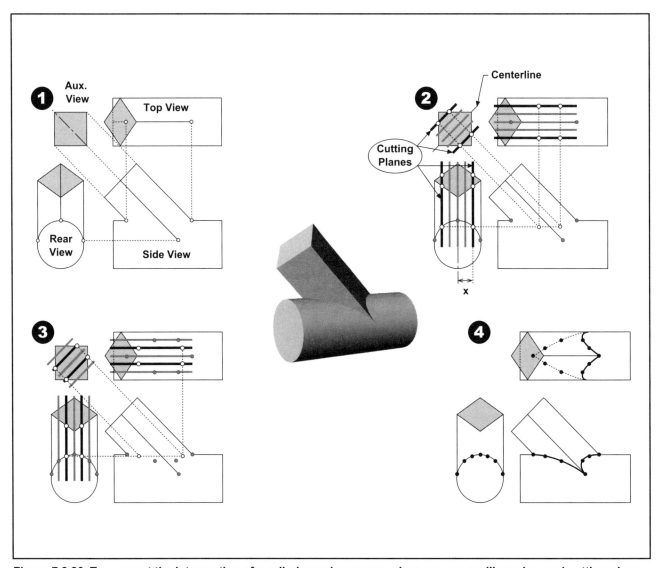

Figure 7.3.26. To map out the intersection of a cylinder and a square prism, use an auxiliary view and cutting planes.

In **Figure 7.3.26**, you can see a cylinder joined at an angle with a square prism. In cases like this, an auxiliary view plus *multiple cutting planes* are needed in order to map out the intersection. Start by creating the auxiliary view and then map out any points you can using the information already available. This is illustrated in **Step 1**.

Next, divide the auxiliary view into *equal sections*. The lines used to divide this view are cutting planes. These planes must cut through the top view of the subject and also through the front and/or rear view as shown in **Step 2**.

The key here is to work with one pair of cutting planes at a time. First, select two cutting planes – one on either side of the centerline. Then, find the points where these two planes intersect with the *cross section* of the prism in the auxiliary view. Next, project lines from these points into the *side view* as shown. In this example, you should also plot the same set of points (four in all) in the *rear view*. These points will be located where the two cutting planes intersect with the cross section of the cylinder as shown.

Note how distance "**x**" is measured from each cutting plane to the centerline of the cross section in the auxiliary view. For each cutting plane, this distance will be the same in the top view, the rear view, and the auxiliary view. Once you have found points along the intersection in the rear view, project horizontal lines from these points back into the side view. Now, find where the two sets of projected lines cross and mark points in these locations as shown. These will be points along the intersection in the *side view*. Finish by projecting these points into the top view.

Continue by selecting the next pair of cutting planes (see **Step 3** of **Figure 7.3.26**). Once all the points are plotted, you should have enough information to complete the outline of the intersection in both the top and side views. Finally, connect the points with a smooth curve as shown in **Step 4**.

Figure 7.3.27. Combining a prism with a cone can create a complex and tricky intersection.

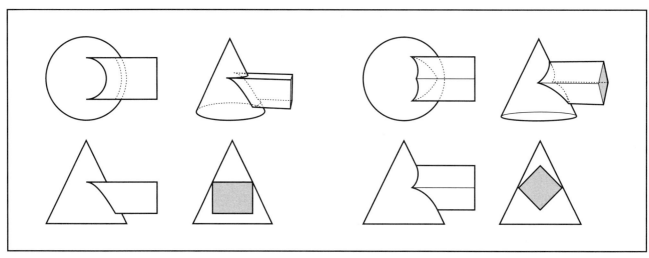

Figure 7.3.28. The shape of the intersection can vary widely depending on the *cross section* of the prism.

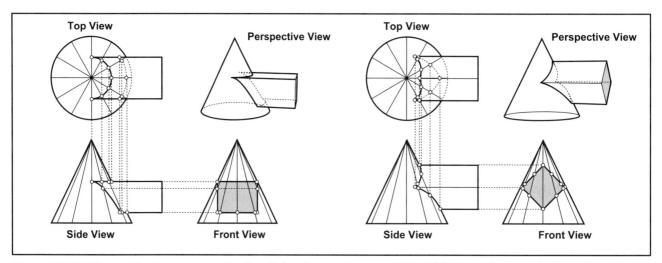

Figure 7.3.29. When objects are perpendicular, divide the cone into sections and use projection to map out key points.

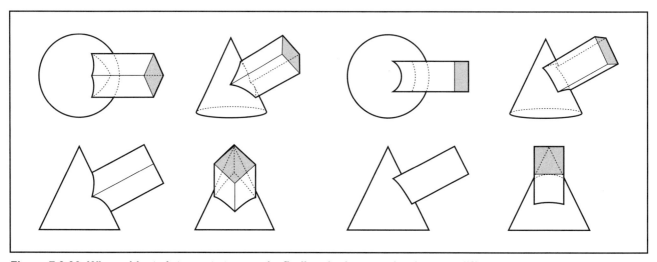

Figure 7.3.30. When objects intersect at an angle, finding the intersection is more difficult.

Cone and Prism

As illustrated in **Figure 7.3.27**, intersections between cones and prisms can be fairly complex. When the objects are perpendicular as shown in **Figure 7.3.28**, the shape of the intersection depends mainly on the cross section of the prism. This cross section can be found in one of the plan views.

Begin by dividing the cone into *sections* using radial lines in the top plan view as shown in **Figure 7.3.29**. Then, project these lines into the side view and also into the front view. Next, plot points on the *cross section* of the prism where they intersect with the section lines on the surface of the cone. Project these points back into the side view and then up into the top view. Finally, connect the points to plot the intersection as shown.

When the objects are joined at an angle as shown in **Figure 7.3.30**, more effort will be required to find the intersection. First, divide the cone into sections using radial lines just as before. This time, however, you will need to create an *auxiliary view* of the cone. This auxiliary view depicts the *cross section* of the prism as illustrated in **Figure 7.3.31**.

Once this view is in place, plot points on the cross section of the prism where they intersect with the section lines on the surface of the cone. Project these points back to the side view and then into the top view and front view. Finally, connect the points to plot the intersection as shown.

Cone and Cylinder

As seen in **Figure 7.3.32**, intersections between cones and cylinders are also somewhat challenging. When the centerline of the cylinder is perpendicular to the vertical axis of the cone, use *horizontal cutting planes* to locate key points in the intersection. This process is illustrated in **Figure 7.3.33**. Create as many cutting planes as you think are needed in order to find a sufficient number of points to draw the intersection.

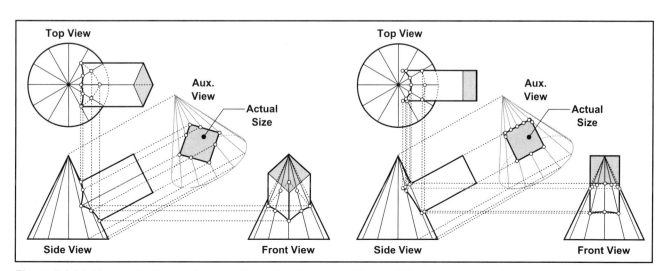

Figure 7.3.31. Use projection and an *auxiliary view* to map out key points of the intersection.

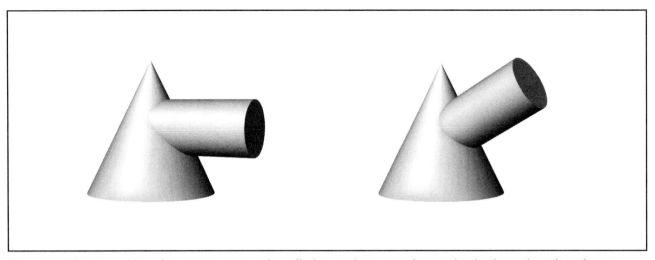

Figure 7.3.32. Intersections between a cone and a cylinder can be mapped out using horizontal cutting planes.

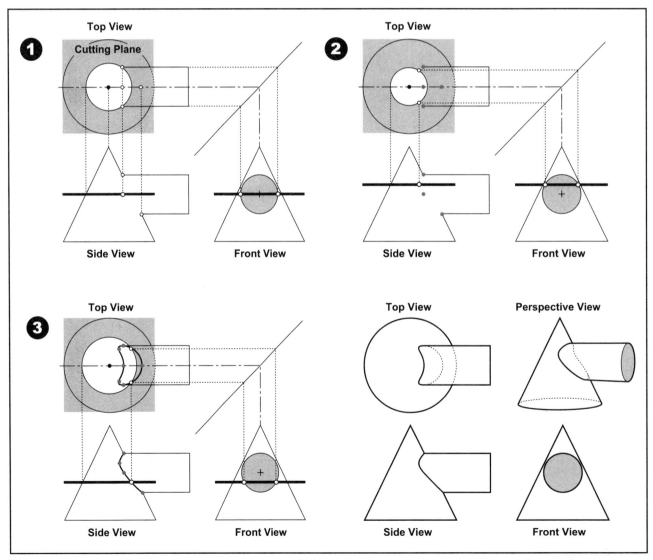

Figure 7.3.33. Cutting planes will be needed even when the cone and cylinder are perpendicular.

Unfortunately, when the cone and cylinder are joined together at an angle, this method will fail. In that event, you must create an *auxiliary view* parallel to the cross section of the cylinder as shown in **Figure 7.3.34**. Divide the cone into sections in the top view using radial lines. Then, project these lines down into the side view as shown in **Step 1**. Once drawn in the side view, project the same lines up into the auxiliary view.

With these lines in place, you will have a "grid" that can be used to "map" the surface of the cone. Find the locations where the radial lines intersect the outline of the cross section of the cylinder in the *auxiliary view*. Project these points back to the side view and then up into the top view as shown in **Step 2**. Finally, project the points into the front view as shown in **Step 3**. Connect the points with a smooth curve to plot the intersection.

Pyramid and Prism

As illustrated in **Figure 7.3.35**, pyramids and prisms make for an unusual combination. Fortunately, these intersections are fairly straightforward to draw. By the time you finish reviewing these examples, you will see how many of the techniques for working with cones can also be used when working with pyramids. You may find, however, pyramids are somewhat easier to work with because their surfaces are planar. As a result, you can map out a "grid" of reference lines on the surface of a pyramid with less effort than it takes to do the same thing with a cone.

If the objects being combined are perpendicular as shown in **Figure 7.3.36**, all the information you need is already contained in the plan views. Start with the *front view* because this view depicts the cross section of the prism. Draw a line from the tip of the pyramid through the edge of the prism and down to the bottom of the pyramid. This line should intersect the extreme

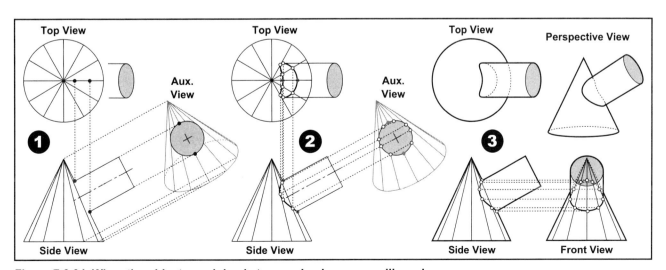

Figure 7.3.34. When the objects are joined at an angle, draw an auxiliary view .

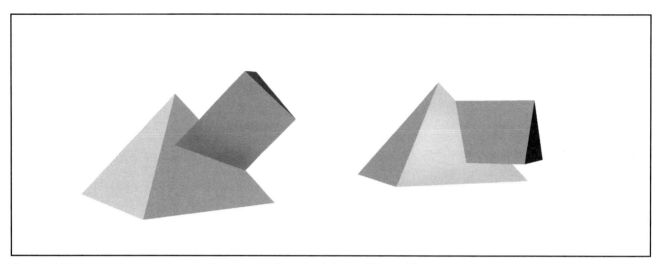

Figure 7.3.35. Treat intersections with pyramids just like intersections with cones.

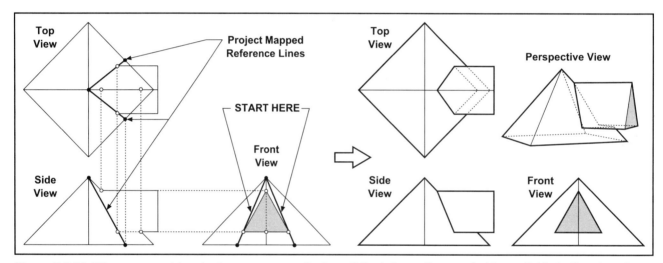

Figure 7.3.36. When a pyramid and prism are perpendicular, all the information needed is available in the plan views.

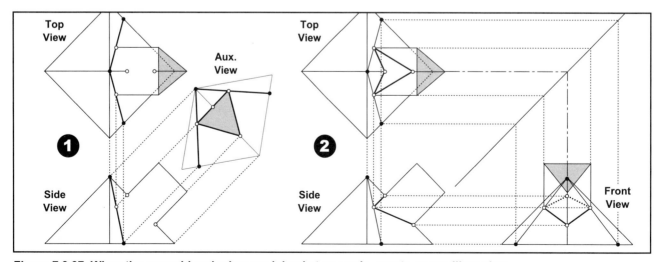

Figure 7.3.37. When the pyramid and prism are joined at an angle, create an *auxiliary view*.

edge of the prism as seen in the front view. Repeat this process for the other side of the prism.

What you have just done is create reference lines on the surface of the pyramid in the front view that show where the prism intersects with the pyramid. Now, project these lines back to the side view and then into the top view as shown. Plot as many points as you can along the intersection and project these points to all views. When you have enough points plotted, connect them with a smooth curve to draw the intersection as shown.

As you can see, this is very straightforward. On the other hand, when the pyramid and prism are joined together at an angle, this method will not work. In this event, you must create an *auxiliary view* that is parallel to the cross section of the prism as shown in **Figure 7.3.37**. This auxiliary view will show the true size of the face of the prism with the pyramid in the background. Now, create reference lines along the surface of the pyramid. Draw these reference lines in the auxiliary view and project them back to the side view. Then, project the reference lines into the top view as shown.

With the auxiliary view now constructed, find the locations in this view where the reference lines intersect with the outline of the cross section of the prism. These will become key points in the intersection. From here, plot these points in the auxiliary view. Then, project them back to the side view and into the top view. Next, project the points from the top view into the *front view*. Finally, connect all the points with a smooth curve to complete the plan view drawing of the intersection.

Sphere and Cylinder or Sphere and Prism

When a sphere and cylinder meet along their centerlines, the resulting intersection is very simple. As illustrated in **Figure 7.3.38**, a sphere is always

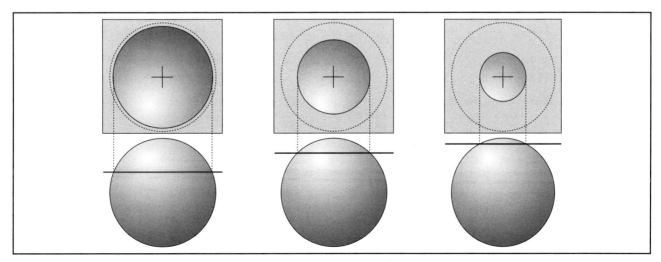

Figure 7.3.38. When a *cutting plane* is parallel to the sphere's axis of symmetry, the intersection is always a circle.

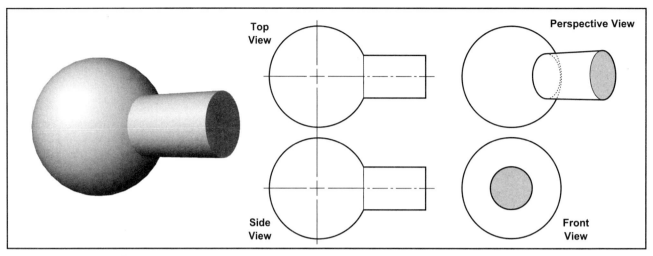

Figure 7.3.39. When the sphere and cylinder are aligned along their axis of symmetry, the intersection is very simple.

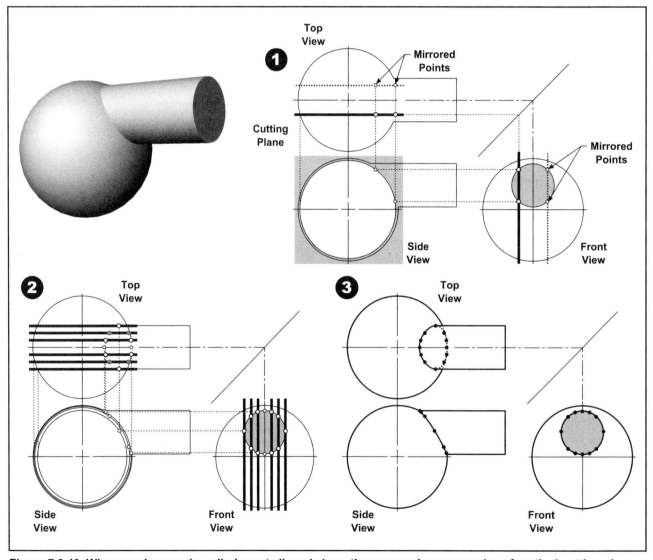

Figure 7.3.40. When a sphere and a cylinder not aligned along the same axis, use a series of vertical cutting planes.

circular in cross section whenever it is pierced by a cutting plane that is parallel to the axis of symmetry. As long as the objects share the same centerline, the intersection of a sphere and a cylinder will simply be a circle as shown in **Figure 7.3.39**.

In contrast, when the cylinder is above or below the sphere's axis of symmetry, the intersection becomes more complex as seen in **Figure 7.3.40**. To solve this problem, pass a *vertical cutting plane* through the sphere as shown in **Step 1**. Then, find where this cutting plane meets the *cross section* of the cylinder in the *front* view. Also, don't forget to plot the *mirror image* of these points on the other side of the centerline.

Remember, the intersection of the cutting plane and the sphere will be a *circle* in the side view. You can use this fact to aid in plotting and projecting points from the front view back to the side view. Also project these points into the top view as shown.

Repeat this process with additional cutting planes to find the remaining points as illustrated in **Step 2**. When enough points have been plotted, connect them with a smooth curve to finish drawing the intersection as shown.

When a sphere and a prism meet, the resulting intersection may look complicated. Fortunately, it might not be difficult to draw. If you start with a plan view that shows the cross section of the prism, you can use a series of cutting planes to map out the resulting intersection as shown in **Figure 7.3.41**.

On the other hand, if the objects meet at an angle, use *revolution* to re-orient them until the *cross section* of the prism is parallel with a plan view. Or, simply create an auxiliary view. Either way, the results will be the same.

7.4: Shortcuts

For sure, creating developments and intersections can be a tedious process. In the examples shown so far, it should be readily apparent that this task can sometimes require a good bit of work. So, the question is: "Are there any shortcuts to make all this easier?"

The answer is: "Yes and No." If you need to make all your patterns on paper using only basic blueprinting techniques, there aren't many options available other than the "brute force" method of working everything out in 2D. On the other hand, if you have access to some 3D modeling tools, you may not need to worry about creating developments and intersections at all.

Low-Tech Shortcuts

For those who can't make the leap to 3D modeling, one practical alternative is to "work smarter, not harder." You can do this by creating blueprints and construction patterns only for those parts that are absolutely necessary.

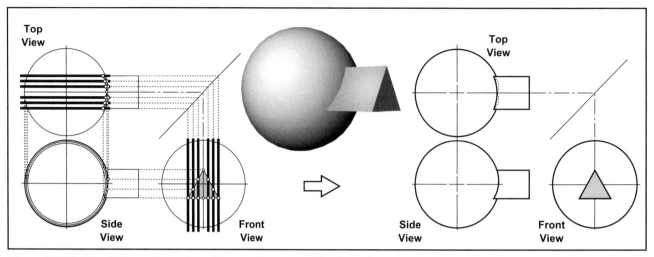

Figure 7.3.41. The intersection of a sphere and a perpendicular prism can be plotted using cutting planes.

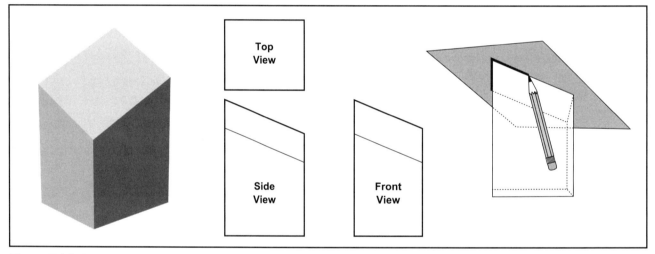

Figure 7.4.1. As a shortcut, consider making patterns directly on the model rather than by plotting everything in 2D.

As you have seen throughout this section, one of the challenges in blueprinting is visualizing exactly how an oblique line or surface appears in a principle plan view. But, if you think about it, in some cases you don't really need to know this anyway. Instead, what you do need are actual construction patterns for the oblique surface. Often these patterns can be derived by working directly on the model.

For example, you might skip the process of determining the true shape of an oblique surface altogether. Focus instead on parts that can be easily drawn in the plan views. Then, start building your model using only these shapes. Once they are assembled, you may be able to create patterns for oblique surfaces "on the fly" by making templates directly on the model itself.

To see an illustration of this idea, take a look at the subject shown in **Figure 7.4.1**. Here you can see a box with an angled surface that needs to be constructed. You might think of this box as a truncated prism. Such a prism is not nearly as easy to develop as a regular box.

The good news is that it's not difficult at all to draw this object in plan view form. As a result, you can easily make patterns for each side of the prism without going to any extra effort. Once you've drawn the prism in each view, you will have the patterns needed to build each side.

On the other hand, making a pattern for the *angled face* of the prism is not a quick and easy task at all. This would require plotting an *auxiliary view*, which could take some time and effort to figure out.

As a shortcut that can make this job easier, consider making patterns for the sides of the prism only. Then, cut out the panels that make up the sides and assemble them. Next, lay a sheet of cardboard on top of the assembled prism and hold it in place. Using a pencil, carefully trace around the edges of the prism where they meet the piece of cardboard. Voila! You have just made an accurate template for the angled face. And, you did it without having to plot an auxiliary view at all.

High-Tech Shortcuts

Modelers who have access to 3D software can have a major advantage in the blueprinting and pattern-making process. Using 3D tools, you can often skip some of the painstaking work needed to create auxiliary views, plot intersections, and create developments. For instance, a program such as *Rhino 3D* can do all this for you – and it can generate perfect 2D orthographic plan views as well.

When deciding which 3D program is right for your needs, you may want to consider choosing a package that includes special features designed to make the blueprinting and pattern-making process easier. The bad news is that not all 3D programs have such features and those that do can be fairly expensive. Thus, cost may prompt some modelers to postpone investing in one of these programs or even avoid using them altogether.

If you do decide to "take the plunge" and invest in a good set of 3D tools, the good news is that it can open up a whole world of possibilities for your modeling projects. By combining the knowledge of 2D design and drafting you've learned in this book with the capabilities and features inherent in a powerful 3D program, you may quickly find yourself achieving new levels of creativity, capability, and productivity.

With this in mind, here are some key points to consider:

- A 3D model can take the place of a conventional "study model" (i.e. a *maquette* or mockup); This allows you to see how your model will look from every angle without having to actually build anything in the physical realm; This is a powerful method for "proving" the accuracy of your finished blueprints, testing parts for fit, or tweaking plans created for challenging shapes.
- When you are trying to create blueprints for a subject using only photographs as reference, 3D tools become invaluable.
- Modeling programs fall into two basic categories – mesh modelers and spline modelers.
- Think of a typical mesh modeling program as "digital clay" that you can sculpt any way you wish; You can quickly build basic elements called *primitives* and then combine, trim, stretch, and "squash" them any way you want to make custom shapes.
- In contrast, *spline modeling* is a different approach altogether; It is a natural extension of the 2D blueprinting process that has been demonstrated throughout this book; Once you know how to make blueprints and construction patterns in 2D, you'll be able to create the profiles needed to build even complex 3D parts quickly and easily.
- You may be able to use special features available in some 3D programs to refine and enhance your 2D drawings and patterns.
- Certain spline modeling programs can even create 2D plans directly from your 3D model so you don't have to do it at all.
- A few programs can *unfold* or *unroll* 3D objects to create developments with a click of the mouse.

As you can see, there are a lot of potential shortcuts available for those modelers who are able to use 3D "power tools." If you haven't already, isn't it about time you made the leap to 3D?

7.5: Summary

A *transition* is a shape that starts out with one cross section and then transitions to another. Transitions are used in modeling where parts with different cross sections must be joined together.

The joining of two dissimilar shapes without a transition results in an *intersection*. Creating developments for shapes that intersect can be one of the most difficult and challenging tasks to perform when making construction patterns. A combination of techniques is often needed to get the results you want. Auxiliary views are commonly used as part of this process. In addition, *cutting planes* can be employed to plot key points in the intersection between objects.

If you need to make all your construction patterns using only 2D blueprinting techniques, there are few options other than the "brute force" method of working out all the details by hand. One alternative approach is to create only those patterns that are absolutely necessary. Then, make templates for the remaining surfaces directly on the model.

If you have access to 3D modeling tools, many of these tasks can become much easier. As a result, modelers who use 3D tools may have a major advantage in the blueprinting and pattern-making process. There are several ways to employ 3D tools to help streamline the design phase of your modeling projects. Many of these options will depend on the program you choose.

What's Next?

As you can now see, the ability to sketch out your ideas forms the *foundation* of the model design process. Thus, the information contained in this volume will help you take your thoughts out of the idea stage and get them on the road to becoming a reality.

Yet, this is only the beginning. There are more advanced tools and techniques available that make it possible to do things you may never have imagined. Are you ready to learn more? Here's a sneak preview of what comes next.

The Model Design & Blueprinting Handbook, Volume 2

In this next volume of the series, you'll see how to turn your 2D blueprints into patterns that can be used to build 3D models. Then, you'll learn how to use powerful 3D tools to make the blueprinting and pattern-making process quicker and easier. With this comprehensive guide, you can gain valuable insight into how 2D and 3D techniques can be combined to streamline the design phase of all your modeling projects:

- Use basic tools to build 3D objects.
- Extract key profiles from your 2D blueprints in order to build 3D shapes quickly and easily.
- Learn more about creating models working only from photos.
- Create 3D study models ("maquettes") to verify the accuracy of proportions, as well as the correct placement of details.
- Employ 3D models to create auxiliary views with ease.
- Make the most of advanced 3D tools to create developments and patterns for complex parts.
- Model challenging intersections and transitions with minimal effort.
- Turn your finished 3D model parts into accurate 2D working drawings.

Please visit: *www.ModelersNotebook.com*

Want to know more about the future of modeling? Be sure to read the **Afterword** that follows.

Afterword

This is merely the first volume in the *Model Design & Blueprinting Handbook* series. These books will introduce some powerful tools and techniques you can use to streamline your projects. This is true whether you are constructing a real model that you can hold in your hand or a "virtual" 3D model that exists only inside a computer.

Moving Ahead

Once you've learned how to make blueprints and construction patterns for your own projects, you'll be ready to tackle a range of advanced modeling applications. Some of these areas will be covered in detail in future volumes. Examples include:

- Making your own custom decals and dry transfers
- Creating artwork for custom-cut painting masks
- Drawing outlines for one-of-a-kind photo-etched metal parts

If that's not enough, how about letting machines make parts for you? For example, you can turn your construction templates into patterns that can be cut with a laser-cutter or computer-controlled (CNC) mill. Or, you can build your models entirely in the computer and then have them carved, printed, or "grown" for you via rapid prototyping. How's that for new frontiers!

Making the Leap to 3D

The topics just mentioned are really only the beginning of what's possible. Indeed, the future of modeling is bright – thanks to new technologies. This does not mean, however, that physical modeling is becoming obsolete. On the contrary, the modelers of tomorrow will combine *both* physical and 3D techniques to obtain simply amazing results.

Since this book provides a foundation for those interested in both traditional and virtual models, it helps build an important *bridge* between the two modeling worlds. Thus, once you've mastered the 2D blueprinting techniques covered here in this first volume, the next logical step is for you to make the leap to 3D design.

Volume 2 of this series will help you make that leap. When you do, you'll discover a whole new world of modeling opportunities awaits you.

Related Books

Several titles are available from the publisher to complement this volume:

Model Design & Blueprinting Handbook, Volume 2

Model Design & Blueprinting Handbook, Volume 3

How to Draw Anything With a Computer:
*A Quick-Start Guide for the Craftsman, Hobbyist,
and Do-It-Yourselfer*

Easy Project Math:
*A Problem-Solving Guide for the Craftsman, Hobbyist,
and Do-It-Yourselfer*

Please visit the following website for more information:

www.ModelersNotebook.com

Appendix A:
Computer-Based Drawing Tips

Overview

There are two very different approaches to computer-based drawing: 1) Computer-Aided Design ("CAD") programs; and 2) Computer illustration programs. Both types of applications are designed for very different purposes. You can actually use either category of program to make blueprints and construction patterns for your projects. Just keep in mind, the process of drawing will be slightly different, depending on which type you choose.

In addition, whether you use a CAD system or a computer illustration program, there may be times when you need to transfer your work to a different program. Thus, the ability to share drawings with other applications can be very useful. As an example, you might draw blueprints in 2D and then decide you want to extract patterns from them in order to build a 3D model. To do this, you will need to open the 2D drawings in a 3D modeling application.

CAD *Systems*

Computer-Aided Design programs have powerful drawing tools and features geared toward *precision*. They are most often used by engineers, architects, and industrial designers who need to produce accurate engineering drawings and technical blueprints. Because these systems are designed specifically for trained draftsmen, they tend to be complex and highly technical.

As a result, beginners may find CAD programs somewhat intimidating. For example, many operations involve typing commands on a keyboard rather than pointing and clicking with a mouse. Thus, the interfaces in these programs can be challenging to learn. Most importantly, a CAD user should be familiar with the standards and conventions of drafting in order to take full advantage of everything these systems have to offer. For this reason, CAD may not be the best choice for someone who is new to computer-based drawing.

Illustration Programs

In marked contrast, computer illustration programs are fairly intuitive and rather easy to use. A product of the desktop publishing revolution in the 1980s,

NOTE: Underlined terms appear in the Glossary. The names of proprietary computer programs appear in *italics*.

For a step-by-step guide that will get you up and running quickly, be sure to read *How To Draw Anything With a Computer: A Quick-Start Guide for the Craftsman, Hobbyist, and Do-It-Yourselfer*, part of the *Modeler's Notebook Reference Series* available from:

www.ModelersNotebook.com

If you don't think you can draw, don't worry. There are actually many ways non-artists can use the computer to make clean and professional-looking drawings for their projects.

There are a number of different CAD packages from which to choose. The industry standard application is *AutoCAD*. Many low-cost packages, however, work just fine for basic drawing. Some programs are even free.

Whether you paint like Picasso or you can barely make a stick figure, the personal computer provides some very powerful and easy-to-use features for creating many different kinds of drawings.

Illustration programs fall into one of two categories: Professional graphics programs such as Adobe *Illustrator* and Macromedia *Freehand* (now owned by Adobe Systems Incorporated); and general purpose drawing programs like *CorelDRAW* and *Deneba Canvas*. You should choose whichever package meets your needs and budget.

Computer illustration programs can be used to make much more than just blueprints. These applications can create artwork that would be tedious or difficult to accomplish when using any other type of application. In fact, illustration programs can come in handy for any of the following model-related tasks:

- Sketching 3-views.
- Generating templates and construction patterns.
- Making profiles and outlines for building 3D model parts.
- Creating artwork for custom decals and transfers.
- Generating outlines for custom photo-etching.
- Making patterns for laser cutting.
- Drawing tool paths for CNC machining.

CAD applications may not be well suited for producing illustrations and artwork such as that needed for making decals and dry transfers.

these applications were created for graphic artists and designers to produce line art for publications. With these programs, just about anyone can create professional quality graphics. And, you need not be at all familiar with the conventions and standards of drafting in order to get started.

Some draftsmen might express cynicism about using anything other than a CAD program for making blueprints. This is probably because the primary advantage of CAD is its accuracy. With these systems, you can make precise drawings to within ten-thousandths of an inch. Yet, as a modeler, you most likely do not need such close tolerances.

The truth is just about any computer-based drawing tool can be employed to create blueprints and construction patterns for modeling projects. In fact, most illustration programs permit you to draw lines accurate to within a thousandth of an inch. This should be more than adequate for most purposes. What's more, because of the flexibility and ease of use inherent in these programs, they can be very simple to learn.

There are other advantages to using a computer illustration program. Some of these will become apparent as you work through the material in this book. In addition, these programs are ideal for creating custom decals or dry transfers. You can also use an illustration program for making artwork to manufacture custom photo-etched parts. Even more, these applications can easily generate templates for producing laser-cut parts.

Thus, as you can see, CAD is most definitely not the only choice when it comes model design and blueprinting. With that said, CAD programs *do* work extremely well for many model design tasks. Still, because an illustration program can do just about everything a modeler requires – while also being easier to use – you may want to start out with this type of program.

If you decide you need features only a more sophisticated drafting system can provide, you can always switch to using a CAD package. Or, in order to have the greatest flexibility, you may opt to use *both* types of programs to aid in designing your projects.

Sharing Data in Computer Drawings

The process of bringing a drawing created by another application into your program is called *importing*. In a similar fashion, sharing your drawing in such a way that it can be opened in another program is called *exporting*.

Importing is useful for incorporating lines and objects created by other programs into your drawing, as well as image files such as scanned photos. Exporting can be used to print your drawings or to send data to a 3D modeling application. For example, you may need your drawings saved in a specific format in order to "plot" or print them on a large-format printer.

File Types

Drawings created with a computer are known as <u>vector-based art</u>. All CAD and computer illustration programs generate this type of art. Vector-based drawings are object-oriented, meaning each line and object is treated as a separate entity. Because of this, all the objects in a drawing can be freely rearranged at will. A major advantage to this approach is that drawing files can be very compact in terms of the disk space required to store them.

In contrast, scanned photos are *bitmap images*. The entire image is a single entity composed of tiny segments called *pixels*. Even though drawing programs generate vector-based line art, nearly all such programs can also open or *import* bitmap images. This permits you to integrate such images into the artwork created with a computer drawing program. For example, this feature can be very valuable when you want to trace all or part of a photograph.

Depending on whether you are using a CAD application or a computer illustration program, there are two distinct groups of drawing file types. CAD programs use one of several popular formats, but the most common is the *AutoCAD*® DWG file. Another commonly used format is called DXF. These are the standard formats for sharing data between CAD systems and also for printing or *plotting* plans on paper from CAD files. Any drawing saved in such a format can be modified by whatever application is used to open it.

In contrast, computer illustration programs have a completely different way of doing things. In general, they are not very compatible with CAD systems and vice versa. (Some illustration programs, however, may be able to import and/or export drawings in DXF format.) All computer illustration programs support the popular Adobe *PostScript*® language designed for creating and printing graphics. This language gave rise to a special file format called EPS, an acronym that stands for "Encapsulated PostScript." You might think of EPS as the foundation and standard for computer illustration files.

The first major computer illustration program was *Adobe Illustrator*® and it is still widely used today. Because this program became the *de facto* industry standard, most similar programs can open and save *Illustrator* files. Depending on the computer platform and version, these files may be saved either with ".art" or ".ai" file extensions.

In addition to working with *Illustrator* format, each computer illustration program can also save files in its own proprietary format, as well as in EPS format. EPS was designed so that computer artwork can be shared and printed with the highest quality possible. Keep in mind, an EPS file can be "locked" or it may be "editable" depending on the options and settings used to create it. In some cases, a file saved in EPS format cannot be modified by another application. As a result, EPS format can be troublesome if you do not have experience using it.

Drawing files can sometimes take up as little space as a word processing document.

See **Appendix C** for more information about printing your plans on paper.

Acrobat Reader software can be downloaded free of charge from the *Adobe* website:

www.Adobe.com

Anyone who has a copy of your work in PDF format can make a screen snapshot of the drawing. Still, you can use *Acrobat's* security settings to make it very difficult for others to extract a copy of your original vector drawing objects. Nothing is foolproof, but most people will not be able to defeat the encryption of a locked PDF file. Thus, the basic security settings in *Acrobat* can be very effective in preventing others from copying your work.

If this level of security is not sufficient, you may want to consider not saving *any* vector drawing elements in PDF format. Instead, convert your drawing to a bitmap image. Anyone will be able to view and copy this image – even if the only way to do so is by making a screen snapshot of it. But, they will not have access to your original drawing objects because those elements will not be included in the PDF file.

With that said, *Illustrator* format is often preferred when sharing data between computer illustration programs. The reason is most programs can easily open *Illustrator* files. In addition, any drawing saved in this format can be modified by whatever application is used to open it – provided the application can actually read the file. This makes sharing your drawings between applications as painless as possible.

A Note About PDF Files

Adobe developed the *Acrobat®* program to allow anyone to open, read, and print data no matter what the computer platform. A special file format called PDF ("Portable Document Format") was developed specifically for this purpose. PDF files can be opened and viewed using the full version of *Acrobat*, as well as the free *Acrobat Reader* software. Other programs can open PDF files if they support the PDF standard. Depending on the security settings of the files, they may or may not be editable by other programs (see below).

Your CAD or computer illustration program may be able to export data in PDF format. Just keep in mind, you may not be able to modify data saved in this manner using another program. This is because PDF is proprietary and encoded. Therefore, this format is most suitable for printing or plotting your drawings rather than for sharing drawings and data with other applications.

Also, be aware that PDF files have *security settings* to protect the information they contain. Depending on the program being used, you may have the option of locking (or "encrypting") the file when you save it. If the file is not locked, the information contained in it can be extracted by someone else.

In some cases, you may be able to open a PDF file in your drawing program. This may be true when the file includes vector drawing objects and the information contained in the file is not locked. In such cases, you may be able to extract or modify these objects using your drawing program.

Importing

If you wish to open a drawing that was created by a different application, launch your program and choose the "Import" command. This is typically found on the "File" menu. You may see a list of available drawing files based on the formats supported by your program.

With a CAD system, you should be able to open any DWG or DXF file. In addition, you may be able to open *bitmap image* files in a variety of formats (for tracing or to use as a template).

Most computer illustration programs should be able to import any file saved in *Illustrator* format, as well as EPS files. Your drawing program may also recognize any of several popular vector file formats. In addition, you may be able to open several different types of bitmap image files.

Exporting

Choose the "Export" command (typically located on the "File" menu) when you wish to save your drawings in a format that can be recognized by another application. You should be able to select from a list of available file formats that are supported by your program. In addition, you may need to use "Export" when you want to save your drawings in PDF format.

CAD systems typically export to both DWG and DXF formats. They may be able to create PDF files as well. Most illustration programs support a large variety of file types (depending on the program). These include most of the popular vector formats. In some cases, DXF format may be available for sharing data with CAD systems. PDF format may be supported as well.

Keep in mind, drawing programs are not designed to modify bitmap images. You may, however, be able to save your drawing in a format that an image editing program can recognize. This may permit you to turn your vector drawing into a bitmap equivalent using a process known as <u>rasterizing</u>.

When a vector-based drawing is *rasterized*, it becomes a bitmap image. For the greatest flexibility and control over this process, you may want to let an image editing program do the rasterizing for you. Since such programs are designed specifically for working with bitmap images, they may be the best choice for this particular task.

Some drawing programs may be able to rasterize vector artwork directly into a bitmap image. In that event, you will need to specify certain parameters such as the size and resolution of the resulting image.

Sharing 2D Data With 3D Modeling Applications

If you create 2D drawings and you wish to use them in a 3D modeling application, export the data in a format recognized by a 3D program. Many popular 3D applications support standard CAD formats such as DWG and DXF. In addition, many programs also support the *Illustrator* standard.

Keep in mind, computer illustration programs create lines called <u>Bézier curves</u>. All curves produced by the *Pen Tool* in a drawing are generated behind the scenes in this manner. The resulting objects are nearly universal to all drawing programs, but they may be quite different from the way CAD systems work. This can sometimes make it challenging when you are trying to transfer data from CAD format to *Illustrator* format and vice versa.

Fortunately, the curves drawn by computer illustration programs are often similar to lines called <u>splines</u> utilized by many 3D modeling applications. As a result, when you import a Bézier curve into a 3D program, it may be treated as a spline. Even so, you can sometimes get unexpected results when importing 2D drawings into 3D modeling software.

If a program is able to import and/or export a particular type of file, it is said to *support* that file format.

Bitmap Image Formats:

- TIFF (".tif")
- Bitmap (".bmp")
- JPEG (".jpg")
- GIF (".gif")
- Photoshop (".pst")
- PICT (".pct")
- PNG (".png")
- Targa (".tga")

See **Appendix B** for a discussion about image resolution, as well as more information on creating templates from scanned images.

Vector Drawing Formats:

- *AutoCAD* (".dwg")
- Generic CAD (".dxf")
- *Illustrator* (".art" or ".ai")
- *Freehand* (".fh4" - ".fh11")
- *CorelDRAW* ® (".cdr")
- Windows Meta File (".wmf")

Some of the formats listed represent older versions of popular programs. No matter how new your program may be, you can often share data using the format for an older version of the same program.

The formula for calculating Bézier curves was pioneered by Pierre Bézier, a noted French engineer, scientist, and teacher.

Some applications may refer to Bézier curves as *paths*. In reality, a path is a *group* of Bézier curves.

Each Bézier curve created by a computer illustration program has a number of *control points* and also a *direction*. When such a curve is imported into another program, this information may not always translate properly.

Fortunately, you may be able to work around this. Start by being aware of the differences in the way CAD, 3D, and computer illustration programs handle curves. You may need to do some tweaking such as reversing the direction of certain Bézier curves after they have been imported. In some cases, you may want to rebuild curves using tools available in the other program. Worst case, you can always use the imported curve as a template to draw a new curve from scratch using the drawing tools in your 3D program.

Exporting 3D Data to Your 2D Drawing Program

If you create objects in a 3D modeling application that you wish to share with your 2D CAD or computer illustration program, the objects must first be "flattened" so they exist in a 2D format. The exact method for doing this depends on the options available in your program. For example, you may be able to *project* an object onto a surface that is parallel with the *horizontal plane* of the program and then export it as a 2D object.

In addition, some 3D programs can generate 2D drawings directly from 3D objects. These drawings will consist of *curves* (i.e. lines) that exist in a two-dimensional plane. In this way, they can be exported either to CAD or to *Illustrator* format and then shared with a 2D drawing program.

If your 3D modeling application cannot export data in a suitable 2D format, you can always create renderings of your finished model and save them as bitmap images. For example, if you were to create plan view renderings of your 3D model, you could import these images into your drawing program to act as a template. These could then be traced to create accurate 2D plans.

Summary

- There are two very different approaches to drawing with a computer – Computer-Aided Design or "CAD" programs and illustration programs.
- CAD programs were designed specifically for draftsmen; They can be highly technical to use.
- Because they were developed for graphic artists, illustration programs can be very easy and intuitive to use; These programs are ideal for modelers because they can handle a variety of model design tasks.
- The process of opening a drawing created by another application is called *importing*; Sharing your drawing with another program is called *exporting*.
- Whether you are using a CAD application or a computer illustration program, there are two distinct types of vector drawing files.
- CAD programs typically use the *AutoCAD* DWG format, as well as DXF format.

- *Illustrator* format is preferred for sharing data between computer illustration programs.
- Your CAD program should be able to import DWG and DXF files, as well as several different bitmap image formats.
- A computer illustration program should be able to import any file saved in *Illustrator* format, as well as EPS files and other popular vector art formats; In addition, you may be able to open a variety of bitmap image files as well.
- CAD systems should be able to export to both DWG and DXF formats; They may be able to create PDF files as well.
- Depending on the program, computer illustration software can export data in a wide variety of file formats.
- To share 2D drawings with a 3D modeling application, export to DWG, DXF, or *Illustrator* format.
- If your 3D modeling application can export 2D lines and curves, choose *Illustrator* format.
- When a 3D program is unable to export vector data in 2D format, make plan view renders of your 3D model; Then, import these images into your drawing to use as a template.

Appendix B:
Working With Template Images

Overview

As discussed in **Chapter 3**, it is very helpful to have some sort of *template* before you begin drawing. The best starting point is either a set of existing plan view drawings or some detailed measurements. Without access to this type of reference, you may be forced to rely on photos instead.

Even if you are lucky enough to have measurements and/or plan view drawings to use as a guide, reference photos can still come in handy for determining crucial details such as *cross sections*. As part of this process, one of the advantages of using a computer drawing program is that you can create an *overlay* by adding lines on top of scanned images. For instance, you can trace a photo or you can even trace an existing set of drawings.

Examples of how to trace scanned images were presented in **Chapter 3**. Here, you will see how to get reference images into the computer in the first place.

The overall process of working with scanned images is as follows:

1. First, *scan* the image so it can be manipulated in the computer.
2. Once scanned, *import* the image into your drawing program.
3. Place the image on a separate drawing *layer*.
4. *Lock* the image layer.
5. *Trace* the image.

Drawings created with a computer are known as <u>vector-based art</u>. All CAD and computer illustration programs generate this type of artwork. On the other hand, scanned photos are <u>bitmap images</u>.

When an image is scanned, the computer divides it into tiny regions called <u>pixels</u>. The number of pixels recorded depends on the *resolution* of the scan. Both the color and the light/dark value of each pixel are individually recorded. These values are then assembled to create an <u>image file</u>. Because of all the information that is being stored, the file size of bitmap images can be quite large. As a result, they can take up a lot of disk space.

NOTE: Underlined terms appear in the Glossary. The names of proprietary computer programs appear in *italics*.

An *image editing program* is needed in order to view or modify bitmap images. Such programs open scanned images and allow you to modify them. Popular image editing programs include Microsoft® *Paint*, Corel® *Paint Shop® Pro*, and Adobe® *Photoshop®*. Using these programs, many different operations can be performed on image files, including:

- Scaling up or down.
- Increasing the resolution (called *up-sampling*) or decreasing the resolution (called *down-sampling*).
- Changing from color to black and white.
- Creating a negative image (called *inverting* the color scheme).
- Making the image lighter or darker.
- Increasing or decreasing the contrast.
- Altering the hue of color images.

Scanners

The first step is to scan the image into the computer. You can do this by hooking up a scanner and installing the appropriate software. If you don't have a scanner, take your photos to a photo lab, photo processing center, or copy center and have them scanned. In this event, the captured images will be saved as image files and placed on a CD or DVD disc.

If you have a scanner, make sure it is configured properly. To do this, correctly establish the following parameters:

- Resolution
- Color mode
- File type
- Filters

Resolution

This is probably the most important parameter when scanning anything. An image can be scanned at just about any resolution. *Low-resolution images* are only suitable for display on your computer screen. You cannot enlarge or magnify these images to see small details. On the other hand, *high-resolution images* contain much more information. As a result, you can "zoom in" to see small details by magnifying these images.

Resolution is measured in *pixels-per-inch* or "ppi." A low-resolution image should be scanned to match the resolution of your computer screen as follows:

- 96 pixels-per-inch for most modern computer screens.
- 72 pixels-per-inch for some older Macintosh screens.

Some scanners will scan an image and then open it in your image editing application without first saving it to disk. To keep from accidentally losing the scanned information, be sure you save the file before doing anything else.

A high-resolution scan in *grayscale mode* will record much faster and take up less disk space than a high-resolution scan in either RGB or CMYK color mode.

On a PC computer running *Windows*, screen resolution is 96 pixels-per-inch or 96 ppi. On some Macintosh computers, screen resolution is 72 ppi.

A high-resolution image is one that is scanned at about 200 ppi or higher. An ideal value to use is 300 ppi since this works well if you later want to print your image. Anything higher than this is ultra-high resolution.

Keep in mind, the higher the resolution, the more data is recorded. As a result, file sizes of high-resolution images can quickly become very large. This, in turn, means the scanner will need more time for scanning each image. In addition, opening and editing large image files takes up a tremendous amount of computer memory. This can slow down the performance of your system.

Color Mode

This parameter tells the scanner whether you want to capture the image in color or in black and white. Color mode can have a big impact on both file size and on the time required to complete a scan.

Because of the amount of information being recorded, full-color scans take the longest – especially when the scanner is configured to make a high-resolution scan. In contrast, black-and-white images take less time to scan.

Since color images contain more information, this also means the resulting image file will take up a lot more disk space. If you have a color photo, however, it's a good idea to scan it in color mode. This way, all the information will be there if you need it.

For color scans, there are two basic choices for image format:

- RGB
- CMYK

These choices are known as "color spaces." RGB (an acronym meaning "red, green, blue") is the method your computer uses to display images on screen. Choose this color mode when you don't need to print the image on a color printer. This works well for photos that are to be traced while making your drawings. It is also the ideal format for any images that will be posted on the Web or sent to others via e-mail.

On the other hand, images that need to be printed should be scanned in CMYK format ("cyan, magenta, yellow, and black"). This is the format used by nearly all printing presses and color printers to create color images. Keep in mind, images scanned in CMYK mode may look strange on your computer screen, but they will print out well. CMYK images also take up more computer memory than RGB images. Thus, they may take longer to scan.

For black-and-white images, there are also two choices:

- Monochrome
- Grayscale

Monochrome images have only black pixels and white pixels. They do not contain shades of gray. As a result, this format is suitable only for scanning line art. The advantage of using monochrome mode is this format takes up the least amount of disk space. Just keep in mind, if you scan an image that has gray tones using monochrome mode, it may look very strange.

Grayscale mode is ideal for just about any black-and-white image. Scanning can be fast and efficient when using this format. Choosing this option saves file space and takes less time than scanning in color mode. You can even scan a *color* image in grayscale format. Doing so, however, will force all colors in the image to be converted into shades of gray.

File Type

Once a scan is recorded, it will be saved to disk by the scanner software. In the process, you will be prompted to select a format for saving the file. There are several possible choices:

- Bitmap (".bmp")
- JPEG (".jpg")
- TIFF (".tif")
- TARGA (".tga")

Bitmap format is commonly used on PC computers. This stores a large amount of data without any sort of *compression*. Thus, the file size can be huge. TIFF format also takes up lots of disk space, but it has the option of moderate compression to reduce the size of the file. JPEG files are the most compact, offering options that substantially compress file size.

Bitmap, TIFF, and TARGA are "raw" formats that can be used to store all the information recorded by the scanner without altering anything. This is ideal for most scans. On the other hand, JPEG always has some degree of compression. As a result, some information will be lost when you save in this format. This reduces the quality of any image saved in JPEG format each time you save the file. Therefore, use JPEG format only if you have very little disk space available.

Filters

Your scanner software may come with a variety of *filters* that can be used to modify the scanned image as it is recorded. Just keep in mind, using filters can slow down the speed of the scanning process considerably.

One of the most important filters is the "de-screen" function. Images that are printed on a printing press (as well as those printed on a personal laser or inkjet printer) are converted into a pattern of tiny little dots in a process called

---

You can actually scan a black-and-white image in color mode. This wastes both time and memory because the computer is storing more information than is actually needed.

If you open a JPEG image and re-save it, the quality will be degraded. This is due to the fact JPEG images are *compressed* each time they are saved.

"screening." These dots blend together so your eye perceives a smooth image. But, if you look at the printed image under a magnifying glass, you may notice the distinct pattern of dots.

Unfortunately, the scanner sees these dots quite well. As a result, scanned copies of screened images often look very poor. The only way to combat this problem is to use a de-screening filter while the scan is being recorded. For more information, check the documentation that came with your scanner. Just remember, using the filter will slow down the speed of the scan.

Recommendations

Be sure to set the size, color, and resolution of your scanned image *before* you import it into a drawing program. You can do this either at the time you scan the image or after you scan it. If the image has already been scanned, open it in an image editing program to make changes and then save the modified file.

If you are scanning photographs or drawings primarily for the purposes of tracing them on screen, be sure to use RGB format for color images or *grayscale* mode for black-and-white images. You can also convert color images to grayscale if the colors in the photo are not needed for reference.

If the image being scanned is simple line art, you have the option of using *Monochrome* mode. Just remember, *grayscale mode* will appear smoother, and it will generally give you a much better scan.

All that remains is to decide on a resolution. The choice will depend on a number of factors such as the size of the photo and the amount of detail it contains. In general, really big images such as an 8 X 10 photo do not need to be scanned at high resolution due to the large format. On the other hand, small photos such as 5 X 7 images should probably be scanned in high resolution so you can zoom in and analyze details close up.

If, however, the file size of the scanned image is overly large, it will take up a lot of memory just to display and work with the image. This can slow down the performance of some computers. If this happens to you, consider converting color images to grayscale mode. Doing this dramatically reduces the amount of memory needed to work with the image. Refer to the documentation that came with your photo editing program for more information on converting scanned images to different formats.

Finally, there is a special case that needs to be mentioned. If the image you are scanning was originally printed in a magazine, newspaper, or book, it has been screened. Therefore, scan it at 300 ppi and be sure to activate the *de-screen function*. Because of the way print screening is accomplished, a resolution of 300 ppi often works best.

Resizing Images

Since most drawing programs are not designed for manipulating photographs, often the best they can do is simply display them on screen. As a result, the size and quality of what you see will depend primarily on the *resolution* of the photo. As you zoom in and out to magnify your view of the drawing, the quality of the displayed image may change dramatically.

For best results, *resize* the template image so it displays at *screen resolution*. This takes some of the burden off the drawing program because it does not have to render the image at high levels of magnification.

When the image is saved at screen resolution, it will look best at a magnification of 100% or below. If you zoom in farther than 100%, the image will *pixelate*. This means it will appear "fuzzy," and you will start to see the individual pixels that make up the image.

By limiting scanned photos to screen resolution, the image will have to be very large in order to display all the detail needed while tracing it. The secret to this process is scanning the image at a high resolution (when appropriate) and then *resizing* it to screen resolution without losing any of the scanned information. To do this, change the size of the image, but do not *re-sample* it. To better understand how this works, take a look at the following example:

> Let's say you want to scan a 5 X 7 photo as a template for making a tracing. First, scan the image at 300 ppi to capture all the detail, thereby creating a high-resolution image. To reduce the amount of memory needed to work with this image, capture and save it in *grayscale mode*. The resulting file should then be saved as a TIFF image.
>
> Open the scanned photo in an image editing program. Because the photo was scanned at 300 ppi, the scanner recorded 300 pixels of information per inch. Therefore, the 5 X 7 photo was turned into 1500 X 2100 pixels of information (5 inches times 300 ppi by 7 inches times 300 ppi).
>
> At 100% magnification, the scanned image will be just 5 X 7 inches on screen. This may not be ideal for tracing the image in a drawing program. In order to capture all the fine detail, the tracing would have to be performed at high magnification. This might slow down the performance of the drawing program.
>
> To make the image easier to trace, save it at *screen resolution*. To do this without losing any of the detail, the pixel count must remain the same. Therefore, the *dimensions* of the photo will need to be changed.
>
> In this case, the scanned photo contains 1500 X 2100 pixels of information. To save the image at screen resolution without losing any detail, increase the overall size while reducing the resolution. To do this, divide the pixel count by the resolution of your computer screen. Thus, 1500 pixels divided by 96 equals 15.625 inches and 2100 pixels divided by 96 equals 21.875 inches.

Most image editing programs have a command or function for resizing images. For example, in *Adobe Photoshop*, choose the "Image Size" command from the "Image" menu.

The "Image Size" command in *Photoshop* can handle all the details of resizing an image without worrying about calculating the new dimensions.

The number "96" was chosen because that represents the resolution of a typical computer screen.

Therefore, without changing the pixel count, this example photo can be resized to **15.625 X 21.875 inches** at **96 ppi**. This is equivalent to 20.83 X 29.17 inches at 72 ppi on some Macintosh computers. In either case, the image will contain the exact same amount of information (1500 X 2100 pixels) as the original 5 X 7 photo scanned at 300 ppi.

Keep in mind, resolution and image size have an *inverse* relationship. As a result, *reducing* the resolution of the image without also *increasing* the dimensions will cause the program to "throw out" some of the scanned information. This is an example of what is known as "re-sampling" an image.

The process of discarding data to make a scanned image smaller is called "down-sampling." If this happens, you could lose valuable information when your image is saved at a lower resolution. Thus, it is a good idea to avoid down-sampling unless it is absolutely necessary. Remember, once the scanned information is gone, the only way to get it back is to start over and scan the image once again.

In general, the only time you might want to down-sample an image is when it was scanned at too high a resolution in the first place. In that event, you could reduce the resolution in order to make the image easier to work with. For example, an image scanned at 600 ppi could probably be down-sampled to 300 ppi without losing very much critical detail.

Summary

When an image is scanned, the computer divides it into tiny regions called *pixels*. The number of pixels recorded depends on the *resolution* of the scan. Each pixel is individually recorded and assembled to create an *image file*. Because of the amount of information that is being stored, file sizes of scanned images can be quite large. An *image editing program* is needed in order to view or modify these images.

The first step is to scan the image into the computer. You can do this by hooking up a scanner and installing the appropriate software or by taking your photos to a photo lab, photo processing center, or copy center and having them scanned and saved to disc. If you have a scanner, decide on the following parameters prior to getting started:

- Resolution
- Color mode
- File type
- Filters

Resolution is measured in *pixels-per-inch* or "ppi." A *low-resolution image* should be scanned to match the resolution of your computer screen. In contrast, a *high-resolution image* is one that is scanned at about 200 ppi or higher. *Color mode* tells the scanner whether you want to capture the image in color

Since you can easily scale any lines or objects you draw on top of a bitmap image, don't worry about sizing the image to match the scale of the drawing. Instead, size the template photo to maximize the clarity and detail in the image. This will make the task of tracing it much easier.

or in black and white. Choices include *Monochrome* and *Grayscale* formats for non-color scans and RGB and CMYK formats for color scans.

Once a scan is recorded, it will be saved to disk as an appropriate image file type. Several possible choices include Bitmap, JPEG, TIFF, and TARGA. JPEG should be avoided because it uses compression that can degrade the quality of the scanned image.

If the image you are scanning was originally printed in a magazine, newspaper, or book, scan it at 300 ppi and be sure to activate the *de-screen function* during scanning.

For best results, resize template photos that are to be traced by making them *screen resolution*. The goal should be to size the photo in such a way as to maximize clarity and detail in the image. This will also improve system performance while tracing the image. Once you are done, scale the tracing as needed to fit your drawing.

Appendix C:
Printing Your Plans on Paper

Overview

When it comes time to print your plans, you will probably find yourself limited by the type of printer at your disposal. For example, most personal and office printers can only accept paper sheets up to 8.5 x 14 inches, with a few going as large as 11 x 17 inches. Obviously, this makes such printers unsuitable when outputting blueprints for anything other than very small projects.

The solution is to output your drawings on a special *large-format printer*. These can be found at your local copy center or reprographics company. There are several options to choose from depending on the type of drawing file you have created. This section will discuss printing concepts, requirements, and available options in detail.

Page or Sheet Size

Illustration programs by their very nature were created to produce artwork that will be output to a printer. As a result, they are designed to make drawings that fit on *pages* of a specific size. So, the first step in creating a new drawing is choosing a page size. Since model plans can be quite large, however, you might think of this as a *sheet size* instead.

In contrast, CAD programs are designed specifically for drafting. Thus, they may be configured to output drawings on any standard-size drafting sheets. In fact, special printers have been created specifically for outputting drawing files created by CAD programs. These printers are called *plotters*. (See "Large-Format Printers" for more information.)

The requirement of determining a sheet size in advance might tempt some modelers to choose a size or *scale* for their drawings based on how big they wish the printout to be. At first glance, this may appear to be a good idea. In reality, however, it's best to make your drawing first, *then* divide up your work to fit onto individual sheets as needed.

Plans should always be scaled to match the size of the model being built. This may take up more space than can fit on any one sheet of paper.

NOTE: Underlined terms appear in the Glossary.

In this context, the term "page" is almost a misnomer. Since most modeling plans take up a large amount of space, they are often arranged on poster-sized "sheets" rather than on pages.

Since it is very easy to move and scale drawing objects as needed, you can easily rearrange your drawings to optimize them for printing after they have been completed.

So, what size sheets should you choose? Most modern large-format printers use giant rolls of paper. They can output anything as large as the length and width of an entire roll. For sure, this should be large enough to accommodate plans for just about *any* model-building project. Therefore, you need not worry about choosing a scale for your computer drawings based simply on the paper size used to print them.

Considerations When Using an Illustration Program

In a computer illustration program, the drawing "canvas" represents the total space available within the program for all the different pages or sheets that make up your drawing. It is, in effect, your "virtual drawing board."

This working area is also known as a *pasteboard* – a term which hearkens back to the days when layout artists assembled their artwork the "old-fashioned" way.

Keep in mind, the size of this virtual drawing board is not infinite. In fact, most programs have a limit on the total drawing area. In general, you can have as many pages/sheets as you want, and each can have different dimensions. That said, *all* the pages/sheets in your document must fit within the total drawing area supported by the program.

The actual dimensions of the virtual drawing board will depend on the units you have chosen for your drawing. Most programs can work with a variety of units, including inches, centimeters, and millimeters. Since illustration programs were created to make pages for print, they may also include unfamiliar choices such as points and picas. These are not appropriate for the purpose of drafting plans.

Using a typical illustration program, drawings can be up to 10-12 feet across. This defines the practical upper limit to the size of any drawings you can create. If you attempt to draw anything larger, you may run into problems when using some applications. In this case, try scaling your drawing down so it is within the limitations of the program. Or, divide the drawing into two or more files.

Whatever you choose to do, you can always make a *copy* of the finished plans and then format the copy for printing as needed. Simply divide the copied drawings into "chunks" that will fit on a specific size sheet. Then, create as many sheets as needed to contain everything you want to print.

Also, don't forget you can easily stretch or shrink drawings to make them fit on any size sheet of paper. Just keep in mind, dividing up your work in such a manner can be done quite easily *after* you are finished drawing.

One of the advantages of using a CAD application is the ability to work with *scaled units*. Since computer illustration programs were not designed to draw blueprints, they don't typically offer this convenient feature.

Large-Format Printers

Large-format printers can be found in copy centers, quick-print shops, and reprographics houses. These devices use large rolls of paper that are limited only in *width*. This means a printout of your drawing can be as wide as the roll of paper and just about any length.

There are two very different approaches for large-format printing. When computerized drafting was first developed, special printers called *plotters* were created. In the beginning, these machines actually held pens that moved back and forth across the paper to produce an image. Later, electrostatic, inkjet, and laser processes were developed. This resulted in large machines that functioned much like a personal printer.

Modern plotters are commonly called *engineering copiers*. These devices can print either in black and white or in full color. They accept large paper rolls up to about 42 inches wide. Some rolls can be as much as 150 feet long.

Printouts created by plotters are known as "plots." Because they were created for the drafting industry, most plotters are designed to accept drawings saved in popular CAD formats. (For more information, see "Plotting" below.)

In contrast, a completely different type of printer was developed for outputting graphics generated by computer illustration programs. These printers are based on Adobe's *PostScript*® printing language (see "Printing" below).

Plotting

To print your plans on a modern engineering copier, your drawing will typically need to be saved in a standard CAD format. The most popular choice is the *AutoCAD*® DWG file. Another commonly used format is DXF.

As an alternative, most plotters can now accept files saved in PDF format. This is a very important option. In the past, anyone using a computer illustration program was unable to print to a plotter because a technological "divide" existed between the two formats (CAD and *PostScript*). Today, however, thanks to Adobe's *Acrobat*® software, this dilemma has been solved once and for all.

Plotting is typically done in black and white, but some modern plotters can now output in color as well. All you need to do is pick a paper stock. Since most plotting is done for architects and engineers, only a small selection of paper stocks may be available at some shops. The most common type of paper is called "copy bond." This is exactly like the "typing paper" used in most personal printers and commercial copiers. A 20-lb copy bond is typical and is often the most economical paper choice available.

Printing

In contrast to plotters that speak the language of CAD, computer illustration programs support the Adobe *PostScript* printing language. A variety of special printers use this standard to output drawing files. These printers are full-color devices for the most part, though some large-format, black-and-white laser printers may be available. In general, however, *PostScript* printing is for color output while plotting is primarily used for black-and-white or grayscale output.

PDF stands for "Portable Document Format." Because plotting of CAD files has traditionally been much cheaper than large-format *PostScript* printing, the advent of PDF plotting has solved what was once a major headache for many computer artists.

Users of computer illustration programs can now print to just about any large-format printer – including plotters – as long as the program can generate a PDF file. If not, you can always purchase Adobe's *Acrobat* software. This program can generate PDF output using the "Print" function in just about any program.

PostScript printers use a variety of technologies to produce stunning color prints. These printers can output to a variety of paper stocks and even other substrates by way of what is known as a *transfer medium*. Inkjet and laser printers are among the most popular choices. Keep in mind, however, the cost of printing in color can be much higher than output in black and white.

To print to a *PostScript* printer, check with the owner of the device to see what file types they accept. You may be able to save your drawing in any of the following formats:

- Adobe *Illustrator*®
- Macromedia *Freehand*®
- *CorelDRAW*®
- EPS
- PDF

Binding

If you are outputting multiple sheets, you may want to have your plans *bound*. The binding process adds a special strip of paper to one edge. Staples are then added to secure the sheets together. This can make multi-sheet sets of plans much easier to handle. Since binding is often a very inexpensive option, you may want to consider having this done when your plans are printed.

Sources

So, exactly where can you get your plans printed? Several options may be available depending on your location. Modern copy centers such as FedEx® Office (formerly known as Kinkos) offer large-format printing services both in black and white and color. Keep in mind, these copy centers may need PDF files in order to print your drawings.

For plotting, simply visit your local reprographics center. Traditionally known as "blueprint shops," these facilities offer a variety of printing services in both black-and-white and in color. They can easily accept drawings in any popular CAD format, as well as most PDF files. A reprographics center may offer the most cost-effective printing options available since plots may be priced at just pennies per square foot. Some shops even have *PostScript* printers for specialty color printing.

Summary

Plans should always be scaled to match the size of the model being built. This, however, might take up more space than can fit on any one sheet of paper. Fortunately, it is very easy to move and scale drawing objects as needed. Therefore, you can easily rearrange your drawings as necessary in order to optimize them for printing.

At the time of this writing, most *PostScript* printers do not accept CAD file formats.

Binding is typically done on the left edge of the paper.

When it comes time to print your plans, output them to a *large-format printer*. There are several options to choose from depending on the type of drawing file you have created.

Special printers called *plotters* are available to output drawings saved in either CAD or PDF format. Modern plotters are commonly called *engineering copiers*. These machines can print either in black and white or in full color on large rolls of *copy bond paper* up to about 42 inches wide.

A completely different type of printer was developed for outputting graphics generated by computer illustration programs. These printers are based on Adobe's *PostScript* printing language and are full-color devices for the most part. To print to a *PostScript* printer, check with the owner of the device to see what type of files they accept.

Modern *copy centers* that offer large-format printing services often require PDF files for output. *Reprographics centers* can plot any CAD file, and they may accept PDF files as well. If you are outputting multiple sheets, you may want to have your printed plans *bound*.

Glossary

NOTE: Underlined terms appear elsewhere in the Glossary.

3-View Drawings. A series of plan views that illustrate the overall form of a subject. Such "primary" views often show the subject's height, width, and depth. This may be all that is needed to adequately describe many subjects. See also First-Angle Projection; Multi-View Drawing; Orthographic Projection; Third-Angle Projection.

Adjacent View. A view that is located to the side of, directly above, or directly beneath another view.

Amidships. A nautical term meaning something is located in or along the middle part of a ship. Typically means located along the ship's centerline. Can also be used to describe a similar location in an aircraft.

Arc. A portion of the circumference of a circle.

Arrowheads. Directional marks in the shape of the tip of an arrow used either to indicate the distance between two points on a dimensioned working drawing or as a pointer to specify a particular object in a drawing.

Auxiliary Plane of Projection. A special plane arranged so as to be parallel with a non-principal plane or surface in order to project an auxiliary view. When any plane or surface on an object is not parallel to a principal plane of projection, it is a non-principal plane and therefore will not appear true size in the corresponding plan views. An auxiliary plane of projection is set up in order to create a true-size view of such a non-principal surface. See also Parallelism.

Auxiliary View. A true-size view of a non-principal plane or surface projected from an auxiliary plane of projection. When any plane or surface on an object is not parallel to a principal plane of projection, it cannot be depicted as true size in the corresponding normal (i.e. principal) plan views. Such a plane or surface can only be depicted true size by creating an auxiliary view. See also Parallelism.

Axes of Motion. The three dimensions about which motion can occur. Labeling for each axis often depends on the context or subject. For objects such as vehicles, the three dimensions may be described as *longitudinal* (fore-aft), *lateral* (side-to-side) and *vertical* (up-down). Longitudinal and lateral motions often correspond with the "x" and "y" axes of a two-dimensional plane. In this case, the "z" axis represents the third or vertical dimension. See also Geometric Center.

Axes of Rotation. The three dimensions about which an object can rotate. Labeling for each axis often depends on the context or subject. For aircraft, the three axes are *pitch* (rotating upward or downward about the lateral axis), *roll* (rotating or "banking" left or right about the longitudinal axis) and *yaw* (turning or "pointing" to the left or right about the vertical axis). See also Geometric Center.

Axis of Rotation. One of the three dimensions about which an object can rotate. See Axes of Rotation.

Axis of Symmetry. The "dividing line" or centerline about which an object is symmetrical. Features on either side of the axis of symmetry will be a mirror image of each other.

Bézier Curves. (Pronounced "BEZ-ee-ay") A curved line created by a computer illustration program. The formula for calculating such curves was pioneered by Pierre Bézier, a noted French engineer, scientist, and teacher. These drawing objects are nearly universal to all computer illustration programs. Some applications, however, may refer to them as "paths." CAD programs may use a completely different approach behind the scenes when creating curved lines. See also Spline.

Bitmap Image. A digital image created from individual dots called pixels. When an image is scanned, the computer divides it into tiny little regions. The number of regions recorded depends on the resolution of the scan. Both the color and the light/dark value of each region are individually recorded and stored as pixels. These values are then assembled to create a digital image file. Because of the large amount of information being stored, the file size of bitmap images can be quite large. As a result, they can take up a lot of disk space. See also Vector-Based Art.

Blueprints. Drawings created to precisely and accurately describe the construction of an object. Presentation plans depict a subject from multiple angles or views. Floor plans and elevations describe buildings and other structures. Design drawings depict objects ranging from furniture and cabinetry to crafts and consumer products. Modelers create plans in order to build their projects. All these drawings are blueprints.

Body Plan. A special plan view that consolidates many different cross section outlines into a single view. Naval architects use body plans to describe the complex curves of boat and ship hulls. By consolidating all the cross section outlines together, the result is a clean and compact representation of the cross section for the entire hull. See also Dividing Line.

Bored. Drilled partially or all the way through. Example: A hole can be bored through an object or a hole can be bored in an object.

Bulkhead. The dividing line between watertight compartments on a ship or a transverse frame member inside an aircraft fuselage. On boats and ships, frame stations mark the points along the hull where either a bulkhead or a transverse frame is positioned. On aircraft, frame stations mark the points along the fuselage where bulkheads are positioned. The structural frame is then "skinned" to form the shape of the hull or fuselage.

CAD. An acronym meaning "Computer-Aided Design."

Centerline(s). A "dividing line" defining the location of a cutting plane that precisely divides an object in half. For symmetrical objects, the centerline is the axis of symmetry. In such cases, features on either side of this line will be a mirror image of each other.

Central Angle. The angle between two lines that form a *sector* of a circle. If you imagine the circle as a pizza, a sector would be a single slice. The straight edges of this slice would be two radial lines drawn from the center of the circle to the outside edge or circumference. The central angle would then be the angle between these two radial lines.

Chordal Distance. An approximation of the distance between two points along the edge or circumference of a circle. Since the precise measurement of such distances requires utilizing mathematical formulas for the length of an arc, measuring the chordal distance is quicker and easier because it can be accomplished graphically. The chordal distance is simply the length of a straight line connecting two points along the edge of a circle. In contrast, the true distance along the circumference is the *arc length* between the same two points.

Clearance. A gap created between two parts to streamline assembly and fitting. Because the proper fit of most parts requires some degree of tolerance, plans should ideally take this into account. In many cases, it is possible to draw parts in the computer much more precisely than they can be built in the real world. Creating "buffer" space around such parts provides some "wiggle room" to allow for a proper fit. In general, a margin of at least 0.01 inch or even more is often a good idea. Machine-cut parts may require less clearance while parts cut by hand often require more clearance. See also Tolerance.

CMYK. An acronym that means "Cyan, Yellow, Magenta and Black." CMYK represents what is known as a "color space." Printing presses and color printers create color images using four different colors of ink. In contrast, RGB ("Red, Green, Blue") is the method of choice for displaying color on television screens and computer monitors. Digital image files that are to be printed should be scanned and saved in CMYK format. This stores more information, however, and therefore takes up more computer memory than color scans saved in RGB format. CMYK images may also take longer to scan. See also Bitmap Image; Grayscale; Monochrome.

CNC. An acronym that means "Computer Numeric Control." A CNC device is a machine that is controlled by a computer. These machines may operate in two dimensions or in three dimensions to cut or shape parts out of wood, metal, or plastic. Such a device moves by means of *stepper motors* that are actuated by a computer-controlled interface.

Conical Helix. A coil formed by wrapping a sloping line around a cone. This type of helix appears as a *spiral* when viewed from directly above. See also Helix.

Constant Cross Section. To have a cross section that does not change either in size or in shape along the entire length of the object. Examples of shapes that have a constant cross section include solid rods, tubes, and pieces of pipe. An object with a constant cross section can be extruded. See also Extruding.

Construction Lines. Temporary lines sketched on a drawing to aid in constructing views of objects. Such lines often extend from one view into another to help locate points and/or features in multiple views at the same time. These lines must be removed to produce a clean, final drawing. Therefore, when using a computer drawing program, it is best to place them on a separate layer. It is also helpful to choose a very light color for your construction lines. See also Tint.

Conventional Revolution. The practice of revolving a symmetrical object or feature until it appears true length in a particular view. For the draftsman, it may be considered poor practice to draw a true representation of certain symmetrical features in a plan view when they are not parallel to that view. The reason is simply that such objects cannot be measured when they do not appear true size in a view. While revolving such features allows them to be measured, the view in question will no longer be a true representation of what the object really looks like. As a result, this convention is somewhat subjective and may cause confusion. See also Parallelism; Revolution; Revolved; Revolving.

Cross Section. A section view created by passing a cutting plane through an object. Though section views may be created at any location necessary to describe the structure of an object, the cutting plane is typically parallel to the frontal plane of projection. See also Section.

Cube. A six-sided, three-dimensional shape where each side is a square.

Custom Guides. Lines and/or objects in a computer illustration program that have been placed on the Guides layer. Standard Guides are limited to horizontal and vertical lines. Creating a Custom Guide permits the use of angled lines (such as a miter line) or other objects that act like standard Guides. This is important because lines and objects can snap to Guides.

Cutting Plane. A plane that "slices through" an object at a particular location. By plotting the intersection of the plane and the object, a cross section outline can be drawn at that location. The cutting plane is represented by a straight line in a view when the edge of the plane is parallel to that view. See also Edge View.

Cylinder. An object with a circular cross section such as a round rod, a tube, or a piece of pipe.

Decimal Inches. A unit of measurement whereby an inch is divided into tenths rather than sixteenths. Thus, 1/2 inch would be 5/10 of a decimal inch. Decimal inches are a convenient measuring system when you need to use a calculator to find measurements. In contrast, fractions must be converted into a decimal equivalent before punching the numbers into a calculator.

Degrees. The basic unit of measurement for angles. A circle is divided into 360 degrees. An alternative to the degree is a unit known as the <u>radian</u>. These alternate units are often used in trigonometry. Radians are also important in calculations pertaining to circles as well as in mathematical formulas for calculating the length of an arc. When working with certain formulas it is sometimes necessary to convert from degrees to radians and vice versa. See also <u>Radians</u>.

Derived. Deduced or calculated from available information. As an example, if you know the overall length of an object and also the length from one end to a certain feature, you can derive the measurement for the distance between the same feature and the opposite end of the object.

Design drawings. <u>Blueprints</u> created by industrial designers or craftsmen for constructing industrial or consumer products. This is a subjective label that can be applied to any number of different items. For example, an industrial designer might produce design drawings for a toy or for a bottle that contains a liquid product. A craftsman might produce design drawings in order to construct a cabinet or a piece of furniture.

Develop. To "unfold" or "unroll" a three-dimensional object in such a way as to create flat patterns that can then be used to construct it from sheet material. See also <u>Developments</u>; <u>Unfold</u>; <u>Unroll</u>.

Developments. Flat patterns that, when assembled, will yield a three-dimensional object. See also <u>Develop</u>; <u>Template</u>.

Diameter. The total overall width of a circle. This value can be accurately measured by passing a straight line through the exact center of the circle.

Dimension Lines. Lines used to indicate the start and end points of measurements noted in <u>dimensioned</u> drawings (i.e. <u>working drawings</u>). To conform to convention, dimension lines should be positioned so as not to cause confusion or clutter. They should have <u>arrowheads</u> at both ends.

Dimension Numbers. Numbers placed over the center of <u>dimension lines</u> to denote the values of the measurements being specified.

Dimensioned. Having key dimensions specified/labeled using <u>dimension lines</u>, <u>dimension numbers</u>, and <u>extension lines</u>.

Dimensioning. The process of marking key dimensions on a drawing using <u>dimension lines</u>, <u>dimension numbers</u>, and <u>extension lines</u>.

Dividing Line. A line added to a top or side <u>plan view</u> to mark the location of the widest point along the hull of a ship or the fuselage of an airplane. All <u>cross section</u> outlines forward of this point will appear in the front <u>plan view</u> while all cross section outlines aft of this point will appear in the rear plan view. The dividing line also helps in the creation of a body plan. See also <u>Body Plan</u>.

Dodecahedron. A three-dimensional geometric shape having 12 faces where each face is in the shape of a five-sided pentagon.

Drafting. The process of creating mechanical drawings of an object in such a way that measurements can be accurately extracted and/or interpreted from them.

Edge View. A view that depicts a plane or surface of an object as an edge. The edge of the plane or surface will appear as a straight line in any such view.

Elevations. Side, front, and/or rear plan views of a building or other structure. An elevation is any view that shows the vertical portions of the building/structure rather than the horizontal layout. See also Floor Plan.

English Units. A traditional system of measurement using inches, pounds, and gallons that is standard in the United States of America. Also known as "US Customary Units." English measurements, sometimes called "Imperial" measurements, are also standard in Great Britain. Note, however, that some measurements have slightly different values between US/English and British/Imperial standards. In stark contrast, the Metric system (called "Système International d'Unités" or "SI") is a decimal-based system of measurement using meters, kilograms, and liters.

Extension Lines. Lines that extend from points on a feature or object to either end of a dimension line. Extension lines are used to indicate the start and end points of measurements in a dimensioned drawing. They help keep the drawing clear by allowing the dimension labels to be placed away from the object while indicating the exact start and end points of the measurement in question. See also Dimension Lines; Dimension Numbers; Dimensioned; Dimensioning.

Extruding. The process of creating a three-dimensional object or structure using a two-dimensional cross section outline. Extruding can be used in the manufacture of products that have a constant cross section. It is also a technique for making 3D computer models. All that is needed to build such a shape is a drawing of the cross section to be extruded. This makes extruding a very fast and easy technique for three-dimensional construction.

First-Angle Projection. Standard for arranging multi-view drawings practiced in Europe and the International community. This system places the top view at the center of the drawing with the front view above it and the left side view to the right of the front view. A completely different arrangement called third-angle projection is practiced in the United States, Canada, and Great Britain.

Floor Plans. Top plan view of a building or other structure looking downward. A floor plan shows the horizontal layout of the building/structure. In contrast, elevations depict the vertical portions.

Focal Plane. A surface onto which light is focused in order to create a clear image either by exposing film inside a camera or by recording information in digital format using a charge-coupled-device ("CCD"). The focal plane is parallel with the body of the camera. Due to the properties of optics, light focused through the lens of the camera creates an upside-down image on the focal plane.

Fold Line. The line along which two sides of an imaginary glass box surrounding a subject meet. Orthographic projection works by "unfolding" such an imaginary box and arranging all the sides on a single plane represented by a sheet of paper. The fold line becomes very important when creating a primary auxiliary view. The draftsman will measure distances from the object to the fold line in order to create a true-size representation of the object in the auxiliary view.

Foreshortened. Not appearing true length or true size. Both lines and planes/ surfaces can appear foreshortened in an orthographic plan view when they are not parallel to the principal plane of projection upon which the view was derived. See also True Length, True Size.

Frame Station. A location along the hull of a boat or ship – or along the fuselage of an aircraft – where a structural framing member is located. On boats and ships, frame stations mark points along the hull where either bulkheads or transverse frames are positioned. (On aircraft, all transverse frames are called bulkheads.) The structural frame is then "skinned" to form the shape of the hull or fuselage.

Frontal Plane. One of the three principal planes of projection that yields the front and rear plan views. Since both views are parallel to one another, the plane of projection that yields the front plan view is parallel to the plane of projection that yields the rear plan view. As a result, these planes of projection can be combined into a single plane known as the frontal plane. See also Parallelism.

Frustum of a Cone. A cone that is missing part of the top. The top surface of the frustum of a cone is parallel with the bottom. In contrast, when a cone has been trimmed such that the top and bottom surfaces are non-parallel, it is known as a truncated cone.

Frustum of a Pyramid. A pyramid that is missing part of the top. The top surface of the frustum of a pyramid is parallel with the bottom. In contrast, when the pyramid is trimmed such that the top and bottom surfaces are non-parallel, it is known as a truncated pyramid.

Geometric Center. The precise center point of an object where the lateral, longitudinal, and vertical axes come together. Since some objects can rotate or move about a point other than the geometric center, this may or may not be the same point as the *center of rotation* (i.e. the point where the three axes of motion meet). See also Axes of Motion, Axes of Rotation.

Geometric Solid. A three-dimensional area of space enclosed either by a curved surface or by a series of flat surfaces that are joined together at the edges (i.e. a "closed" surface). Geometric solids include cubes, cylinders, prisms, cones, pyramids, spheres, and polyhedrons (or "polyhedra").

Gore. A portion of the development of a sphere. A gore is also known as a lune. Since a sphere has compound curves, it cannot be precisely developed.

The process of creating gores or lunes permits the surface of a sphere to be approximated as a series of flat patterns. This process is commonly used to create globes from printed paper parts.

Grayscale. An image format for storing digital photographs, images, or scans that displays the image in black, white, and shades of gray, but not in color. One of two possible formats for storing non-color images in digital form. The other option is called Monochrome. See also Bitmap Image; CMYK; Image File, RGB.

Guides. Parallel lines appearing on the screen of a computer illustration program. Guides replace horizontal and vertical construction lines traditionally drawn by the draftsman on paper using a parallel rule and T-square. See also Custom Guides.

Half-Round. One half of a cylinder, split lengthwise down the middle.

Half Section. A section view where one half of the object is omitted to save space. This is most often done when the object in question is perfectly symmetrical, meaning it is not necessary to draw the entire object. See also Section.

Hatching. A series of equally spaced parallel lines used to create the appearance of *shading* in a techical drawing or blueprint. In the past, such drawings were nearly always monochrome. Thus, they did not contain any shades of gray. As a result, it was necessary to find a way to use solid black to create the *illusion* of gray. Placing hatched lines closer together creates the effect of darker shading. Lines placed farther apart indicate lighter shading. In drafting, this is often done to indicate the presence of a solid structure – particularly in "cutaway" drawings like section views.

Helix. A coil formed by wrapping a sloping line around a cylinder. A regular helix appears as a circle when viewed from directly above. See also Conical Helix.

Hemisphere. One half of a sphere.

Horizontal Plane. One of the three principal planes of projection that yields the top and bottom plan views. Since both views are parallel to one another, the plane of projection that yields the top plan view is parallel to the plane of projection that yields the bottom plan view. As a result, these planes of projection can be combined into a single plane known as the horizontal plane. See also Parallelism.

Icosahedron. A three-dimensional geometric shape having 20 faces where each face is in the shape of a triangle.

Image Editing Program. Software designed to open and modify bitmap images. These include digital photographs, scans, and other digital artwork that is stored as a series of pixels in an image file.

Image File. An assemblage of individual pixels that make up a digital image such as a scanned photograph. When an image is scanned, the computer divides it into tiny little regions and records both the color and the light/dark value of each region. These values are then assembled to create a digital image file. Because of the large amount of information being recorded, image files can take up a lot of disk space. See also CMYK; Grayscale; Monochrome; RGB.

Inclined Line. A line that is parallel only to one principal plane of projection. Inclined lines are non-normal lines.

Inclined Plane. A plane that is not parallel to any of the principal planes of projection, but is perpendicular to one plane of projection. Inclined planes are non-normal planes.

Incomplete View. A view that is "cleaned up" to eliminate unnecessary hidden lines. Sometimes an object is so complex that including every single hidden line would produce a very "busy" and potentially confusing drawing. In this case, some of the hidden lines may be omitted in an effort to produce a cleaner drawing.

Interpret. To examine and analyze a photograph to understand exactly what is being depicted. Interpreting photos is a valuable skill that can help a modeler extract critical information that can be used to accurately recreate the subject.

Intersection. The location where two surfaces meet in three dimensions. An intersection in 3D space is defined by a three-dimensional line. This line can then be projected into any orthographic plan view. Accurately plotting intersections can be one of the most challenging aspects of model design. Fortunately, 3D computer modeling tools can make this process much easier.

Isometric. A "pictorial" representation of an object that depicts three-dimensional information without including any visual perspective. Measurements can be taken from an isometric view just as they can from an orthographic plan view. Since the eye always sees visual perspective in everything, however, an isometric view may not be intuitive.

Lateral Axis. An axis running from one side of an object to another defined by a line that extends through its geometric center.

Lathing. A process of creating a perfectly symmetrical three-dimensional object using a two-dimensional profile. The profile is revolved around the axis of symmetry. This process can be used to carve shapes from wood and other materials on a tool called a *lathe*. It can also be used in 3D computer modeling to quickly and easily build three-dimensional shapes.

Layer. A plane in a computer drawing that can contain lines and other drawing objects. Also known as an "overlay." Layers are used to organize drawings and reduce clutter. In the past, when drawings were made by hand, sheets of vellum or clear acetate were assembled to create the multiple layers of a complex drawing. Today, computer programs make it possible to organize a drawing using an almost infinite assortment of different layers.

Leader Lines. Thin lines that connect a note(s) about an object on a drawing to the area or feature in question. Such lines should begin next to the first or the last word in the note rather than in the middle. A leader line pointing to a feature ends in an <u>arrowhead</u> while a leader line pointing to a surface or area ends in a round dot. See also <u>Dimension Lines</u>; <u>Dimension Numbers</u>; <u>Dimensioned</u>; <u>Dimensioning</u>.

Line of Sight. An imaginary line between the eye of an observer and an object or feature. The line of sight defines a specific viewing angle or point of view on the part of the observer.

Lofting. The process of creating a three-dimensional shape by combining or "blending" multiple <u>cross sections</u> along a given path. This process is very similar to <u>extruding</u>. A lofted shape, however, can have different cross sections at points along its length whereas an extruded shape has a <u>constant cross section</u>.

Longitudinal Axis. An axis running down the length of an object, defined by a line that extends through its <u>geometric center</u>.

Lune. A portion of the <u>development</u> of a sphere. A lune is also known as a <u>gore</u>. Since a sphere has compound curves, it cannot be precisely developed. The process of creating gores or lunes, however, permits the surface of a sphere to be *approximated* as a series of flat patterns. This process is commonly used to create globes from printed paper parts.

Mesh. The three-dimensional surface of an object inside a 3D computer modeling program. Mesh surfaces are composed of <u>polygons</u> that are stitched together. In most cases, each polygon is a triangle. Sometimes, however, they may be 4-sided quadrilaterals. A program that creates mesh objects can be thought of as forming "digital clay" that a 3D modeler can then "sculpt" using a number of different computer-based tools. In sharp contrast, a <u>spline</u>-based modeling program creates precise surfaces from curves based on mathematical formulas. Unlike mesh modeling, spline modeling is a natural extension of the 2D <u>drafting</u> process. See also <u>Multigon</u>; <u>Bézier Curves</u>.

Metric. A decimal-based system of measurement using meters, kilograms, and liters that is standard in Europe and the International community. Also known as "Système International d'Unités" or "SI" for short. The labels for each unit of measurement in the Metric system are based on a decimal percentage of the fundamental unit. As an example, a "centimeter" is 1/100 of a meter while a "millimeter" is 1/1000 of a meter. In stark contrast, a more traditional system of "US Customary Units" based on the inch, pound, and gallon remain the standard in the United States of America. These <u>English</u> units are based on the "Imperial" units developed by Great Britain.

Miter Line. A line positioned 45-degrees from the horizontal that is used to transfer points between <u>non-adjacent views</u>. The miter line is one of the key concepts that makes <u>orthographic projection</u> work. Acting as an angled "mirror," the miter line is used to "reflect" construction lines from one view into another.

Modifier Key. A key on a computer keyboard that, when depressed, modifies the behavior of a command executed in a computer drawing program. The key must first be depressed and then the command is chosen from a menu (or a button is clicked). When the desired action is complete, the modifier key is released.

Monochrome. An image format for storing digital photographs, images, or scans that displays the image using only black and/or white pixels, but not shades of gray or color. One of two possible formats for storing non-color images in digital form. The other option is called grayscale. Monochrome format uses the least amount of computer memory when storing an image. See also Bitmap Image; CMYK; Image File; RGB.

Multigon. A two-dimensional geometric figure with three or more sides. In this book, the term "multigon" is used in place of the word "polygon" because a polygon is a special type of object used in 3D modeling that exists in three dimensions. See also Polygon.

Multi-view drawing. The process of preparing multiple orthographic plan views of a subject using orthographic projection. In fact, multi-view drawing is often synonymous with the term "orthographic projection." An imaginary "glass box" is said to surround the subject and views of the object are projected onto each side of this box. It is then "unfolded" so that all views are in the same plane. See also 3-View Drawings; First-Angle Projection; Third-Angle Projection.

Non-Adjacent View. A view that is not located to the side of, directly above, or directly beneath another view. As an example, when views are arranged according to the intuitive layout shown in this book, the side view is adjacent to the front, rear, top and bottom views because they are arranged around it (above, below, and on either side). On the other hand, the front and rear views are *not* adjacent to the top or bottom views. Rather, they are adjacent to the side view. When views are not adjacent, a miter line can be used to transfer points between them.

Non-Normal Line. Any line that is not a normal line. Non-normal lines may be either inclined or oblique. See also Normal; Parallelism.

Non-Normal Plane. Any plane that is not a normal plane. Non-normal planes may be either inclined or oblique. See also Normal; Parallelism.

Normal. A direction perpendicular to the face of a surface or plane. As an example, if a plane is a horizontal plane represented by the "x" and "y" axes, a line *normal* to this plane would be a vertical line representing the "z" axis. See also Parallelism.

Normal Line. A line parallel to two principal planes of projection, but perpendicular to the third. See also Parallelism.

Normal Plane. A plane that is parallel to two principal planes of projection at the same time. See also Parallelism.

Normal View. An orthographic plan view derived from one of the three principal planes of projection. All six principal plan views (top, bottom, left, right, front, rear) are normal views. On the other hand, an auxiliary view is not a normal view. This is because it is projected from an auxiliary plane of projection that is not parallel with any of the principal planes of projection. See also Parallelism.

Oblique. (Pronounced "oh-BLEEK") Not parallel to any normal view (as in an oblique line or oblique plane). Also, not upright, or appearing to "lean" to one side (such as an oblique cylinder, cone, or prism). See also Parallelism.

Oblique Cone. A cone that appears to "lean" to one side. If a line is drawn from the tip of such a cone to the exact center of the circular base, it will not be perpendicular to the plane containing the base.

Oblique Cylinder. A cylinder that appears to "lean" to one side. The ends of such a cylinder are parallel to each other, but are cut at an angle such that they are not perpendicular to the longitudinal axis of the cylinder.

Oblique Line. A non-normal line that is not parallel to any principal plan view. An oblique line appears foreshortened in all normal views. See also Parallelism.

Oblique Parallelepiped. (Pronounced "oh-BLEEK pair-uh-lel-uh-PIPE-id") A six-sided, three-dimensional shape very similar to a cube, but where each side is a *rhombus* rather than a square.

Oblique Plane. A non-normal plane that is not parallel to any principal plan view. An oblique plane appears foreshortened in all normal views. See also Parallelism.

Oblique Prism. A prism that appears to "lean" to one side. The ends of such a prism are parallel to each other, but are cut at an angle such that they are not perpendicular to the longitudinal axis of the prism.

Octahedron. A three-dimensional geometric shape having 8 faces where each face is in the shape of a triangle. An octahedron can be assembled from two square-base pyramids.

Odd Angle. Any angle that is not commonly used in construction. Common angles include 90 degrees, 60 degrees, 45 degrees, 30 degrees, 22.5 degrees (i.e. 1/2 of 45 degrees), and 15 degrees. Most angles chosen in construction come from this list of commonly used values, are multiples thereof, or are otherwise rounded to the nearest five degrees. Any other choice might be considered an odd angle.

Order of Importance. When lines overlap in a drawing, this principle is used to decide which lines to show and which to omit. Visible lines must always be shown. Therefore, they have priority over all other line types. Hidden lines are next in priority, while centerlines are last.

Orthographic Projection. A method whereby a subject can be drawn from any angle without including the distortion caused by visual perspective. The process of preparing orthographic plan views of a subject is also known as multi-view drawing. An imaginary "glass box" is said to surround the subject and views of the object are projected onto each side of this box. It is then "unfolded" so that all views are in the same plane.

Parallelism. The state of being parallel where two objects are perfectly aligned with one another and face in the same direction. If two lines are parallel, they are equidistant from one another at all times. Such lines neither converge nor diverge. Even if the lines were extended to infinity, this alignment would be maintained along their entire length. In contrast, when two lines or planes are arranged at right angles to one another, they are said to be *perpendicular*.

Partial Section. A <u>section view</u> that depicts less than one half of a feature or subject. When an object is perfectly <u>symmetrical</u>, a <u>half section</u> may be used to describe its structure while taking up less space in the drawing. For some subjects that have radial symmetry (such as a wheel), even less information may be required. In such cases, a partial section may be used to describe only a portion of the object.

Partial View. A portion of a <u>normal view</u>. If a subject is perfectly <u>symmetrical</u>, it may not be necessary to describe the entire object. If space is limited, a partial view may suffice.

Pasteboard. The total drawing area available inside a computer illustration program. All pages or sheets that make up a drawing must fit on the pasteboard. This term originates from the traditional method of creating print layouts by hand using paper and paste on a work surface such as a drawing table. The pasteboard is also known as a "virtual drawing canvas."

Pixels. The tiny regions or "dots" that makes up a digital image. Unlike a television screen that has a picture made up of *scan lines*, images on computer monitors are broken down into individual dots called pixels. All digital images must be stored as a pattern of pixels before they can be displayed on screen. Each pixel can appear white, black, a shade of gray, or any one of millions of possible colors. When an image is scanned or "digitized," the computer divides it into pixels and records both the color and the light/dark value of each. These values are then assembled to create a digital image file. See also <u>Bitmap Image</u>.

Plan View. An "orthographic" representation of a subject from a particular angle or point of view. Orthographic renderings are prepared in such a way that distortion caused by <u>visual perspective</u> is completely eliminated. An orthographic plan view can be any one of the six <u>principal plan views</u> (top, bottom, front, rear, left, and right) derived from the three <u>principal planes of projection</u>. See also <u>Orthographic Projection</u>.

Plane. A perfectly flat surface. Because it is perfectly flat, a plane is actually a two-dimensional object, but it can be oriented in any direction in three-dimensional space.

Plans. <u>Blueprints</u> created for the purpose of building a scale model of a subject.

Platonic Solids. Five special types of regular <u>polyhedrons</u> (or "polyhedra") where the same number of sides or "facets" always come together at each point or vertex. These geometric figures – named after the Greek philosopher Plato – are unique because every side, angle, and edge is the same all around the object. The five Platonic Solids are the <u>tetrahedron</u>, <u>cube</u>, <u>octahedron</u>, <u>dodecahedron</u>, and <u>icosahedron</u>.

Polygon. In geometry, a two-dimensional figure with three or more sides. In 3D modeling, the polygon is the basic element that makes up a <u>mesh</u> surface. See also <u>Mesh</u>; <u>Multigon</u>.

Polyhedron. A three-dimensional area of space enclosed by a series of flat surfaces or "facets" that are joined together at the edges (i.e. a "closed" surface). Each face of a polyhedron is a <u>multigon</u>. See also <u>Platonic Solids</u>.

Presentation Plans. <u>Blueprints</u> that depict only the overall form of a subject, but not the structural detail needed to recreate it.

Primary Auxiliary View. A <u>true-size</u> view of a non-principal <u>plane</u> or surface projected from an <u>auxiliary plane of projection</u>. The primary auxiliary view is derived from information contained in the normal <u>plan views</u> via <u>orthographic projection</u>. In contrast, a <u>secondary auxiliary view</u> is derived from information contained in a primary auxiliary view.

Principal Plan Views. The six orthographic views projected onto the sides of an imaginary "glass box" surrounding a subject using <u>orthographic projection</u>. These are the top, bottom, front, rear, left, and right views. All six principal plan views are <u>normal views</u>.

Principal Plane. A <u>normal plane</u>.

Principal Planes of Projection. Three planes of projection from which the six <u>principal plan views</u> are derived. According to the theory of <u>orthographic projection</u>, an imaginary "glass box" can be placed around a subject and the six principal plan views projected onto the six sides of this box. Each side of the box is therefore a *plane of projection*. Since views on either side of the imaginary glass box are parallel to one another, the plane of projection that yields a view on one side is parallel to the plane of projection that yields the view on the opposite side. As a result, the six planes of projection can be reduced to just three principal planes of projection.

Prism. (Pronounced "PRIZ-uhm") A three-dimensional shape with a base and top made from identical <u>multigons</u> and where the sides are either rectangles or parallelograms.

Profile. In a 2D drawing, a <u>cross section</u> outline appearing in the side plan view. A profile is created by passing a <u>cutting plane</u> through an object where the cutting plane is parallel with the <u>profile plane</u> of projection. In a <u>spline</u>-based 3D modeling program, a profile is a two-dimensional line, curve, or other shape used to create a three-dimensional surface. Profiles are used with 3D processes such as <u>extruding</u>, <u>lofting</u>, sweeping, or <u>lathing</u>.

Profile Plane. One of the three <u>principal planes of projection</u> that yields the left and right side plan views. Since both views are parallel to one another, the plane of projection that yields the left plan view is parallel to the plane of projection that yields the right plan view. As a result, these planes of projection can be combined into a single plane known as the profile plane.

Projected View. An outline projected onto the side of an imaginary glass box surrounding a subject using the techniques of <u>orthographic projection</u>.

Pyramid. A three-dimensional shape where the base is a multigon and the sides are triangles.

Radian. A special unit of measurement for calculating values related to angles, circles, and arc lengths. Also used in trigonometry. Even though the concept may be confusing, the radian is a "dimensionless unit." Many common mathematical formulas require that values be input in radians, and some formulas may produce results in radians. In this event, it is necessary to convert radians to degrees and vice versa. Many scientific calculators have a built-in function for converting between the two forms of angle measurements (i.e. degrees and radians).

Radius. The distance from the exact center of a circle to the outside edge or circumference. This distance is exactly one half the diameter of the circle.

Regular Helix. See Helix.

Regular Polyhedron. One of five special types of polyhedrons (or "polyhedra") where the same number of sides or "facets" always come together at each point or vertex. See also Platonic Solids.

Regular Pyramid. A "right" (i.e. upright, not oblique) pyramid with a base in the shape of a regular multigon. (A regular multigon is a two-dimensional shape with three or more sides that are all identical in length.)

Removed View. A view created to illustrate an object, detail, or feature positioned in such a location that it cannot be clearly seen in any normal view.

Resolve. To uncover, deduce, reconstruct, or calculate based on available information, i.e. to "fill in the blanks" using existing information as a guide. If the blueprinting process is imagined as being similar to solving a picture puzzle where some pieces are missing, existing information could be used to reconstruct or "resolve" the puzzle to find the missing pieces.

Revolution. The process of revolving an object or feature about an appropriate centerline until it is parallel with a normal view. The goal of revolution is to find a view of the part where it appears true length or true size and can therefore be measured. This technique is a practical alternative to the process of creating an auxiliary view. See also Conventional Revolution.

Revolved. Rotated about an appropriate centerline using the process of revolution. A "revolved view "is a true-size representation created by rotating an object or feature until it is parallel with a normal view. This is often a quick and easy alternative to the process of creating an auxiliary view.

Revolving. The process of rotating an object or feature about an appropriate centerline. See Revolution; Revolved.

RGB. An acronym that stands for "Red, Green, and Blue." RGB represents what is known as a "color space" and is the method both televisions and computers use to display color images on screen. In contrast, CMYK is the format used by printing presses and color printers to create color images using four different colors of ink. Digital image files that will be viewed only on screen or sent to others via e-mail should be scanned and saved in RGB format. (On the other hand, images that are to be printed on any sort of printer should be scanned and saved in CMYK format.) RGB images contain slightly less information and therefore takes up less computer memory than images saved in CMYK format. See also Bitmap Image; Grayscale; Monochrome.

Right Cone. An "upright" (i.e. not oblique) cone that does not "lean" to one side. If a line is drawn between the exact center of the circular base and the tip of a right cone, it will be normal (i.e. perpendicular) to the plane containing the base of the cone.

Right Cylinder. An "upright" (i.e. not oblique) cylinder that does not "lean" to one side. Both the base and the top of a right cylinder are parallel. In addition, a line drawn between the exact center of the circular base and the exact center of the circular top is normal to both surfaces.

Right Prism. An "upright" (i.e. not oblique) prism that does not "lean" to one side. Both the base and the top of a right prism are parallel. In addition, a line drawn between the exact center of the base and the exact center of the top is normal to both surfaces.

Scale. The proportional relationship (*ratio*) between the size of a facsimile of an object and the original object.

Secondary Auxiliary View. A true-size view of a non-principal plane or surface derived from information contained in a primary auxiliary view via orthographic projection. In contrast, a primary auxiliary view is derived from information contained in the normal plan views. Secondary auxiliary views can be challenging to draw. As a result, employing revolution is often an easier alternative.

Section. A view created by passing a cutting plane through an object to "expose" the true shape of both the visible and hidden internal structures. Though section views may be created at any location necessary to describe the structure of an object, the cutting plane is typically parallel to the frontal plane of projection.

Snap. A feature of both CAD and computer illustration programs that permits precise alignment and placement of lines and objects. In a computer illustration program, objects can "snap to" Guides. This means any object placed close to a Guide will automatically be positioned by the software so it is perfectly aligned with that Guide. Some programs may allow you to snap to *points* on lines or objects while drawing. A CAD application typically offers many more options for "snap," allowing for extremely precise placement of objects relative to one another.

Spline. A two-dimensional (or three-dimensional) line or curve used to build a 3D surface or object in a 3D modeling program. Not all 3D modeling programs use splines – many programs create mesh objects instead. Mesh modeling is a completely different approach and is more like "digital clay" that can be sculpted into many different shapes. In sharp contrast, a spline-based 3D modeling program creates precise surfaces from curves that are based on mathematical formulas. Because curves are the starting point for creating each 3D object, spline modeling is a natural extension of the 2D drafting process. In addition, some spline modeling programs offer incredibly powerful features such as being able to unfold or unroll certain 3D objects to create developments and/or to make 2D line drawings automatically. See also Bézier Curves.

Symmetrical. The property whereby features or points on either side of an object are a mirror image of each other. A symmetrical object has a "dividing line" or centerline called the axis of symmetry. Points and features on either side of this axis are equidistant from the centerline.

Template. An illustration depicting the true-size outline of a "flattened" pattern needed to make a part(s). Also known as a "construction pattern." In traditional construction, templates are often printed on paper, cardboard, or thin sheet stock. They can then be traced and used as an aid when cutting the final part(s) from some other material. Templates can also be drawn with modern computer-based tools and then printed on paper or some other substrate. Computerized templates offer many options that are not available with traditional techniques. Utilizing vector-based art, computer drawing files make it possible to cut parts by machine rather than by hand. Examples include laser-cutting, computer-cut vinyl (used by sign makers), and CNC milling. See also Developments.

Tetrahedron. A three-dimensional geometric shape having 4 faces where each face is an identical triangle, i.e. a three-sided triangular pyramid.

Text Tool. A tool in a computer illustration program that permits text to be added to a drawing.

Third-Angle Projection. A standard for arranging multi-view drawings that is practiced in the United States, Canada, and Great Britain. This practice places the front view at the center of the drawing with the top view above, bottom view below, right side view to the right, and left side and rear views to the left. The front view is labeled arbitrarily. Thus, it is not necessarily the true front of the object. This can sometimes cause confusion. A completely different arrangement called first-angle projection is practiced in Europe and within the International community.

Through-Holes. Holes bored (i.e. drilled) completely through an object.

Tint. A screened, muted, or "washed out" color that is of lighter intensity than the color upon which it is based. For example, shades of gray are tints of the base color *black*. In the same way, a pastel blue might be considered a "tint" of bright blue. In a computer illustration program, tints can be created by specifying a percentage value of the base color, i.e. medium gray = 50% black. A very light gray can be created as a tint of 10% black. In fact, a 10% tint of an intense base color such as bright red, green, or blue yields a very light color that is ideally suited for drawing construction lines.

Title Block. An area in the bottom right-hand corner of a drawing where the subject, name of the draftsman, title, company, page or sheet number, date, revision history, and any other desired information can be specified.

Tolerance. A variation in size or thickness from the expected or stated value. Some manufactured materials differ from their stated dimensions due to variations inherent in the manufacturing process. As a result, tolerance should be taken into account when designing parts that must fit together precisely. See also Clearance.

Transition. A change in cross section over the length of a part or assembly. A transition can be used to join two parts that have dissimilar cross sections without creating an intersection between them.

Transverse Frame. A structural framing member that runs laterally or side to side. On boats and ships, both transverse frames and bulkheads are used to form the shape of the hull. A bulkhead is actually a dividing line between watertight compartments on a ship. On aircraft, all transverse frames are called bulkheads. These structural frame members are "skinned" to form the shape of the hull or fuselage.

True Depth. The entire depth of a bored hole. Most drill bits have tips that are angled at 120 degrees. Thus, the tip of the drill bit creates a cone-shaped depression when it bottoms out in the hole. The true depth includes this cone-shaped space. In contrast, the usable depth does not. See also Usable Depth.

True Length. The accurate length of a line or the accurate measurement along a surface. Many lines and surfaces do not appear true length in a drawing because they are visually "compressed" or foreshortened. Understanding this concept is *critical* to properly understanding and interpreting blueprints. According to the principles of orthographic projection, an object can appear true length in a normal view only if it is *parallel* to the principal plane of projection for that view. In the case of an auxiliary view, it will appear true length only if it is parallel to the auxiliary plane of projection that created the view. See also Parallelism; True Size; Foreshortened.

True Size. The true dimensions of a plane or surface. See also True Length; Parallelism; Foreshortened.

Truncated. Trimmed in such a way that one or both ends are cut at an angle. Examples include the truncated cone, truncated cylinder, truncated prism, and truncated pyramid. Cones and pyramids are a special case. See also Frustum of a Cone; Frustum of a Pyramid.

Truncated Cone. A cone with its tip cut at an angle. See also Truncated; Frustum of a Cone.

Unfold. To create a development for a three-dimensional object or surface composed of flat faces or "facets" (or to create a development that approximates a sphere). The object is "unfolded" in order to flatten it. See also Development; Unroll.

Uniform Cross Section. Having a cross section that does not change in shape – but may change in *size* – along the length of the object. Objects with a uniform cross section are often easy to draw because the cross section merely needs to be *scaled* at different points along the length of the object. It may also be possible to create such an object using the lofting tool of a spline-based 3D modeling program.

Unroll. To create a development for a three-dimensional object or surface that has a rounded shape such as a cylinder. The object is "unrolled" into order to "flatten" it. See also Development.

Usable Depth. The depth of the cylindrical portion of a bored hole. Most drill bits have tips that are angled at 120 degrees. Thus, the tip of the drill bit creates a cone-shaped depression when it bottoms out in the hole. The usable depth does not include this cone-shaped space. See also True Depth.

Vector-Based Art. Object-oriented art consisting of lines and objects that is created either with a computer drawing program or with a CAD program. A vector-based drawing object is formed by recording start, middle, and end points. In a computer illustration program, various properties of an object such as "stroke" and "fill" can also be controlled. Objects can be modified and rearranged as needed since each is treated as an independent entity. The amount of information needed to record the properties and locations of drawing objects is minimal. Thus, the file size of vector-based drawings can be very small. In fact, vector-based artwork can sometimes take up as little disk space as a word processing document. In stark contrast, digital images stored as pixels take up far more computer memory. Since many individual pixels must be changed in order to alter the appearance of a digital image, they are also much more memory-intensive to modify. See also Bitmap Image; Bézier Curves.

Vertex. The point where two sides of a multigon meet. Or, a point where two lines that form an angle between them converge. Or, the point where three or more sides of a three-dimensional object such as a geometric solid meet.

Vertical Axis. An axis running from the top to the bottom of an object. This axis is denoted by a line that extends through its geometric center.

Vertical Plane. An alternate term for the frontal plane of projection.

Visual Perspective. A natural phenomenon that allows the eye to perceive three-dimensional objects. Perspective also creates dramatic visual distortion. The amount of distortion depends on the size of the object, as well as on how far away it is from the viewer. The closer the object, the more perspective distortion is present. Orthographic projection was developed to eliminate all visual perspective from blueprints so that objects in drawings can be accurately measured.

Working drawings. A set of blueprints that includes detailed measurements and other information needed to accurately recreate the subject. By nature, a working drawing is always a dimensioned drawing. See also Blueprints; Presentation Plans.

Index

Symbols

OTHER BOOKS IN THIS SERIES

MODEL Design & Blueprinting HANDBOOK
Volume 2

In the *Model Design & Blueprinting Handbook, Volume 2*, you'll see how to turn 2D blueprints into patterns that can be used to build 3D models. Then, learn how 3D "power tools" can make the blueprinting and pattern-making process quicker, easier, and more accurate. This comprehensive guide will demonstrate how both 2D drawing and 3D modeling tools can be used *together* to streamline the design phase of all your modeling projects and ideas.

MODEL Design & Blueprinting HANDBOOK
Volume 3

In the *Model Design & Blueprinting Handbook, Volume 3*, you'll explore new modeling frontiers as you learn how to turn your finished drawings into usable materials and components in the real world.

- Find out how to bring 3D models to life using rapid prototyping technology.
- Gain an understanding of the capabilities and methods surrounding machine output – including laser-cutting, 3D printing, and CNC processes.
- Learn how to convert 2D drawings into useable artwork for making decals, dry transfers, and even custom photo-etched parts.

This unique guide brings it all together in an easy-to-understand format that will help you take your modeling projects to the next level.

> **To learn more, please visit:**
>
> *www.ModelersNotebook.com*